Photos courtesy of Johnson Motors

ONCE UPON A TIME there was little to do at a beach but sit in the sun and splash in the water. Then came surfing, water skiing and scuba diving—and the water world became a whole new kind of playground. If you go for scuba diving, you'll find plans for a scuba sea tow on page 2362

Photo courtesy of The Coleman Company, Inc.

EXPERTS SAY that camping is the fastest growing activity in the country, not only because it's fun, but because it stretches vacation dollars. Thousands of new campers hit the tenting trail every year, and new campsites are being opened as fast as the state and federal governments can complete them. If camping looks like a solution to your vacation problem, you'll be interested in camping equipment. The story on page 2374 tells you all about buying sleeping bags

BEFORE YOU think about adding a room, or about redoing the exterior of your home, read the article on page 2348. It tells you about the many different kinds of siding available to you today. There's bound to be one that's just right for you

IF YOU HUNT, that shotgun means a lot to you. You need to know how to use it and care for it. The shotgun tips on page 2334 will be helpful. And the directions on how to pattern your gun on page 2336 will improve your hunting considerably

Photo courtesy of American Hardboard Association

Photo courtesy of Winchester-Western

Photo courtesy California Redwood Association

THE TWO PHOTOS above give you an idea of what you can do with wood stains. Both walls are redwood. The article on page 2464 tells you about the different types of stains available and how to use them

YOU MIGHT CALL this the mini-garage. It's one of a group of tiny shelters shown on page 2309 for that rolling stock that currently is making your garage a difficult place to move around in

Popular Mechanics Do-It-Yourself Encyclopedia

in 16 volumes

A complete guide to

- home maintenance
- home improvement
- hand-tool skills
- craft projects
- power-tool know-how
- hobbies
- automotive upkeep
- automotive repair
- shop shortcuts
- boating
- fishing
- hunting
- model making
- outdoor living
- radio, TV and electronics

Volume 13

Book Division, Hearst Magazines, New York, N.Y. 10019

© 1968, The Hearst Corporation
All Rights Reserved

No part of the text or illustrations in this work may be used without written permission by the Hearst Corporation.

Printed in the United States of America

VOLUME 13

shelters
    Park 'em in their own garages   2309
shelters, camping
    Kitchen canvas for campers   2318
    Shelter fly rolls out from luggage rack   2320
shelves
    Shelves around a corner   2322
    Plants on a pole   2323
shock absorbers
    Shock absorbers shot?   2324
shortwave receivers
    Buyer's guide to shortwave receivers   2329
shotguns
    Tips for shotgunners   2334
    For better hunting, pattern your shotgun   2336
shovel, power toy
    Little digger for junior engineers   2342
shrink plate
    How to make a shrink plate   2346
siding
    Choose the right siding   2348
    Use the right nail for siding   2351
signs
    Carving signs with templates   2352
skiing
    Ski parallel in one day   2358
skin diving
    Hitch a ride on this scuba sea tow   2362
slate floors
    Lay a slate floor in your entry   2365
sleds
    Tob-sled   2369
    Ski sled with outriggers   2370
    Here comes the snow boat   2372
sleeping bags
    How to choose a sleeping bag   2374
slide projectors
    Sound track for your slides   2378
slide rest, lathe
    Compound slide rest for lathe   2380
sliding doors
    How to hang sliding doors   2386
slitting saws
    Pee-wee saws   2392
slotting
    Metal slotting with a twist drill   2395
smelting furnace
    Gas-fired smelting furnace   2396

snow fort
    Snow fort for winter fun   2400
socket checker
    Triple check on three-wire outlets   2402
solar motors
    Light powers this electric motor   2404
    Electric motor spins in the sun   2406
soldering
    Soldering tricks   2407
sparkplugs, auto
    Sparkplugs are built-in engine analyzers   2410
sparkplugs, marine
    Match the sparkplug to your outboard   2416
speedometers
    Is your speedometer telling the truth?   2420
speed reducers
    Speed reducer for your bandsaw   2421
spice chest
    Great-grandmother's spice chest   2424
spice racks
    Two ways to add spice to your kitchen   2426
    Early American spice rack   2430
spindle sander
    Make a spindle sander   2432
spinning wheels
    Make this spinning wheel   2434
sports boat
    Build a sleek sports boat   2440
spotlight, photo
    Make glamour pictures with a homemade spot   2450
spray painting
    Paint with air   2454
stagecoach
    Stagecoach fits on a wagon   2462
staining, wood
    Wood stains and how to apply them   2464
stairs
    Secrets of building stairs   2472
stake plate
    Stake plate has many shop uses   2478
starting, auto, cold weather
    Hot tips for cold starts   2482
starting, auto, hot weather
    Cool tips for hot starts   2490

Project-a-plans   2495

How to use your Encyclopedia

Browse. Glance through this volume, or any other volume of the Encyclopedia. Likely you will find the solution to a particular home-maintenance problem that has been bothering you, or a shop project so appealing that you will immediately head for your bench. Browsing not only is enjoyable, but is a source of ideas.

Seek specific information. Perhaps you want to find out how to cure that leak in your basement, how to keep the exterior paint from peeling, or how to tune and set the carburetor on your car.

Four reader aids, all cross-referenced, will enable you to find specific information:

1. *Alphabetical headings.* Located at the top of the page, these headings cover broad classifications of information. If you are looking for information on how to keep paint from peeling, for example, look up "Paints" alphabetically, then find the particular section dealing with peeling paint.

2. *Alphabetical cross-references.* These are shown in a box at the bottom of the page. Some material can logically be classified under more than one alphabetical heading, so if you don't find what you are seeking alphabetically (as described above), be sure to check the *alphabetical cross-references* at the bottom of the page; there you may find precisely the classification you are seeking. For example, you and your son decide to build a model airplane, and are looking for plans. You look up "Model airplanes" and find nothing under that alphabetical heading. However, if you glance at the bottom *of that same page* you will find an alphabetical cross-reference that reads: **model airplanes,** see airplane models.

3. *See also references.* These are shown at the end of many articles. They refer you to related articles which may also be of interest.

4. *Instant index.* Located at the end of Volume 16, it is thoroughly cross-referenced to help you find information under any heading.

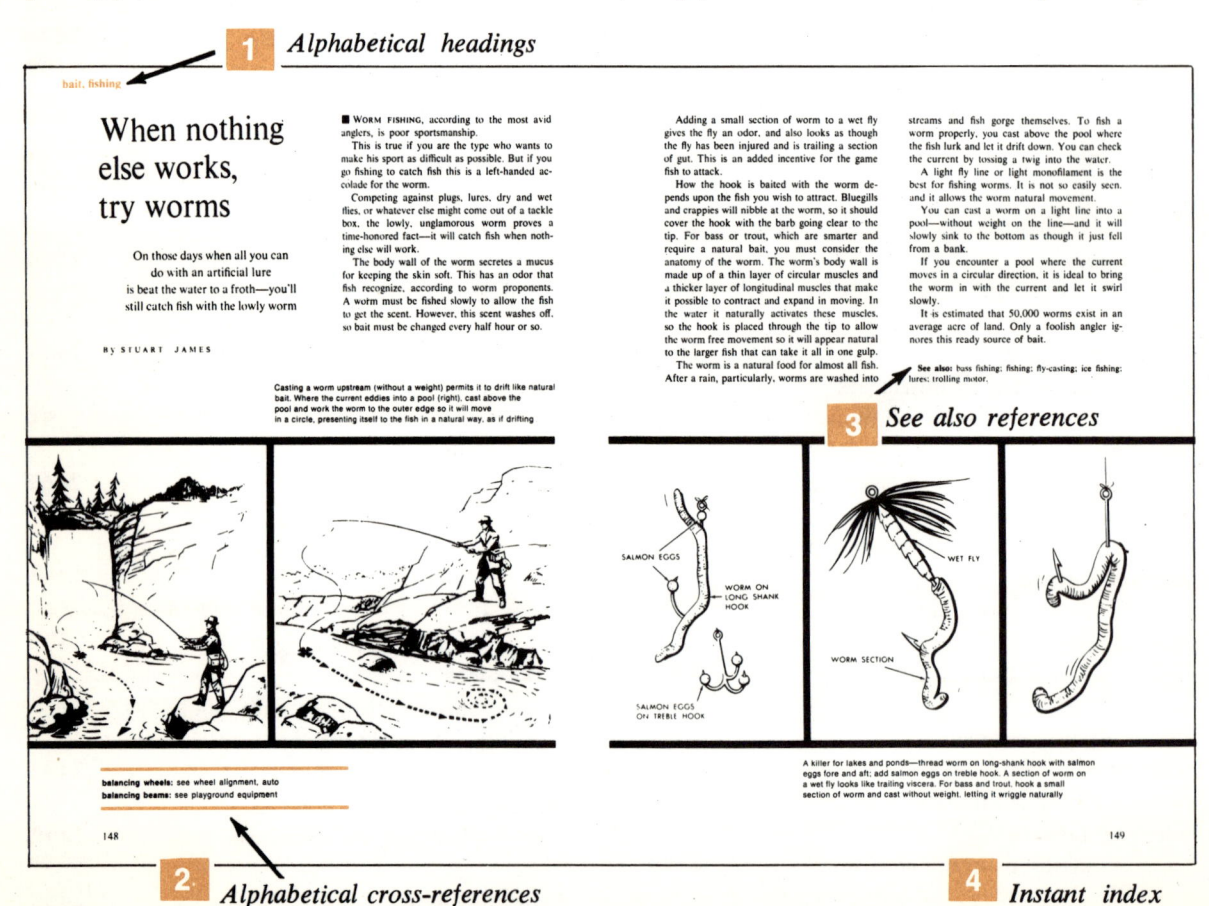

shelters

If your
garage
is full,
build these
shelters
for extra
equipment

Park 'em in their own garages

■ IF THERE IS ROOM in your garage for that riding mower you bought last summer, you're lucky. In most cases, there's little or no extra space to park such a vehicle. The average garage is already crowded to the rafters with a hundred and one household items that hardly leave room for the family car.

A bulky vehicle such as a motorbike, riding mower or a family-size yard tractor is usually left out in the cold when it comes to sheltered

2309

shelters

While suitable for any of the three vehicles, the tapered design of this tractor barn makes it ideal for the average yard tractor such as the one shown here. The fold-back roof (below) is equipped with a handle to make it easy to lift the hinged sections. When open, these stand by themselves

special garages, continued

parking. And while a tarp, perhaps, offers the next best thing to a permanent shelter, it provides far less protection and convenience than a separate little "garage."

This is particularly so in the case of a motorbike which may be used daily to provide transportation to and from the station. Having a cozy little stall where it can be wheeled in and out and kept high and dry makes overnight parking as handy as can be.

Equally as handy for a rider mower or yard tractor, one of these little huts located right out in the yard at the rear of the lot makes for real convenience, too.

You can drive in as well as drive right out of this drive-through shelter since it has doors at both ends. Roof sections lap one another, fold up and over. One is held vertical by long hooks and screw eyes. Twin ramps rest level with the floor; they can be hinged to fold up inside the drive-through unit

Of course, any of these little shelters can be put to good use as utility buildings to care for garage overflow, or to take over where there is no garage at all. Ideal for out-of-season storage, they'll provide a place to keep folding patio furniture, screens and storms, kids' toys, snow shovels—you name it. Even to keep rakes and hoes handy to the garden, these little structures will prove extra convenient to have around. Handiest of all for this purpose is the canvas curtain lean-to. Here, in addition to being completely accessible from the front, both ends swing open wide. All it would take to make this one serve as a dandy garden toolshed would be a tool

2311

shelters

DRIVE-THROUGH

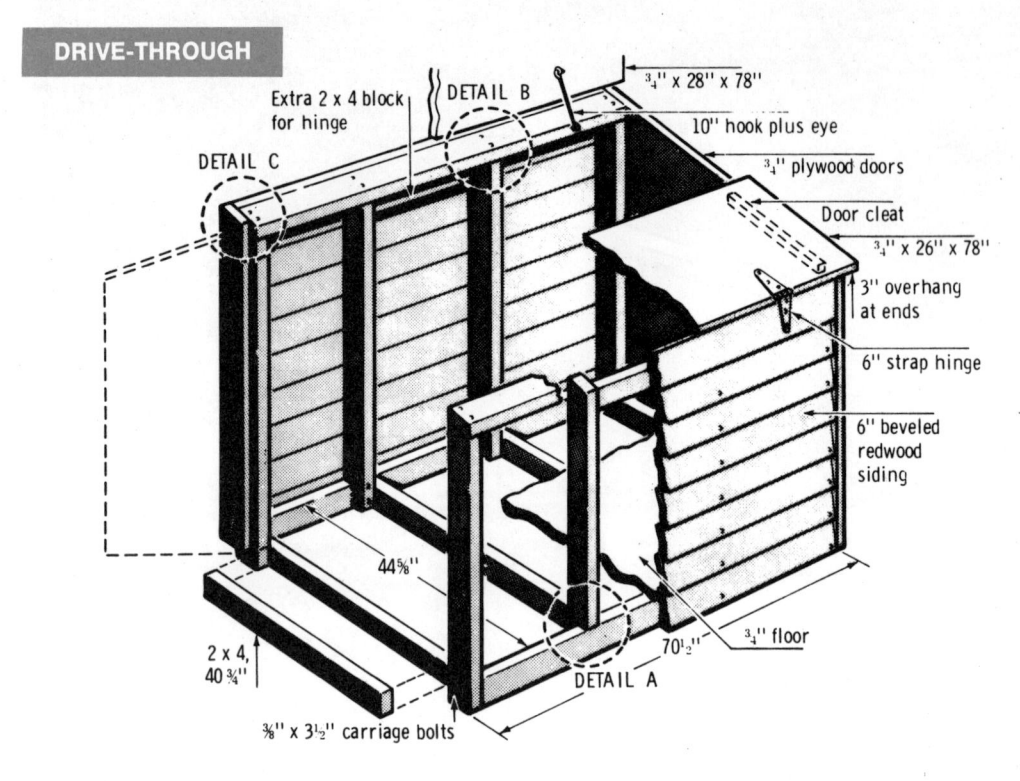

special garages, continued

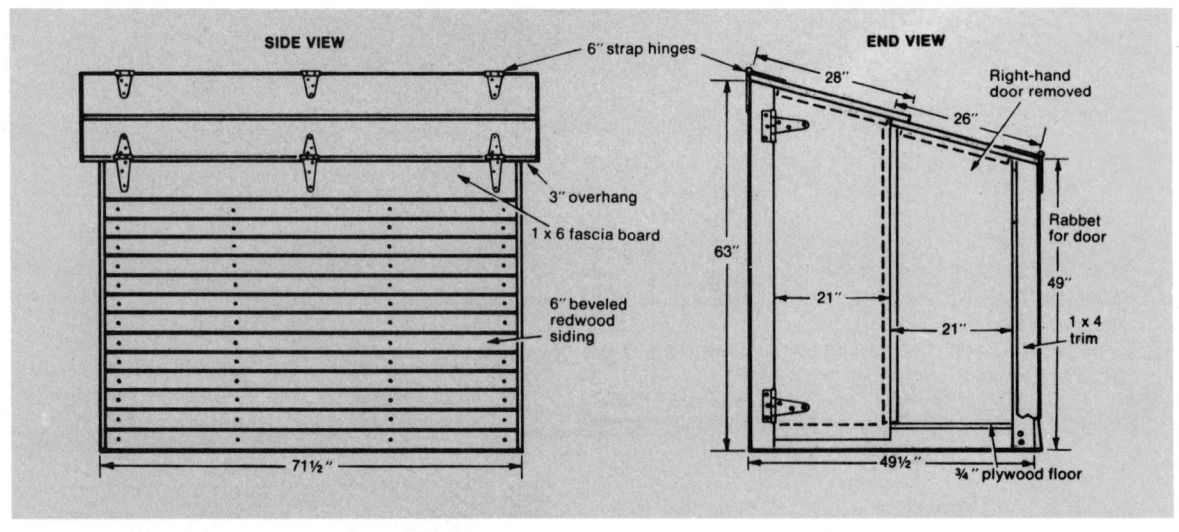

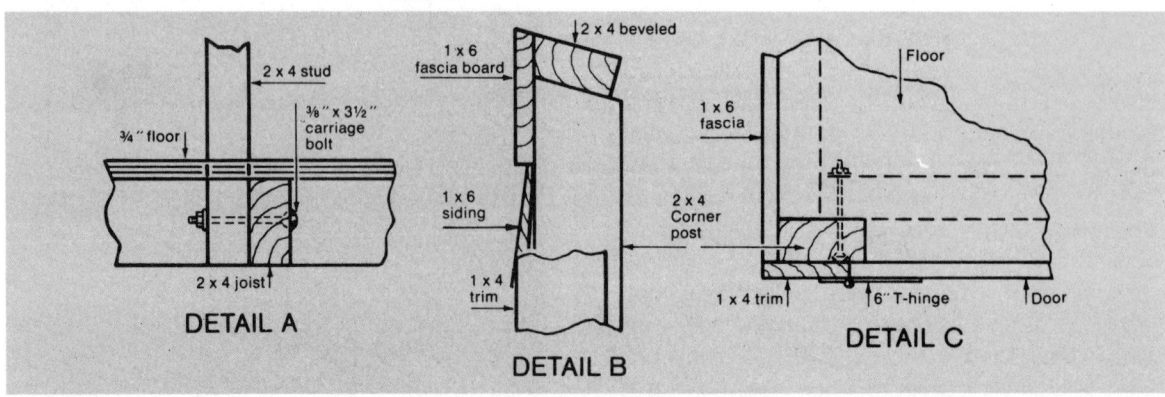

SIDE VIEW

END VIEW

DETAIL A

DETAIL B

DETAIL C

TRACTOR BARN

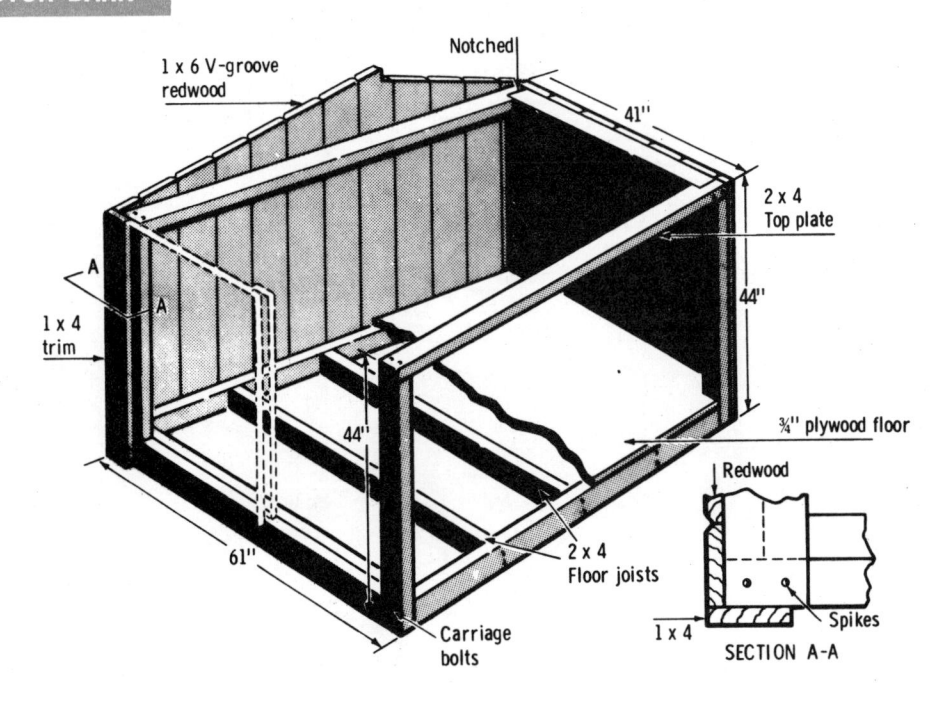

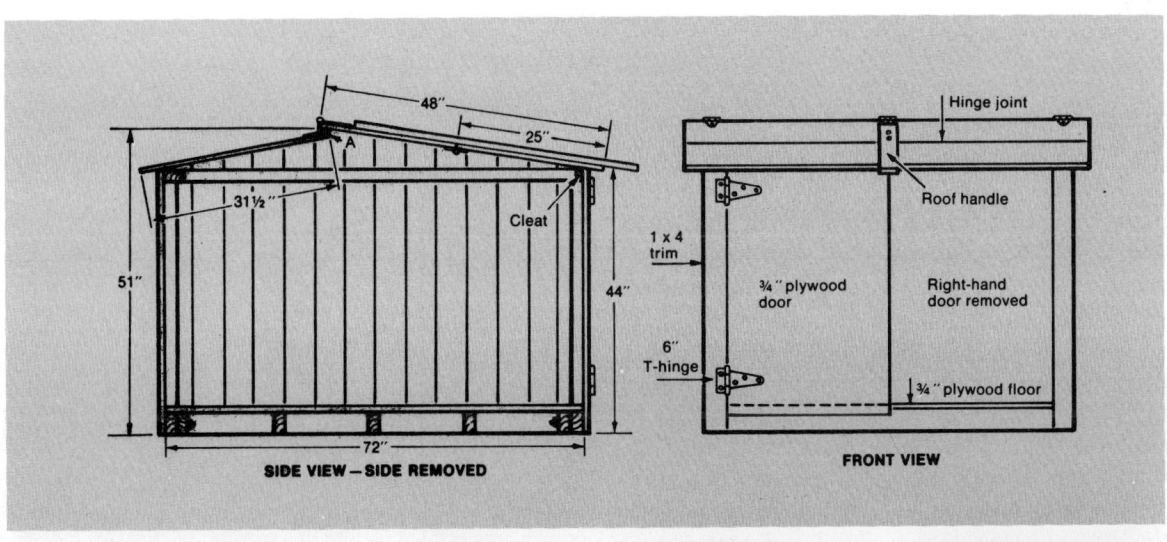

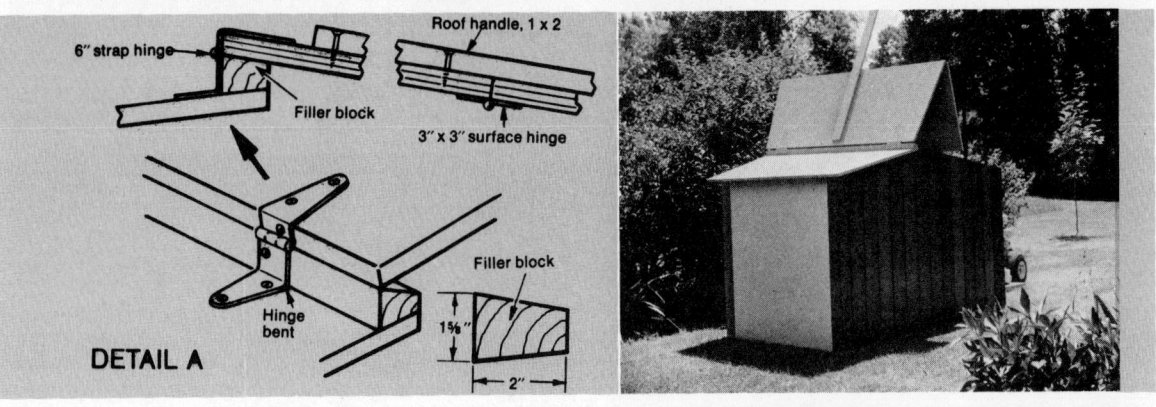

Top illustration labels:
- 1 x 6 V-groove redwood
- Notched
- 41"
- 2 x 4 Top plate
- 44"
- 1 x 4 trim
- A
- 44"
- ¾" plywood floor
- 61"
- 2 x 4 Floor joists
- Carriage bolts
- Redwood
- 1 x 4
- Spikes
- SECTION A-A

Side View — Side Removed:
- 48"
- 25"
- 31½"
- Cleat
- 51"
- 44"
- 72"

Front View:
- Hinge joint
- Roof handle
- 1 x 4 trim
- ¾" plywood door
- Right-hand door removed
- 6" T-hinge
- ¾" plywood floor

Detail A:
- 6" strap hinge
- Roof handle, 1 x 2
- Filler block
- 3" x 3" surface hinge
- Hinge bent
- Filler block
- 1⅝"
- 2"

2313

shelters

CANVAS LEAN-TO

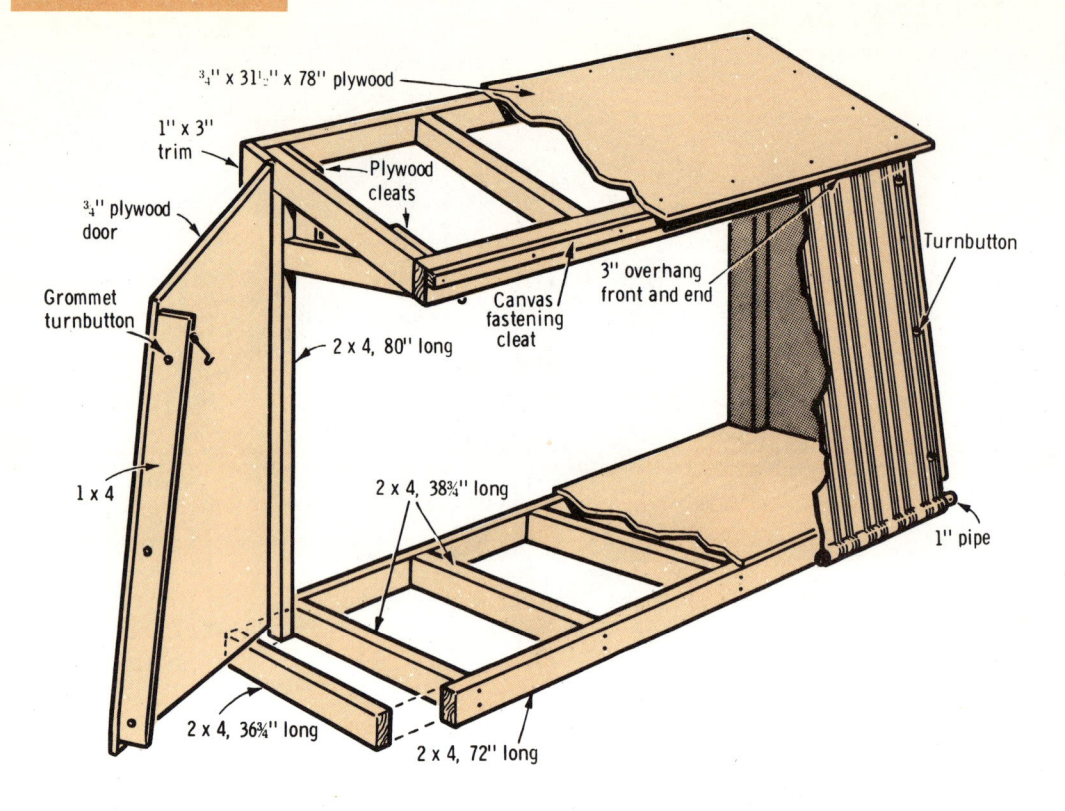

special garages, continued

panel of perforated hardboard across the back and a shelf near the roof. And you'd still have room to park a rider mower or lightweight motorbike.

You'll notice that two of the designs (the drive-through and the lean-to) permit you either to ride or wheel the vehicle in and out, each structure being fitted with doors and ramps at both ends. There's plenty of headroom in the canvas lean-to design to let you ride in, and in the drive-through design, the hinged roof opens up to provide the necessary head clearance. In the fourth design—the tractor barn—a portion of the roof folds back to let you ride right in, although here the vehicle must be backed out. If desired, you can hinge the ramps so they will swing up inside before you close the doors. In the case of the motorbike hut, the door doubles as a ramp and is held shut by the cover.

The basic framing of all four units consists of 2 x 3s and 2 x 4s, and, while plywood was used for the floors, doors and roofs, we also used redwood siding to relieve the plainness. Beveled red-

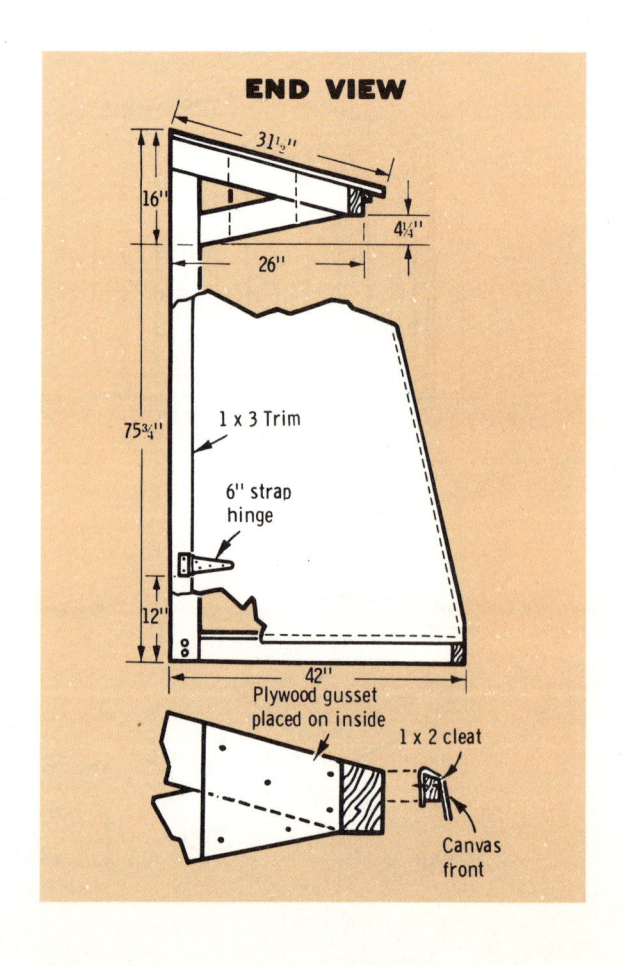

Designed to attach to the side of a building, this canvas lean-to version, with a drop-curtain front, opens wide. Canvas buttons to strips on the doors

shelters

The side panels of ½-in. Trentex plywood are fastened to inner frames of 2 x 3s with flathead screws. Countersink them

Wheel-guide members are bolted to the plywood platform with carriage bolts. Do this before the wall panels are added

special garages, continued

wood siding, applied horizontally, was used on the drive-through model; V-joint redwood, applied vertically, was used on the tractor barn. You could substitute hardboard siding, of course, as well as aluminum—or even colorful fiberglass. All plywood, whether rough-sawn white pine or smooth Douglas fir, should be exterior grade.

Each garage is clearly detailed in cutaway drawings. Door posts are anchored solidly to the floor platforms by bolting them to the inner corners before the floor is nailed. Your platform should not rest directly on the ground. A few concrete blocks partially buried make ideal piers.

While each of our models has a wood floor, yours wouldn't have to. If you'd prefer to pour a concrete slab, you could. In fact, your floor could be nothing more than gravel with your corner posts being treated with a preservative and set in the ground like fenceposts. You could use a floor of flagstone. Since the roofs are pitched to shed water quickly, a couple of coats of porch and deck paint will do without need for actual roofing. While overall dimensions given will accommodate average-size vehicles, it may be necessary to vary the length and the width to suit actual measurements.

See also: building; framing; garages; motorcycles; mowers; storage buildings.

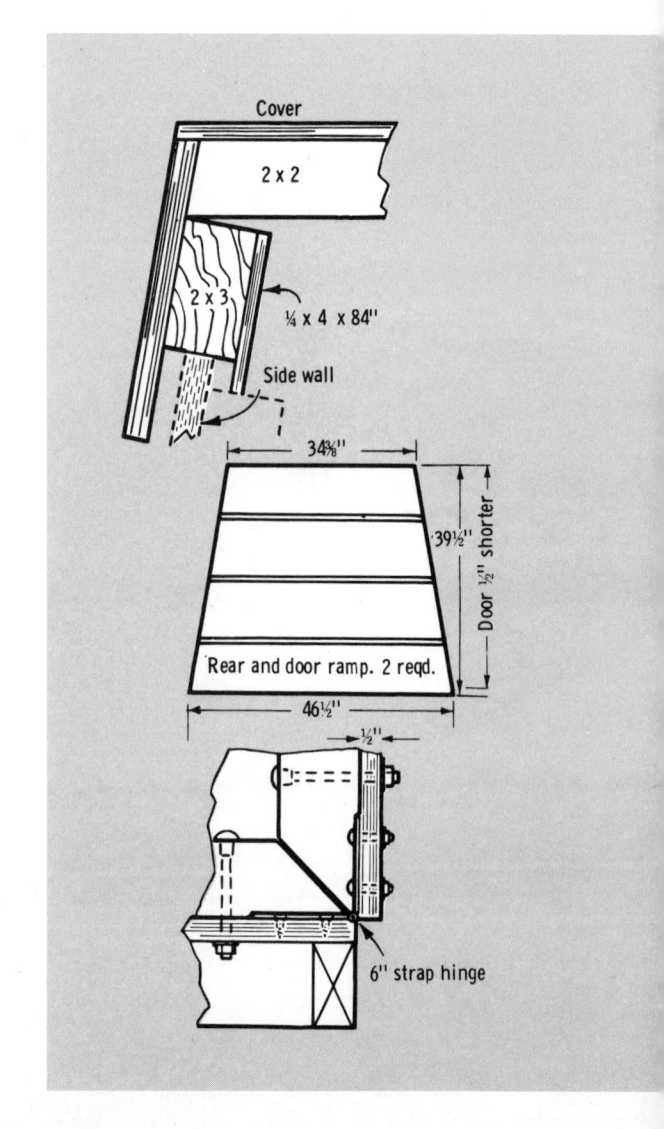

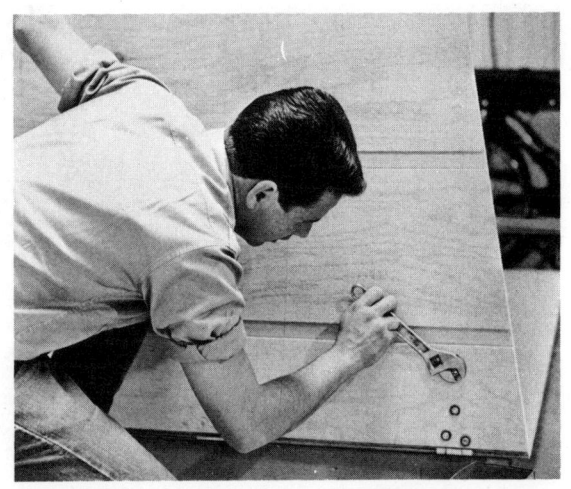

Strap hinges which support the drop-front ramp are fastened to the plywood with rust-resistant 1/8 x 1-in. stove bolts

The roof fits over the tapered sides of the hut like the cover of a box, serves to hold the hinged front closed without a catch

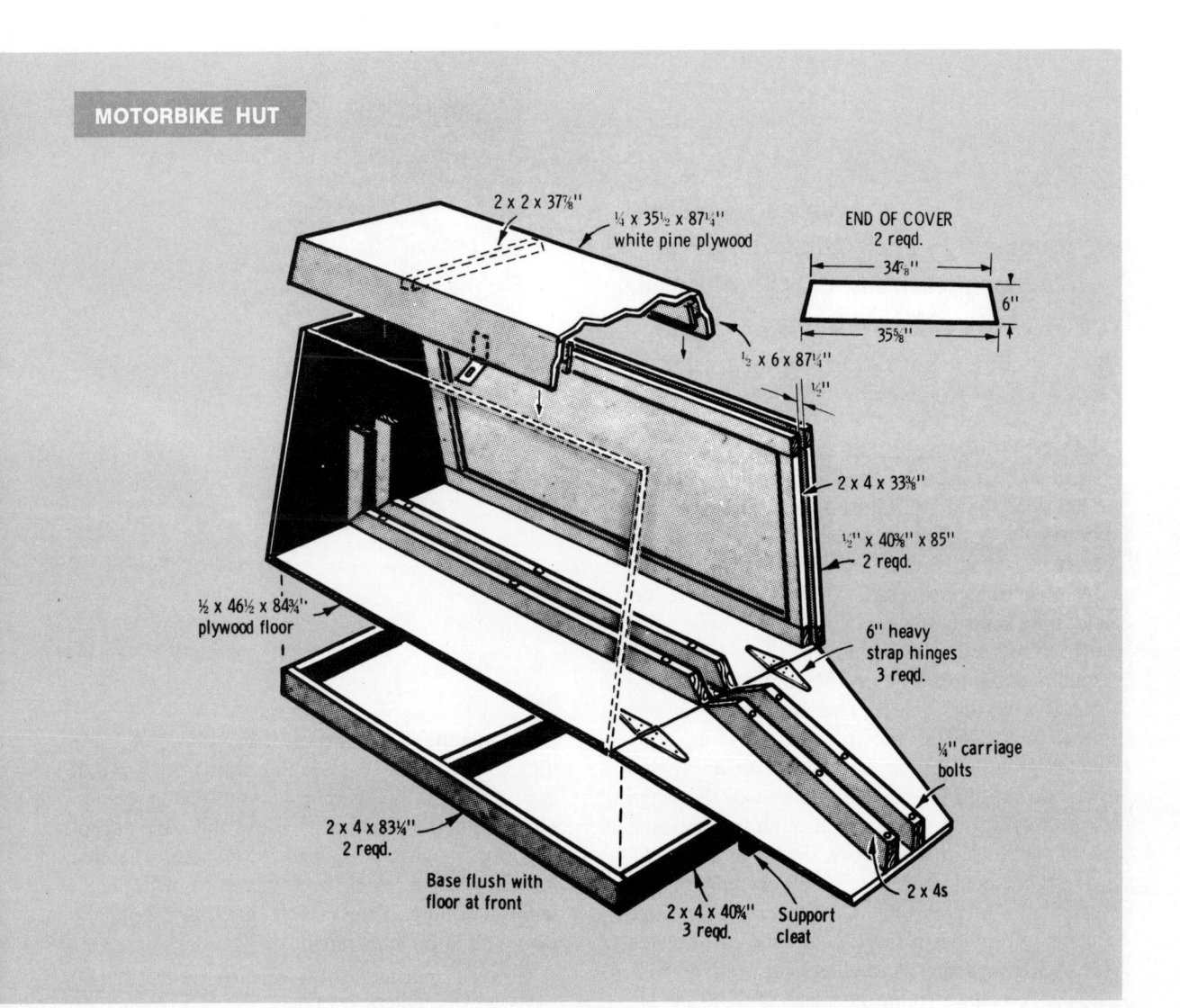

MOTORBIKE HUT

- 2 x 2 x 37⅞"
- ¼ x 35½ x 87¼" white pine plywood
- END OF COVER 2 reqd. — 34⅞" / 35⅝" / 6"
- ½ x 6 x 87¼"
- ½"
- 2 x 4 x 33⅜"
- ½" x 40⅜" x 85" 2 reqd.
- ½ x 46½ x 84¾" plywood floor
- 6" heavy strap hinges 3 reqd.
- ¼" carriage bolts
- 2 x 4 x 83¼" 2 reqd.
- 2 x 4s
- Base flush with floor at front
- 2 x 4 x 40⅜" 3 reqd.
- Support cleat

2317

shelters, camping

Kitchen canvas for campers

BY CARL PELANDER

There's a way you can eat your meals on camping trips in dry comfort. An outdoor kitchen shelter is all you need. It's easy to assemble and transport by car top or trailer

■ FEW THINGS SPOIL a camping trip like a cloudburst at mealtime. You needn't risk it. With this outdoor kitchen shelter, called a kitchen fly, you'll always be able to prepare and eat your meals in dry comfort. It's easy to assemble, transports readily by car top or trailer, and has a built-in table.

The tarpaulin (nominally a 12 x 14, which actually measures 11½ x 13½ ft.) is supported by a 2 x 6 ridge board. This can be left in one piece, or spliced as shown for easier transporting. A grommet of the tarp slips over an angled ⅜-in. dowel pin inserted in one end of the ridge (see drawing). A guy rope through the opposite grommet rides in the groove shown in Detail C, an arrangement that permits slackening of the rope if the tarp shrinks. Cantilevering the ridge unevenly provides a large overhang on one side for sheltering a stove and other gear.

The A-shaped frame is made of 2 x 2s. Its cross members support a ½-in. plywood table top, which is set 26 to 30-in. above the ground, depending on the height of your camp chairs. Holes drilled in the 2 x 2s above the table accept pegs for hanging pots, dish towels, etc. The side poles, of 1¼-in. stock, are square, to pack neatly without rolling. They're 5 ft. long, and hold the tarp with ⅜-in. steel pins.

See also: camping; car-top carriers; car-top sleeper; sleeping bags; trailers.

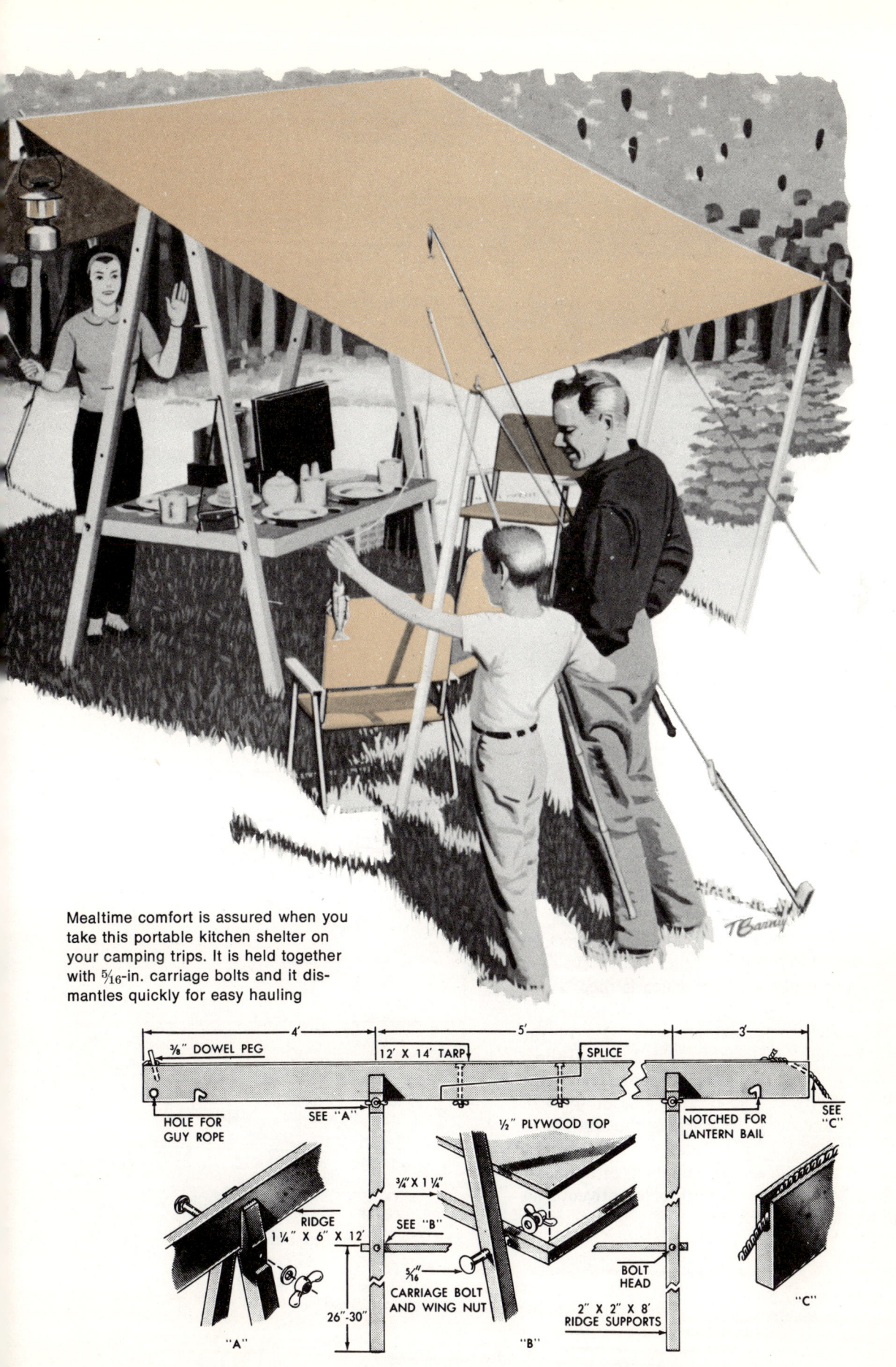

Mealtime comfort is assured when you take this portable kitchen shelter on your camping trips. It is held together with 5/16-in. carriage bolts and it dismantles quickly for easy hauling

shelters, camping

Shelter fly rolls out from luggage rack

BY FRANK N. STEPHANY

FROM QUICK ROADSIDE MEALS to extended auto camping trips, you'll welcome the protection from sun and rain offered by a pair of 6 x 8-ft. tarps mounted on the luggage rack of your car. For traveling, poles and stakes are simply rolled into the tarp which is then lashed to the carrier.

To make them, hem the long edge of the tarps over an 8-ft. length of 2 x 2. Install three grommets along this edge to permit tying the pole to the rack. Use 6-ft. lengths of thinwall conduit for corner posts, plugging the upper ends with dowel and driving roundhead wood screws part way in to engage the grommets in the outer corners of the tarps. Drop flies for privacy can also be made.

shelters, ice fishing: see ice fishing
shelters, storage: see storage buildings

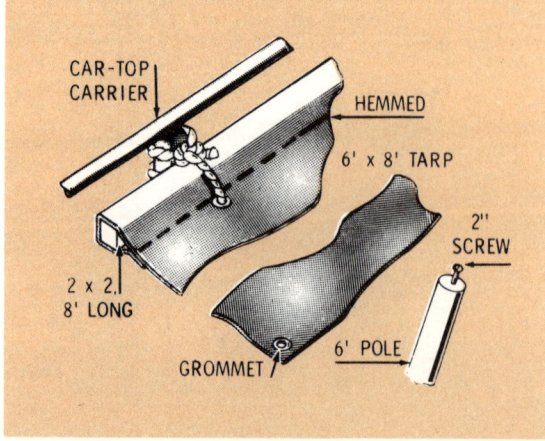

clever ideas

A pipe bushing can be used to repair a broken push-broom handle. Make hacksaw cuts across the threads on the inside and outside of the bushing. Taper the end of the handle until it will turn into the bushing tightly. Then turn the bushed end of the handle into the hole in the broom.

A drop light can be prevented from swinging with a bracket made from a wire coathanger. Bend the hanger to a W-shape and staple it to the wall to form the bracket. Bend the hanger hook to take the lamp socket snugly. Now slip the socket in place in the holder and screw in the bulb.

Add handy pockets to the back of your lawn chairs when you re-cover them. The pockets will hold magazines, cigarettes, matches, swim caps, etc. Just buy additional material and after sewing the backing in place sew excess matching fabric to the back of the chair to form two wide pockets.

Crushed ice will always be available for your ice-cream freezer if you fill ½-gal. milk cartons with water and keep them in the food freezer. Crush the ice by striking the carton squarely on each side with a short length of 2 x 4, or, lacking this, the flat side of a hatchet.

Bundle old newspapers and magazines with masking tape rather than cord and you'll avoid the three-handed struggle of keeping the stack in order while you knot the end of the cord. Wind the tape around the stack, keeping it tight as you wrap. Once or twice around each way does it.

Shelves around a corner

BY HANK CLARK

Mounted on unused walls over a desk, they make an ideal place to display a hobby collection

WHAT GOOD IS a collection if you don't have a space to show it off? This four-shelf corner unit provides the perfect answer to the problem.

Originally developed to hold a boy's model planes and ships, it was mounted in an unused corner over a desk. Since the models were so light in weight, expensive commercial shelf standards and brackets would have been an unnecessary luxury. The mounting system shown here is sufficiently strong to support figurines, dolls and similar objects. For heavier loads, use corner irons with each shelf.

Construction should offer no problems, but be especially careful when cutting the joints at the corner so that the shelves will bear against both walls. Easiest way to assure this is to lap the boards at the corner, scribe a 45-deg. line on one board and make the cut, then place both boards in the corner and scribe the other board along the cut in the first. When using boards of different widths, the first cut should run from the corner out to where the edges of the boards meet.

To assure perfect alignment, drill the holes for the dowels through all four shelves at one time. Notch the shelves for the square corner post, and begin assembly by first gluing each pair of shelves together at the mitered joint. Then add the post and dowels. The completed unit is hung by nailing through the square post and into corner wall studs, and screwing angle brackets to the outer ends of the top shelves.

See also: book storage; children's furniture; hardware; remodeling; remodeling ideas; remodeling shortcuts; vacation homes.

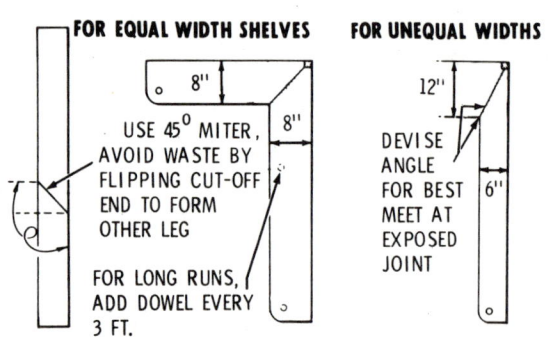

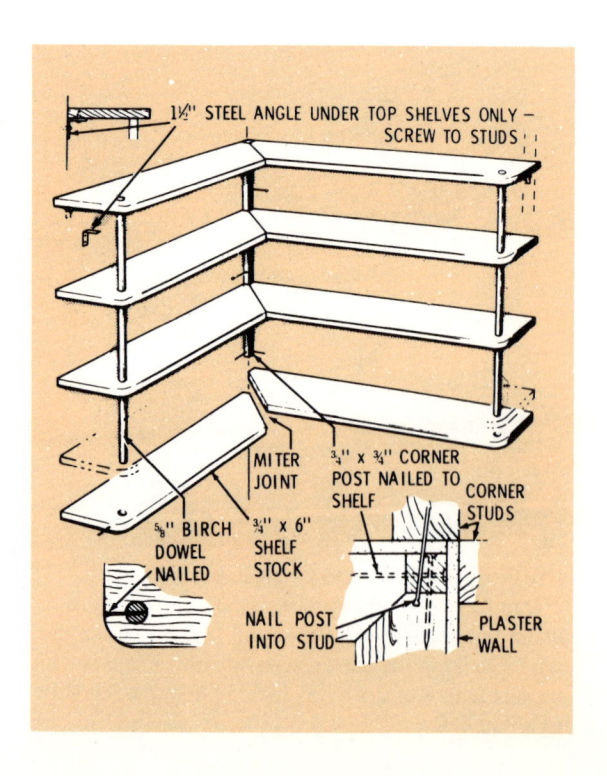

shelves

Plants on a pole

BY L. D. LaBARGE

■ BRIGHTEN A CORNER where you are with a pole tier of colorful plants. By supporting the shelves on a single free-standing pole wedged between floor and ceiling, you can place plants in a sunny corner of a porch or a bare corner of living room.

For my pole I used a unit called Timber Topper. This is a 1⅝-in. wooden pole which has a spring-loaded top to bear against the ceiling. You'll need to cut off the pole itself 3 in. short of your floor-to-ceiling height. I fitted the pole with three shelves, but more can be added.

If you nest the shelf patterns, three can be cut from a 2 x 4-ft. sheet of plywood with a minimum of waste. Each shelf is attached to the pole by a 2¼-in. locking screw which is driven through the edge of a square block fastened to the underside of the shelf. To bore the large hole through both shelf and block you'll need a hole saw or a fly cutter. Both of these tools work best in a drill press—particularly the fly cutter—but you can use a hole saw in a portable electric drill. Note that the hole should be made slightly larger (1¾-in.) than the diameter of the pole so the shelves will slide in place freely.

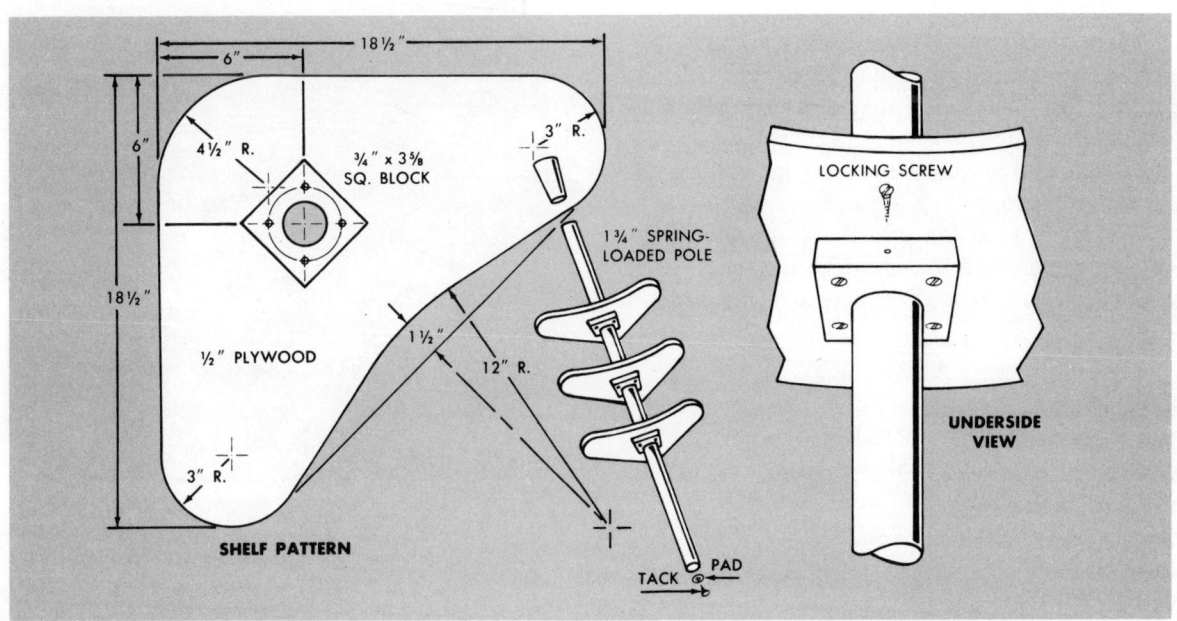

2323

shock absorbers

Shock absorbers shot? Service 'em yourself

BY MORTON J. SCHULTZ

More and more car owners know they should be concerned about the car's shock absorbers. In many cases, they don't know how to recognize trouble, nor what to do if they do recognize it. But at least they know the subject deserves concern.

Evidence is in the growth of the shock absorber replacement business. During one recent period, replacement sales increased *fifteen times*

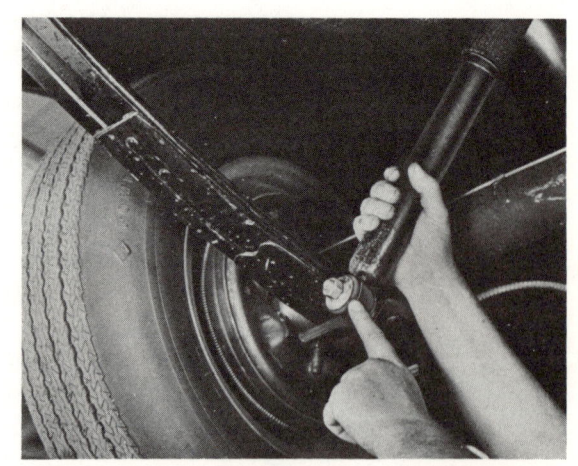

To check shock absorbers' mountings, shake them hard. If there's any significant looseness in either mount, tighten up on the mounting nuts (indicated by the forefinger above). If bushings are worn, however, you will have to tackle the replacement job

---

shoes, jumping: see play bouncers
shoji screens: see remodeling
shooting: see ammunition; chronograph; marksmanship; shotguns; targets
shop air system: see air system, shop
shop vacuum cleaners: see vacuum cleaners, shop

---

shock absorbers

2324

as fast as vehicle registrations. So maybe we should say that concern has reached the level of a fad.

But in any case, you're financially better off to know your shocks as thoroughly as possible—so you replace them when needed, but not before. You're better off in a safety sense, too, if you know how to be sure they're in good shape. This new awareness, therefore, is all to the good. And, while identifying failing shocks isn't easy, you can do well enough if you know what to look for, and are warned about pitfalls in advance.

The useful life of a set of shocks can range anywhere from *2000 to 50,000 miles*. Ten miles of driving on back-country washboard roads, for instance, can work shocks harder than 1000 miles of freeway driving. Moisture, dust and temperature are other factors affecting shock life.

To know the condition of your own shock absorbers you must test them. It would be easy to spot faulty shock absorbers if they went flat like a punctured tire. But shocks are coy. They wear out gradually. And because they do, a driver accustomed to the same car day after day gradually learns to accept whatever ride his car gives until the ride gets really bad.

Thus you may well trust a friend's opinion more than your own. If he's rarely in your car—almost always in a newer model with shocks known to be in good shape—give him a ride and ask for his reaction to the railroad tracks and other bumps.

Another point: The driver's seat is almost midway between the front and rear wheels. That means any poorly controlled pitching fore and aft is further concealed from the everyday driver. So let your observer ride in the rear—the farther back the better. If you're checking out a station wagon, let him ride all the way back next to the tailgate.

Deteriorating shocks will advertise themselves by one or more of the following signs:
- Excessive bounce on bumps.
- Under-par steering control.
- Chassis noises and rattles.
- Skidding or loss of control on curves.
- Uneven or premature tire wear.
- A "too soft" or "too hard" ride.

Unfortunately, pinpointing shocks as the underlying cause of these symptoms will be difficult unless you're finely attuned to the difference in riding motion between a car with new shocks and one with an old, well-worn set. Also, many of these same troubles can be caused by any one of a number of weak or worn parts in the steering or suspension systems, including a weak or broken spring, loose ball joints, defective wheel bearings or a rough idle. So don't rush into replacing a set of shocks before you're reasonably sure that new ones will help. You may find you've spent a sizable chunk of money to no avail.

shocks do lots of work

Shocks absorbers are double-acting hydraulic devices. Double-acting simply refers to their damping action in two directions: on the rebound, when the shock absorber extends itself; and during compression, when the shock collapses.

The relationship of rebound-to-compression load varies with the speed to which a shock absorber is subjected. In other words, a particular velocity results in a particular load on the shock. Normal operating pressures range from zero p.s.i. to 700 p.s.i. When subjected to really violent road shocks, the pressure can go as high as 5000 p.s.i.

Since shocks are filled with a carefully measured amount of fluid and sealed in manufacture, you can't reload them if they lose fluid; and you can't disassemble them to replace worn parts. The only first aid you can administer to a shock absorber is to replace worn rubber bushings and tighten loose mountings.

Practice the following three techniques for the care and coddling of your shock absorbers:

(1) *Stay alert for changes in driving "feel."* If you detect any, check the shocks. If they're

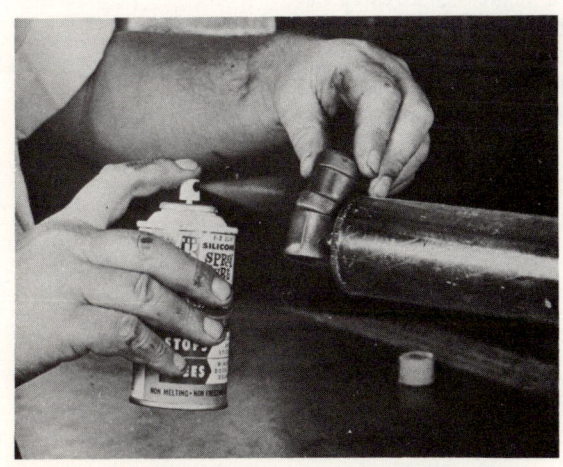

Spraying silicone lubricant on new bushings makes the replacement job lots easier. Otherwise they're often difficult to work into their seats. Be sure, however, to steer clear of any petroleum-base lubricants; they will attack the rubber and cause fast deterioration

shock absorbers

COMPONENTS AND ASSEMBLY OF A TYPICAL SHOCK ABSORBER

1. Mounting Section
2. Piston Rod
3. Seal Cover
4. Rod Seal
5. Seal Retainer
6. Seal Spring
7. Rod Guide
8. Pick-Up Washer
9. Intake Spacer
10. Star Spring
11. Intake Valve Disc
12. Piston
13. Rebound Valve Disc
14. Rebound Valve Disc Spacer
15. Rebound Spring Seat
16. Rebound Spring
17. Nut

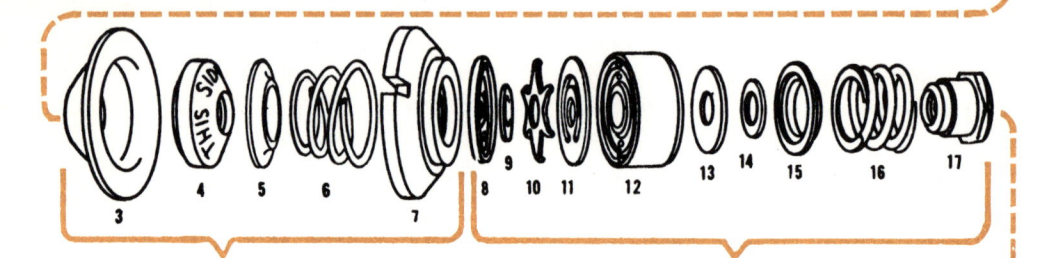

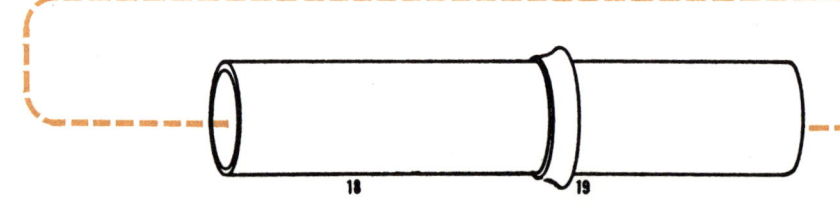

18. Pressure Tube
19. Baffle Ring
20. Compression Stem
21. Compression Valve Plate
22. Compression Valve Cage
23. Compression Valve Sleeve
24. Compression Valve Spring
25. Conical Replenishing Spring
26. Valve Retainer

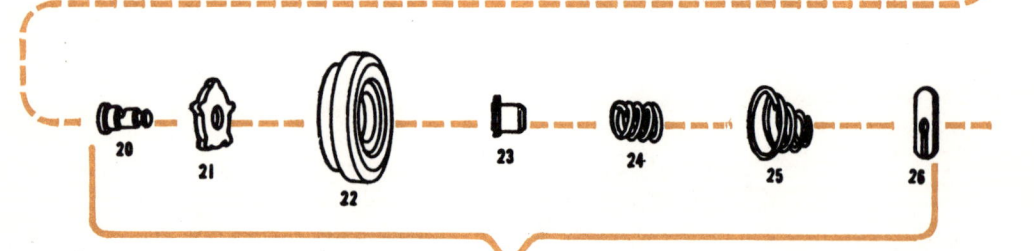

service shock absorbers, continued

okay, check out the remainder of the suspension system—*and* the steering.

(2) *Inspect shocks every time the car is on a lift.* Look for fluid leakage; also for dents in the casings. The latter may signal damage to the internal valving. If so, the shock should be replaced.

To test a shock for stability, grab it and shake it (there should be only *slight* movement, if any). If it's loose, tighten up the mountings. If this doesn't help, remove the shock, then bang out the old bushings and insert new ones. Admittedly, inserting new bushings can be a rough job. To ease this chore and make the new rubber bushings more pliable, spray them with a silicone lubricant. Then work the bushings into their seats. Note: Never apply a petroleum-base lubricant; petroleum attacks rubber and causes rapid deterioration.

(3) *Run a thorough inspection of your shocks when your car reaches 20,000 miles, then every 5000 miles thereafter.*

"How about that time-honored test of the used-car buyer—bouncing the car up and down?" you may ask.

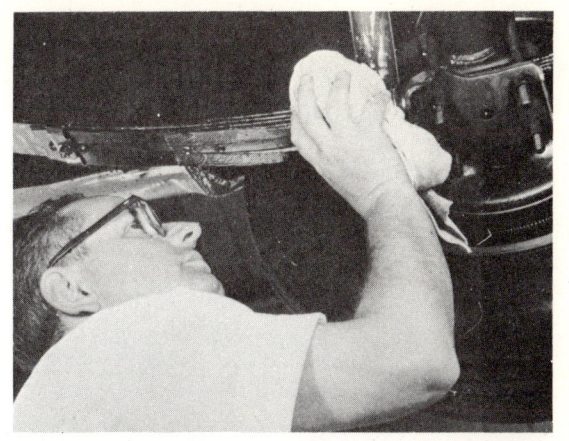

During the inspection, clean off the shock's casing and watch for fluid leakage as well as casing dents. Leaking fluid or dents that indicate damage to the internal valving mean the shock absorbers, both of them at that end of the car, must be replaced

With your car on a frame-grip hoist, the kind that takes weight off the wheels, a long-reach jack can make it easier to remove the lower end of the shock absorber. Set the jack under the leaf spring near the shock mounting and jack the spring up slightly

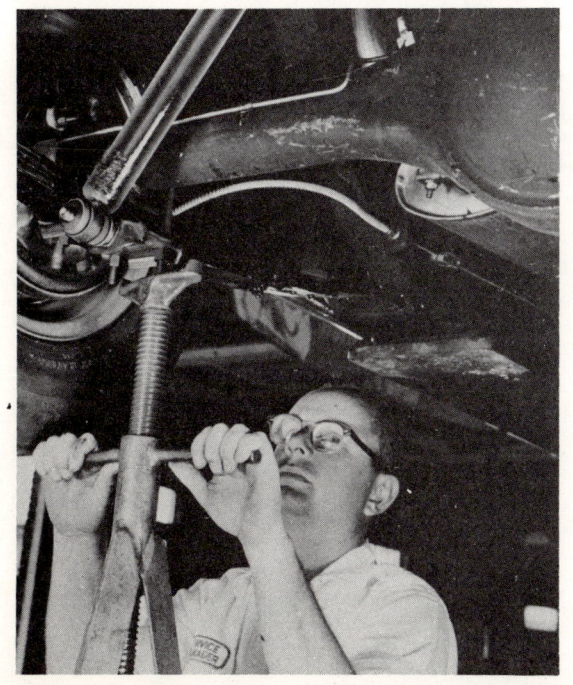

As a matter of fact this *is* a legitimate, if perfunctory, method of determining the general action of your shocks. Just jounce the car by hand or foot at each of its corners. A considerable amount of resistance should be felt at both the upward and downward thrusts of the car.

As a rule of thumb, try it this way: Get the corner of the car oscillating up and down pretty well. Give it a last hard push down, and let go. On rebound, the car body will usually go past the center point—*once.* Then, if the shocks are all they should be, it will come back down to its normal position and stop. More oscillations are cause for concern, but their lack is no great reassurance. Repeat the procedure at each corner or at least each end of the car.

Don't delude yourself, however, that you have conducted a thorough, technically precise test. There just isn't any reliable way for the ordinary consumer to accumulate enough experience to justify any sense of certainty in this area.

The resistance you feel in trying to jounce the car is also a guide. But remember that it's just that; a guide and nothing more.

For one thing, interpreting the results takes experience. What might seem like sufficient shock resistance to you, *wouldn't* to a trained mechanic.

Shock-absorber failure occurs in one of two ways: the seals rupture and fluid leaks out of the casing, or worn parts cause internal failure.

Fluid leaks are easy to spot. Once a shock begins to leak it must be replaced. Internal fail-

shock absorbers

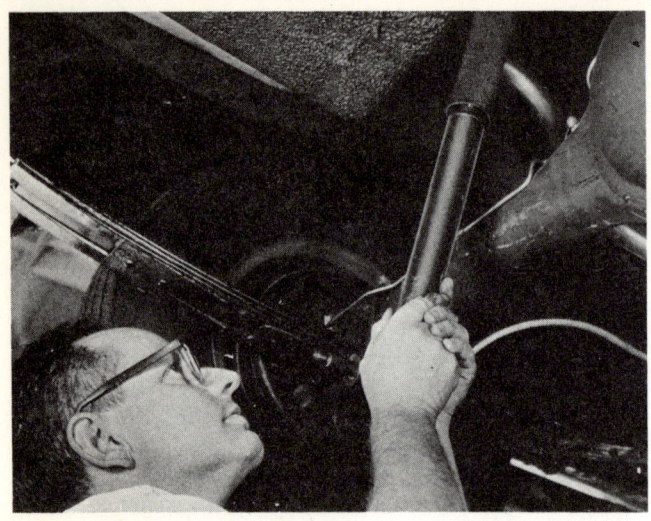

So the springs' strength doesn't hide failing shocks, remove the assembly from the lower mounting and cycle the shock in and out. It should resist firmly. But shock absorbers mounted within coil springs must be taken completely off the car and bench-tested

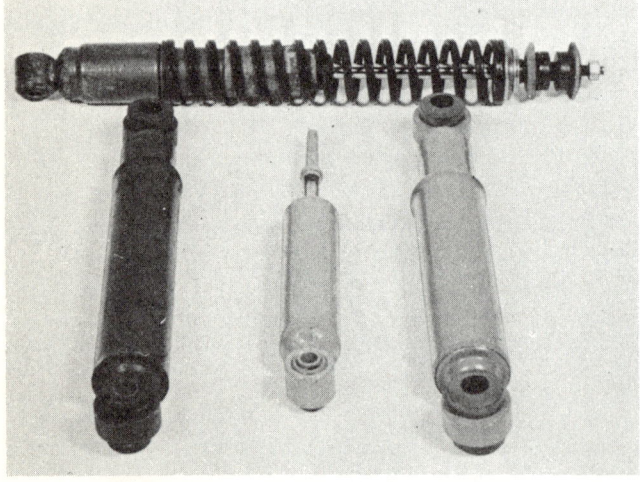

Four typical replacement shock absorbers are shown here. At the left is an Autolite front shock, with an Autolite rear shock next to it in the center. At the right is a Delco assembly. Across the top is a Monroe load-leveler shock absorber

service shock absorbers, continued

ure will make itself known by the "feel" of the ride.

To service or replace a shock, put the car on a lift, then clean all road dirt and grease from the upper and lower mountings. The toughest part of the job is removing the mounting hardware, especially if it has rusted. So give the mounting bolts and nuts a good shot of penetrating oil and let it soak in for several minutes. This will facilitate loosening the nuts with a wrench.

If your car is on a frame-grip lift that takes the weight off the wheels, removal of the lower end of the shock will be made easier by jacking up the spring near the shock.

Now compress the shock by hand as it hangs from the top mounting. This will require plenty of force *if* the shock is in good condition.

Front shocks that are mounted inside coil springs are the only type that must be removed from the car for testing. To test one of these, clamp it upright in a vise so the lower mounting is held firmly. Then force the shock in and out of the casing. Any erratic or low resistance indicates the shock should be replaced.

The replacement shocks you buy are generally not the same as those originally on the car. Original factory shocks are built to give the softest ride. Replacement shocks are designed to give the best *control* to a car that has put many thousands of miles under its wheels. Thus replacement shocks will be found to be generally sturdier than the original units.

shocks for heavy loads

However, if you use your car to haul heavy loads—a boat or trailer, for example—you should consider installing the so-called *load-leveler* type shocks for greater control and easier handling. In any case, always buy well-known, brand-name replacement shocks which are marketed by such companies as Autolite, Monroe, Gabriel, Columbus, Delco and MoPar. The safety involved is too important to trust to off-breed bargains.

Here are some pointers to bear in mind when installing new shocks:

• Follow the manufacturer's installation instructions *to the letter*. Early failure can be expected in the form of broken shocks if they aren't mounted correctly.

• To avoid so-called *shock rattle* caused by air trapped in the working chambers, move each shock up and down a few times before mounting it. This cycling forces the air out of the chamber.

• Always replace old shocks in pairs—two in the front or two in the rear. Although only one of a pair of old shocks may be bad, chances are the one you *don't* yank won't match the performance of the new shock. Result: an unbalanced ride. Replacing shocks in pairs will equalize their damping effect.

See also: auto repair; chassis, auto; steering, auto; tires.

Buyer's guide to shortwave receivers

BY LARRY STECKLER

Here's a run-down of things to look for when buying a shortwave receiver, whether you're looking for an economy model or an all-wave rig with all the extras

■ TO TAP THAT WORLD of airwave adventure surrounding you—police calls, marine communications, satellite signals, radio amateurs, aircraft or foreign broadcast stations—you may think that you need only to switch on any shortwave radio receiver.

But step into a radio showroom, or leaf

shortwave receivers

shortwave buyer's guide, continued

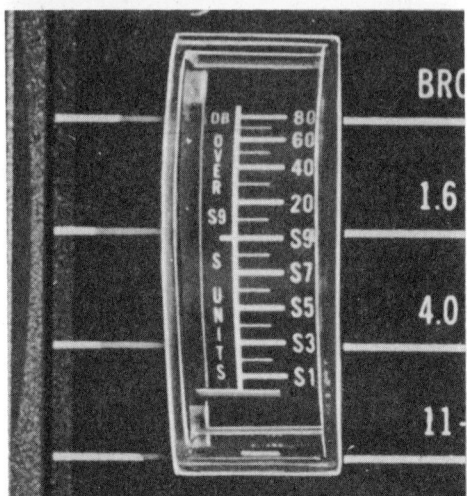

S-meters measure signal strength. Standard types (top) are easiest to read and their large scales make them the most accurate. The current trend is to smaller, vertical dials. Avoid the uncalibrated ones (bottom)

What the Shortwave Dollar Will Buy

PRICE: Under $75

4 bands
No r.f. stage
540-kc to 30-mc
May not have S-meter
Fixed frequency BFO
May not have headphone jack

PRICE: Under $100

4 bands
May not have r.f. stage
540-kc to 34-mc
S-meter, but may not be calibrated
Fixed frequency BFO
Headphone jack
May have basic Q multiplier
May have basic noise limiter

PRICE: Under $150

4 bands
R.F. stage
540-kc to 34-mc
25:1 tuning ratio
S-meter
Automatic noise limiter
BFO, may be fixed-frequency circuit
Antenna trimmer
Headphone jack

PRICE: Under $200

5 bands
R.F. stage
540-kc to 34-mc
30:1 tuning ratio
Calibrated S-meter
BFO with pitch control
Automatic noise limiter
Basic Q multiplier
Dual conversion
Antenna trimmer
Headphone jack

PRICE: Under $300

5 bands
R.F. stage
540-kc to 34-mc
60:1 tuning ratio
Calibrated S-meter
Variable i.f. selectivity
Noise limiter automatic
Automatic volume control
Single-sideband reception
Dual conversion
Antenna trimmer
Headphone jack

PRICE: Under $450

6 bands
2 r.f. stages
540-kc to 109-mc
AM and FM (27-MC to 109-MC)
60:1 tuning ratio
Single sideband reception
Automatic volume control
Automatic noise limiter, adjustable
Triple conversion
Adjustable i.f. selectivity, notch filter
Plug-in crystal tuning
Push-pull 10-watt audio output
Clock timer
Antenna trimmer
Headphone jack

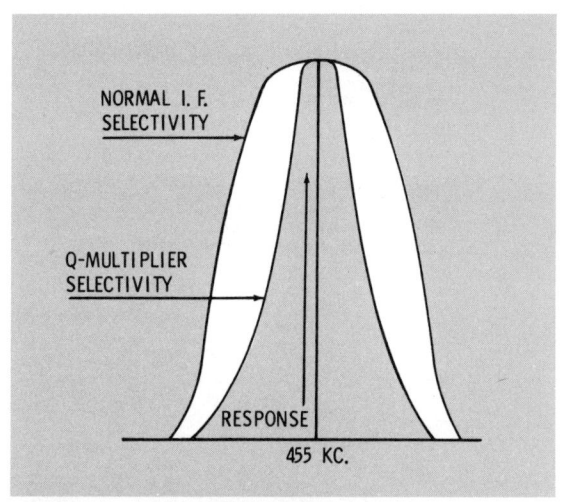

Q-multipliers narrow bandpass of the i.f. amplifiers resulting in greater selectivity in the receiver. For you, this means less jumble and more stations

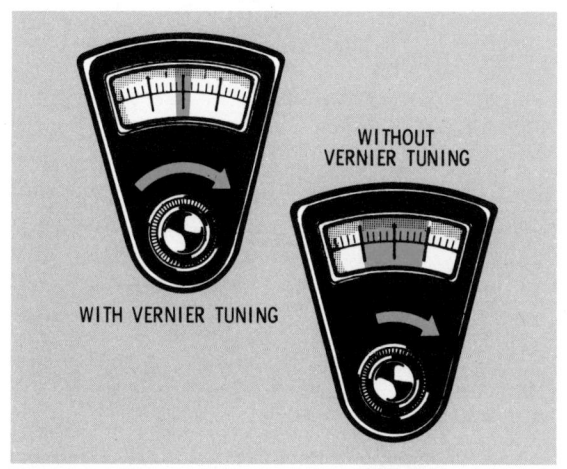

High-ratio dial at left covers less tuning distance per turn than low-ratio dial at right, simplifying tuning

through the radio receiver pages of an electronics catalog, and you enter a world of confusion.

Suddenly you're looking at amateur and "all-wave" receivers ranging in price from little more than that of a good clock radio to well above the cost of a radio-TV-phonograph console. You also have to sort out a veritable alphabet soup of mysterious abbreviations (BFO, ANL, AVC, Q multipliers, to name only a few) which may or may not be important to the type of short-wave listening you have in mind.

Prices fluctuate, but you'll find units tending to fall into groups, the features of which generally determine construction costs and, thus, prices. Using the check lists shown here, determine those features you want and can afford. When making a choice between two apparently equal sets, pick the one with the most tubes or transistors—it'll cost more but perform better.

Before you walk into the showroom you should decide what type of listening you intend to do—amateur radio or general-purpose "all-wave" shortwave listening. The amateur receiver concentrates on the amateur radio bands at 3.5-, 7-, 14-, 21- and 28-megacycles. The bandspread dial on these sets is calibrated for these bands.

The general-purpose set, on the other hand, carries labels at around 1.6-mc. (1600 kc) for police radio, 2.5-mc. for ship-to-shore phones, as well as amateur frequencies and the most commonly used foreign-broadcast frequencies.

It is interesting to note that the 1.5 to 4-mc. area is generally good for reception up to 300 miles and nighttime listening. From 4 to 8-mc.,

Formerly available only as accessories (right), Q-multiplier circuits are now built in (left), help separate shortwave stations that are crowded together and overlapping

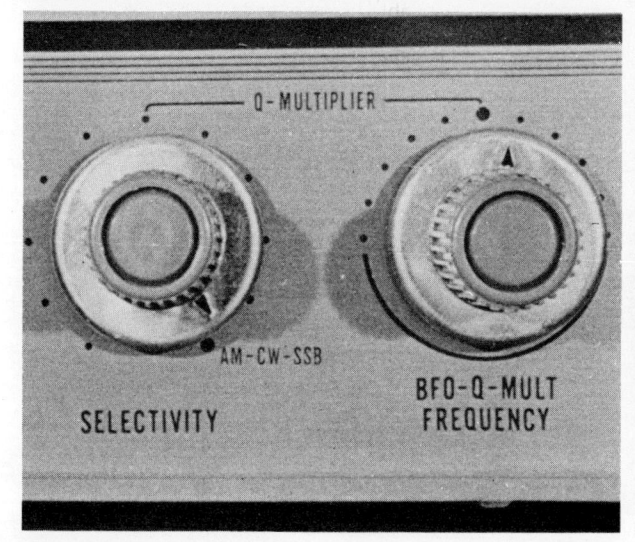

2331

shortwave receivers

Preselector (left) brings in long-range broadcasts, is found only on best shortwave sets.
Control cluster looks good, but some knobs are switches, don't adjust; others aren't calibrated

expect 300 miles daytime and up to 1500 miles at night. From 8 to 14-mc., look for under 2000-mile range during the day and over 2000 miles at night. For 14-mc. to 34-mc., expect 1500 miles or more with best results in the early morning or evening.

Portable all-wave sets are usually transistorized and come with a built-in pole-type antenna. In general, they will not perform as well as a nonportable receiver selling for the same price. The built-in antenna can only deliver a small fraction (as little as one tenth or less) the signal picked up by a long 150-foot single-wire antenna. Also the portable's transistor circuitry is inherently noisier. When you are listening to a strong station, this noise cannot even be heard.

	KNOW YOUR RECEIVER FEATURES		
R.F. STAGE	Radio frequency amplifier located ahead of other receiver stages. If you want really long-range reception make sure your receiver includes this circuit. Best sets have 2-stage circuit (preselector)	VARIABLE SELECTIVITY	Electronic circuit that adjusts bandwidth of i.f. stages, enabling reception of weaker more distant stations. Look for range of adjustment and crystal filters. See diagram on page 2331
S-METER	Signal-strength meter. Look for large calibrated dials and a long scale. Vital if you intend to obtain QSL cards. Large dial eases tuning and taking accurate signal-strength readings for QSL's	ANL (AUTOMATIC NOISE LIMITER)	Circuit designed to reduce background noises of all types. A real help if you live in an area where a lot of electronic static is present. Look for a sensitivity control if circuit is not automatic
TUNING RATIO	Ratio of distance tuning control knob turns to distance station; selector dial actually moves. Larger the ratio, the more selective your tuning. See the diagram on page 2331 for greater detail	ANTENNA TRIMMER	Matches receiver input to antenna for best performance. Look for front panel control. It often helps to readjust trimmer after tuning station. Brings the desired station up out of the clutter
BFO (BEAT FREQUENCY OSCILLATOR)	Absolute must if you intend to listen to Morse-code broadcasts. Keeps tone of signal constant making code reading easier. Look for a variable pitch control so you can select the tone you want	HEADPHONE JACK	A must for listening to distant stations. Phones eliminate otherwise distracting local noises. Look for front panel jack. Other locations are not as convenient. Found on almost all receivers

However, tune in a weak distant signal and you may find yourself getting more noise than signal. For best performance for the price, then, stick to a nonportable vacuum-tube type receiver.

When comparing receiver performance in the store and trying some of the tests mentioned in this article, ask the salesman to be sure that the sets you try are all connected to the same antenna. Most stores have a setup for switching any radio on display to a particular antenna. But if you really want to play it safe, don't rely on the switching. Try one set plugged into one particular antenna jack, then unplug it and hook up the next one. A good set hooked to a poor antenna will not perform as well as a poor set connected to a good antenna.

Three main factors determine quality. They are stability, sensitivity and selectivity.

Stability refers to the set's ability to stay tuned to a station and not drift off frequency. Check by tuning in a weak station for 10 minutes or so. The station may fade in and out (volume level may change) but you should not have to touch the tuning control again.

Sensitivity is the ability of a radio to receive a weak station. Check by tuning in the same weak distant station on several sets. If one delivers a stronger, clearer signal than the rest, it's the most sensitive set.

Selectivity is the receiver's ability to pick out one station from a group of stations crammed tightly together. Tune a receiver to a crowded portion of any band. Then, using the bandspread control, see how many stations you can sort out of the jumble. Test several sets this way.

The alphabet soup. Almost all short-wave radios include a headphone jack and an S-meter. The jack should be mounted on the front panel for easy access. Headphones are a must for good listening to weak or distant stations, and adding a jack to a set that doesn't have one can sometimes be difficult.

If you start collecting QSLs (confirmation cards from the stations you listen to), you want the S-meter to give you a signal-strength reading to relay to the station when asking for a card. But the S-meter should be calibrated and have a large easily read dial. If you have a real basic set that does not include an S-meter, there's an accessory meter you can add.

Noise limiters are electronic circuits intended to protect your ears against sudden loud bursts of static. Almost all receivers above the economy class include such a circuit. Automatic noise limiters (ANL) are handy, but should have a sensitivity control so you can select the point at which they go into operation.

To compare such circuits, tune to a noisy spot on the dial, then flip in the circuit and judge how effectively the noise level is cut back, without eliminating the station signal you are trying to receive.

Beat-frequency oscillator (BFO). Most short-wave radios have this oscillator which is triggered by code signals you may want to tune in. The BFO keeps the pitch of code signals you receive constant. But receivers that have a BFO should include a variable pitch control so you can select both the most pleasing tone and one which can be most readily distinguished from background noise.

Preselector. Only better receivers include this extra tunable r.f. amplifier in front of the other receiver circuits. It helps bring in weak, hard-to-hear stations. To check its effectiveness, tune to a weak station on a set *without* a preselector and compare reception of the same station on a set *with* a preselector.

Variable selectivity of the i.f. (intermediate frequency) circuits is quite popular. One version of this circuit, called a Q-multiplier, lets you narrow the range of frequencies your receiver is amplifying. This helps separate crowded stations. Test by tuning to a crowded portion of some shortwave band, and seeing how many different stations you can get using the Q-multiplier and with it off.

Calibrator (CAL). On some receivers this circuit is built-in. It produces audible tones at precise frequencies, so you can zero the set's dial tuning indicator to conform exactly to the specific frequency it indicates. Make sure the dial itself can be easily adjusted. If you want even more tuning precision, your set should have a crystal-type calibration circuit, which cannot drift off frequency.

Bandspread. The ratio of how far you have to turn the tuning knob to how far the dial moves determines how finely you can tune to a station. Generally speaking, the more expensive the set, the higher the tuning ratio. But make sure the tuning control moves smoothly and easily.

How many bands? Most all-wave sets cover all frequencies between 550-kc. and about 34-mc. (Some special sets cover other frequencies.) But within the normal frequency limits, a set divides its range into a number of bands, usually four, five, or six. The more bands there are, the finer the tuning.

See also: electronics; oscillator, audio; radio repair, AM; tester, radio; transmitter, FM.

shotguns

If you miss despite careful aim, maybe your gunstock doesn't fit you. Try lengthening the stock by placing a pad under the buttplate; or raise the comb by lacing a cheek pad over it as shown at the upper right

Tips for shotgunners

BY W. CLYDE LAMMEY

■ WHEN A COCK PHEASANT roars out of thick cover, or a covey of quail takes off almost literally at your feet, you have only seconds to get in a shot that counts. What happens during this brief interval while the birds are still in range largely determines whether you go home with the limit for the day—or nothing.

Probably no two shotgunners point a scattergun in precisely the same fashion, but some requirements appear to apply to nearly everyone. One of these is the right stock drop and stock length for the individual shooter. The detail below at the right shows what most top shotgunners like to see when the gun is shouldered. Here the actual line of sight, as in the illustration above, is above the breech of the gun with the bird in full view. With the view at lower left, you still see the bird, but you may shoot under him. You can correct this pointing defect with pads.

Another rather common pointing defect, difficult to overcome, is the tendency to cant the gun when shouldering it to take the shot. Usually this can be corrected with the installation of special sights as shown at the bottom of the next page. Due to space limitations, the leads shown are under those required in actual practice.

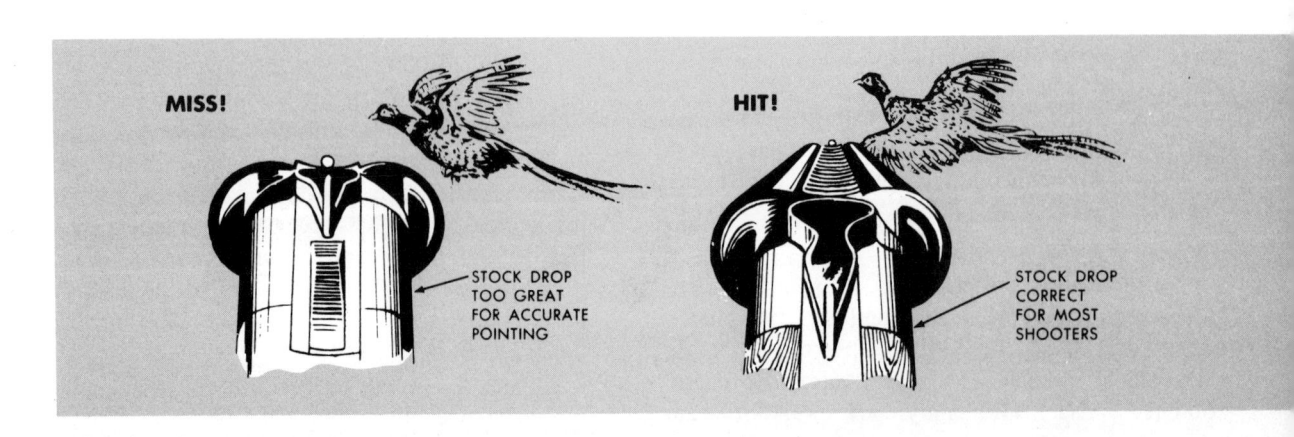

Older shotgunners and those with poor vision often find a muzzle block (or "bandage") helpful in getting onto a flushed bird. It's just a block of wood (size determined by trial), painted flat black and taped to the barrel at the muzzle. Young shooters and beginners shouldn't use this device while training, however

Test the stock length by cradling the gun in your shooting arm as shown below. When raised to this horizontal position, the stock should seat snugly in the bend of your elbow

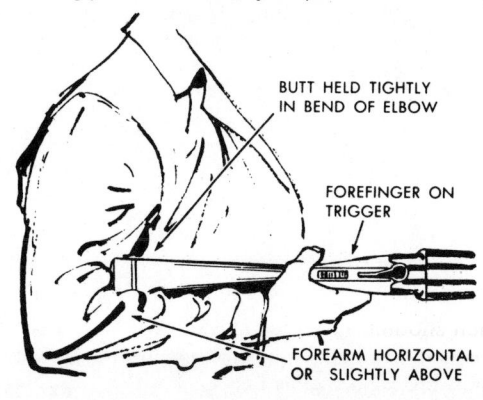

Shotshell reloaders should carry a pocketful of dowel plugs to insert in fired shells. The plugs keep the sleeve from being crushed until it can be reloaded later

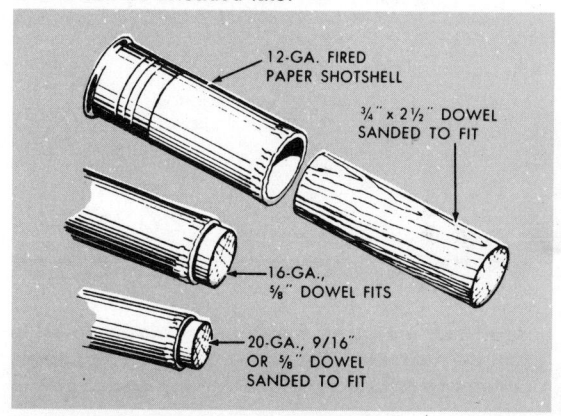

Consistent misses can result from a tendency to cant your gun sideways when shouldering it, as shown below, left. Correct this fault by installing a block front sight or adding a middle sight as indicated in Figs. 2 and 3

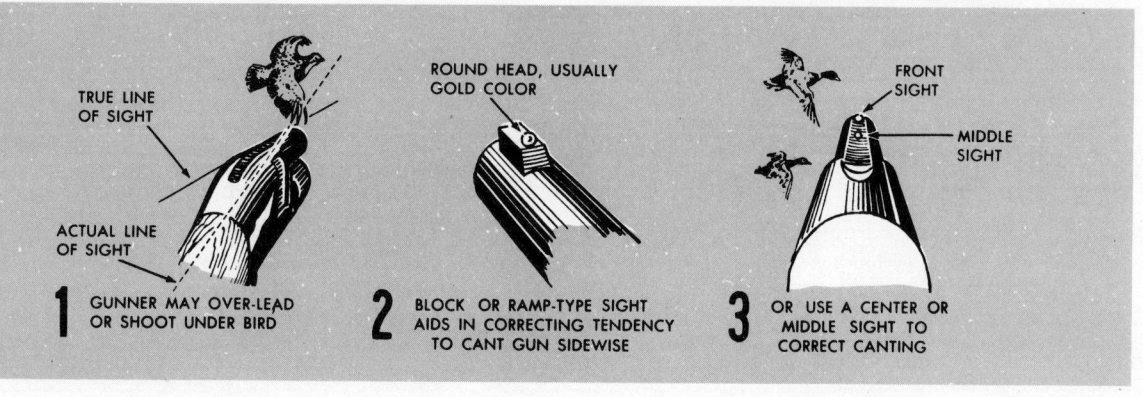

1 GUNNER MAY OVER-LEAD OR SHOOT UNDER BIRD

2 BLOCK OR RAMP-TYPE SIGHT AIDS IN CORRECTING TENDENCY TO CANT GUN SIDEWISE

3 OR USE A CENTER OR MIDDLE SIGHT TO CORRECT CANTING

2335

shotguns

For better hunting, pattern your shotgun

BY W. CLYDE LAMMEY

When you swing
your shotgun on live or clay birds
it's important to know
where the shot charge goes

Fire a single shot at each patterning sheet, then either count the number of pellet holes at the time, or label or otherwise mark the sheet for later reference

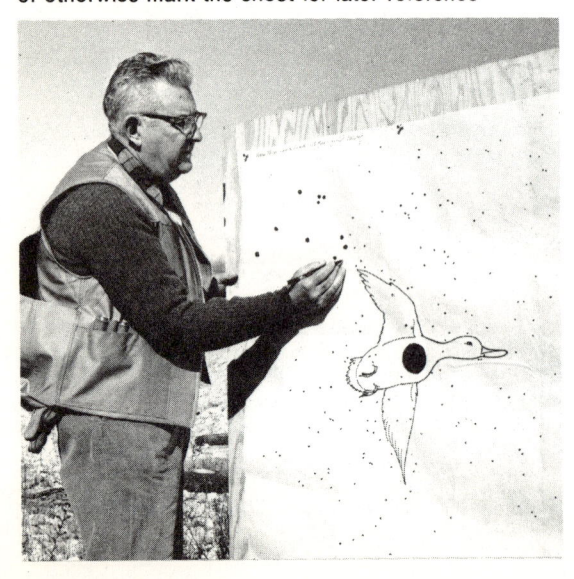

Although stance is important when shooting, it should be relaxed and natural, as suits the individual, with the forward knee slightly bent

Shotgun charges that register consistently off center on the patternboard can tell you how your shotgun fits you. In practice you don't aim a scattergun as you do a rifle and this is why correct shotgun fit is just as essential, perhaps even more essential to high score shooting, as is rifle fit. In shotgun handling one must move fast. Only speed, coordination and proper gun fit count when at most you have only seconds to get off a shot that connects. This is why one should pattern every shotgun he owns, whether these be newly acquired, or old, untested favorites.

If, for example, you are shooting a scattergun with a stock a bit too short for you, you may find on pattern-board testing that the charges register consistently to the right of center and possibly a little low. On the other hand, if the stock pull length is greater than you require individually, you may discover that the charges tend to pattern a little to the left of center and likely a trifle high, assuming, of course, you are right-handed. In either case the bird is likely to be caught in the fringes of the shot pattern or may be missed entirely. If the stock drop is too great, you may find the charges landing con-

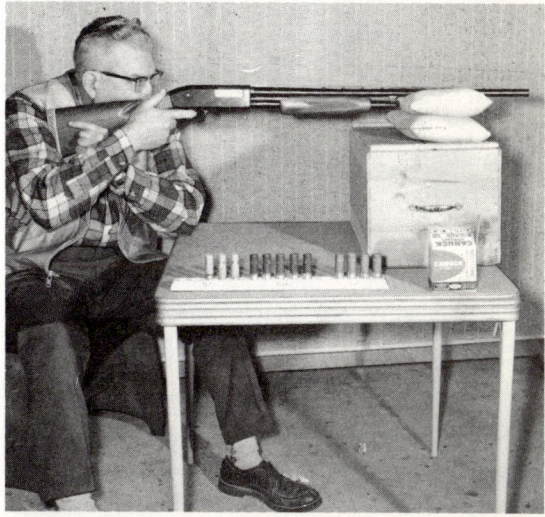

Here's a simple setup for firing from rest. As a safety measure when firing varying gauges, use varicolored shells—red for 12, blue for 16, and yellow for 20 gauge

This is another view of what is generally accepted as a proper stance for offhand firing at a pattern board. Dry firing can be of help in taking the stance quickly

To determine pattern uniformity, also, percentages, scribe a 30-in. diameter circle around the greatest concentration of pellet holes. See p. 2338 for detail

2337

shotguns

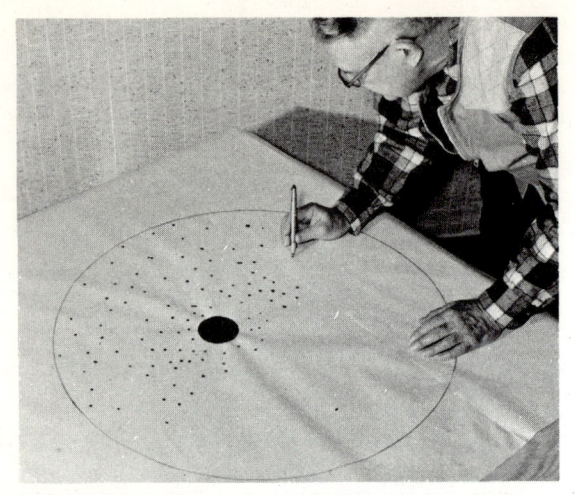

Using a felt marker and counting as you go, check the number of pellet holes inside the circle. The number of pellets may vary from shot to shot, but the average should be fairly close

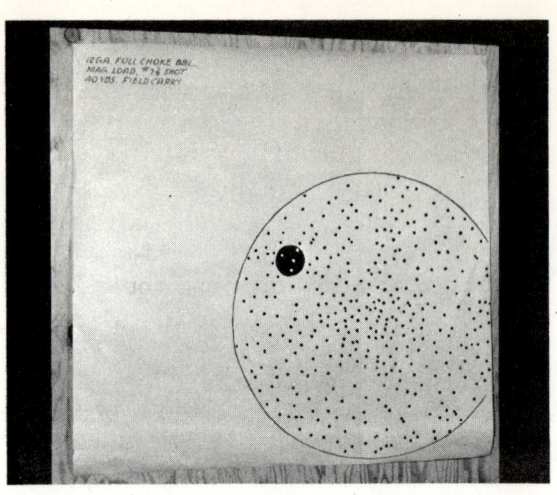

If your gun stock is too short you may find that shot charges are registering consistently low and perhaps a little to the right, as indicated by the distribution in this pattern

sistently low and if the stock is too straight for you individually, the charges may register consistently above center. There are, of course, other factors governing gun fit but these variations usually are considered primary.

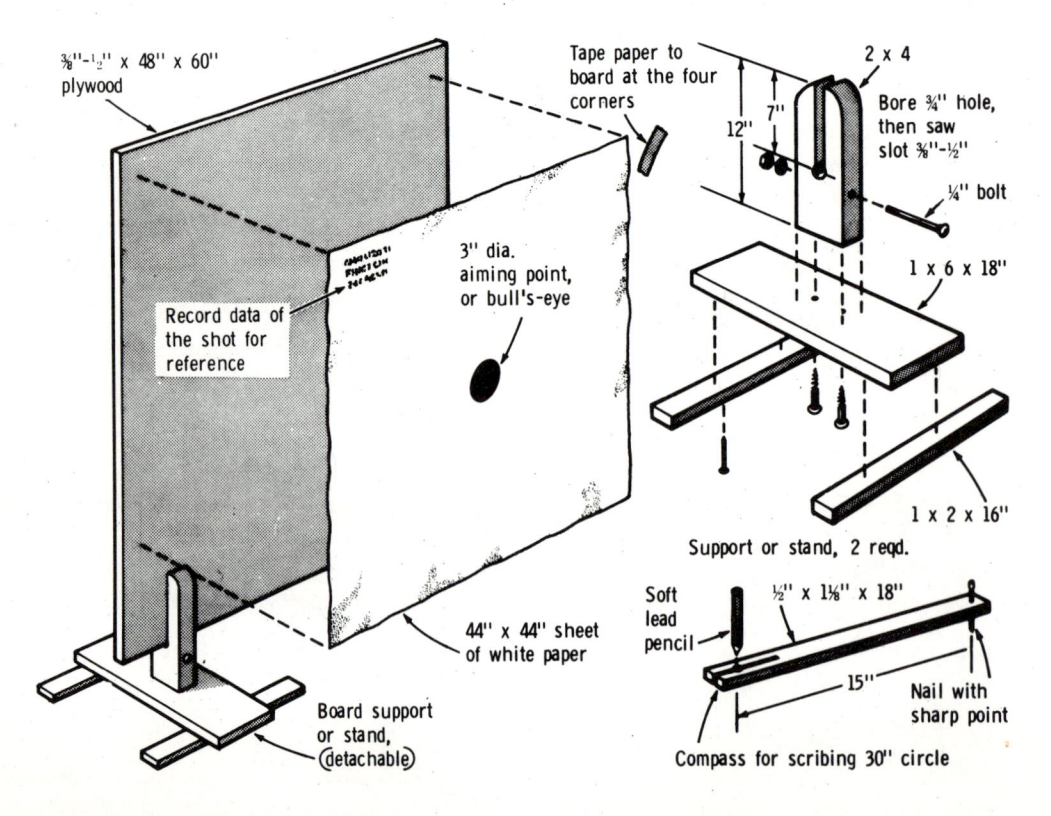

Patterning is a simple procedure but one must be prepared to burn considerable ammo in order to arrive at definite conclusions. You'll need the pattern board and quite a number of sheets of paper roughly of the size and dimensions detailed, the paper sheets each having a bull's eye or bird outline as an aiming point. The pattern board should be set up before a steep slope or in some other location where it is safe to fire a shotgun. A distance of 40 yds. from the pattern board is the generally accepted range for testing full choked 12, 16 and 20-gauge shotguns. The smaller gauges, 28 and .410 bores, also the more open borings in the larger gauges, are usually tested at shorter ranges. Make a mark or drive a stake at the 40-yd. firing position. Don the clothing you normally wear afield—for the first tests a light hunting shirt and jacket.

Move diagonally away from the stake a few steps to the right or left, then turn and approach the stake with the gun in the field-carry position. On reaching the firing point mount the gun and fire quickly, without "aiming," just as you would at a moving target. The first trials of this maneuver may be difficult to bring off consistently as you will be more fully conscious of the gun, the target, and also of the fact that in this procedure the factors of gun swing and lead have been eliminated. But if one persists—dry runs may help—in the maneuver, it's possible to duplicate a typical field stance and to carry out gun mounting and pointing with a consistency and accuracy sufficient for the purpose. Fire only one shot at a time and carefully note the position of the charge as tagged by the pattern paper. Then remove the paper, replace with a fresh sheet and repeat the performance until a consistency in placement of the charges becomes unmistakably evident. All charges may continue to land on center—allowing for inaccuracies in pointing—or they may tend to land right, left, high or low.

try heavier clothing

Before you make any corrective stock alterations, such as lengthening or shortening the pull length, or raising or lowering the comb height, change to heavier clothing such as you would wear in cold weather, and run another series of test shots. It's likely you will turn up some variations, using the same gun and ammo. As an example, if your gun places its charges consistently to the right and low you may discover

AVERAGE NO. OF SHOT PELLETS IN COMMON LOADINGS*
Weight of charge in ounces

Shot Size	¾	⅞	1	1⅛	1¼
9	439	512	585	658	731
8	308	359	410	462	512
7½	263	305	350	394	438
6	169	197	225	254	281
5	128	149	170	191	213
4	101	118	135	152	169

* Figures are only approximate for the number of pellets for each shot size.

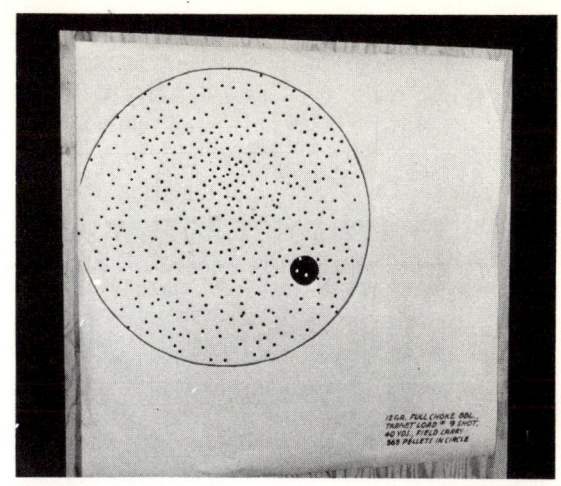

On the other hand, if the shot charges consistently land to the left and high, the stock may be too long for you individually. A gunsmith can correct this at a nominal cost

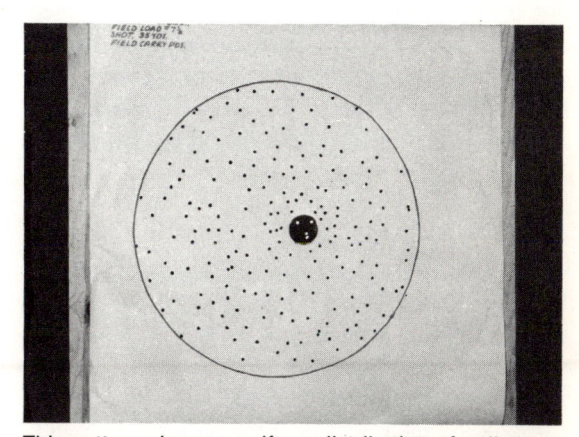

This pattern shows a uniform distribution of pellets from a 20-gauge modified choke barrel at 35 yds. The concentration is to the left—likely a pointing error

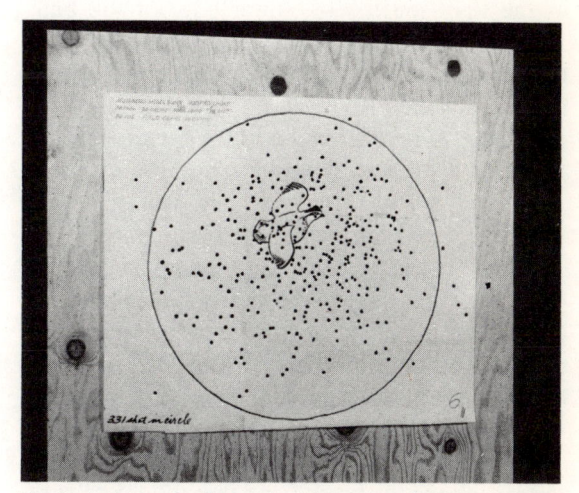

No. 9 shot size is shown in this pattern from a .410 bore insert in a 12-gauge full choke barrel at a range of 25 yds. Note that the charge is centered and rather tightly concentrated

that when you don heavy clothing the charges tend to land on center, give or take a little. In this case the extra thickness of heavy clothing has, in effect, lengthened the stock. Should the stock be a little too long, you may find you're throwing charges halfway off the board when you're heavily clad. Usually there's less variation when the gun tends to throw charges high or low of center consistently, but you may detect some variable even here when comparing the effect of light and heavy clothing.

On discovery of any of these variations you have two corrective choices: either alter the stock as required or adapt your shooting practices to correct the tendency. The latter can be done with practice in handling. You can raise the comb if required with a lace-on type pad. The stock can be lengthened with spacers placed under the buttplate or butt pad. Other stock alterations involving reworking the wood, such as thinning the comb, should be done by an experienced gunsmith, unless, of course, you have had experience in this exacting work. But many of the variables can be corrected simply by altering handling practices.

patterning from rest

Many trapshooters, also skeet shooters and hunters, like to "float" the bird, that is, see it over the gun barrel or barrels, and to determine even more precisely where the gun throws its charge they often pattern from a rest. A sturdy card table will do for this testing. You'll also need a small box and padding to serve as a rest for the gun barrel or barrels. With this setup it's the usual practice to let off each shot just as the sight touches the lower edge of the bull. Here a steady hold is important and at first you may have a little trouble with trigger pull, which usually is somewhat heavier on a shotgun than on a rifle. Also, one may have to become accustomed to the relatively heavy recoil of a shotgun, especially in larger gauges and with magnum loadings. If you flinch, the shots will go wild.

When properly carried out, this test will show just where the gun places its charge relative to the aiming point. Also, it offers an opportunity to test placement of charges from the right and left barrels of side-by-side doubles and over-under guns. Your line of sight in this test—as in those described previously—should be about ¼ to ⅜ in. above the breech and one should be sure the line of sight is centered over the rib before firing.

If desired, patterning tests can be carried farther to determine other governing factors and a "best" load for your particular gun. In patterning for a best loading you may discover a special compatibility of your gun for a certain factory or hand loading in light, medium or heavy chargings of powder and shot. One scattergun may consistently turn in its best patterns with a magnum loading. Another of the same gauge and boring may perform best with a light target (skeet or trap load) or field loading. In this testing, as well as those described previously, you may have to fire a dozen or more shots to reach a more or less definite conclusion.

aim for consistency

The perfect pattern is a consistent uniformity of shot distribution inside a 30-in. circle at ranges suitable to the boring—40 yds. for full choke (12, 16 and 20 gauges), 30–35 yds. for modified and improved modified borings and between 20 and 30 yds. for the skeet and improved cylinder and full cylinder borings. Shot distribution should show a reasonably consistent uniformity at these ranges. There should be no large, irregular holes in the pattern print and no undue bunching or cartwheels, and only a small number of flyers, the latter being deformed pellets which land wide of the main concentration. If you fire the newer shot shells with combined plastic shot cups and wad columns, you may see few, if any, flyers. The 28-gauge and .410-bore guns usually give the best pattern prints at the shorter ranges, 25 to 30 yds. average, and these generally perform best with the smaller shot sizes, such as No. 7½, 8 and 9.

determining shot percentages

It's easy to arrive at the shot percentages. Make a simple compass of 15 in. radius like that detailed, lay the pattern sheet on a flat surface, determine the greatest concentration of pellet holes and strike a circle around this area. Then, using a felt marker, mark the shot holes in the paper within the 30-in. circle, counting as you go. Some testers count the shot holes on the line as well. Then, for example, if there are, say, 300 holes in the circle and the average number of shot pellets per shell is 400, then 300 times 100 divided by 400 equals 75, or 75 percent pattern. These are only convenience figures, of course, but they show how percentages can be arrived at. The percentages will vary somewhat from shot to shot and if you desire a further average, then it will be necessary to fire a minimum of 10 shots or so to determine this figure.

clever ideas

Small squares and rectangular workpieces to be drilled are rather difficult to hold with conventional clamps on the drill-press table. Use a machinist's clamp having two steel pins in each jaw and you'll get the job done easily and more accurately. The jaws of a machinist's clamp are machined all over to the same dimensions; they lay perfectly flat and hold the workpiece securely when the jaws are tightened. Try this idea the next time you have a small piece to drill on your press.

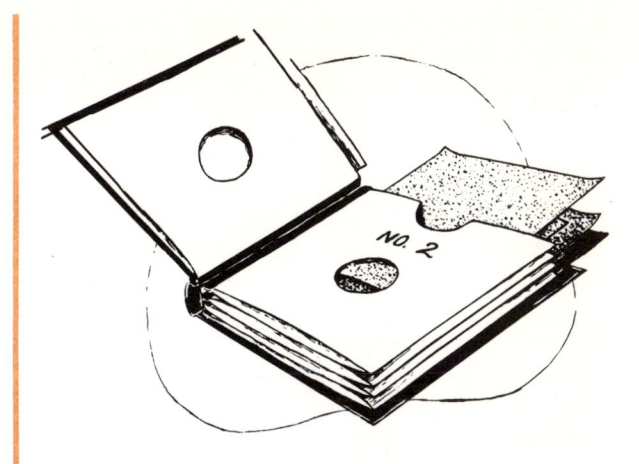

No doubt you have often wished for some simple way to store sandpaper where any grit size you might need would be readily findable and the sheet always in good condition for use, clean and unwrinkled. Then why not use a record album? It's ready-made, inexpensive and suits the purpose to a "T." Several sheets of a single grade of sandpaper can be kept in each album envelope and you can mark the sizes on the envelope or read them through the round opening.

Suppose you need to know the diameter of a piece of tubing, pipe, or any other round of metal or wood and there's nothing at hand but an adjustable wrench and a folding rule. You can't measure the round accurately with either tool, but by combining the two in the simple setup pictured you can come so very close that the measurement will do for all practical purposes. Don't tighten the wrench jaws on the tube; just run the adjustable jaw up lightly, measure between the tips, and you have the diameter.

Indentations of the regular C-clamp pad are difficult if not impossible to remove without changing the dimension of the stock either by planing or sanding. You can easily avoid this damage by placing a plastic or rubber caster cup under the regular C-clamp pad before tightening the screw. The caster cup does two things: protects the surface of the work from dents and distributes the clamping pressure over a much greater area. The caster-cup pads can be used with all types and sizes of C-clamps.

2341

shovel, power toy

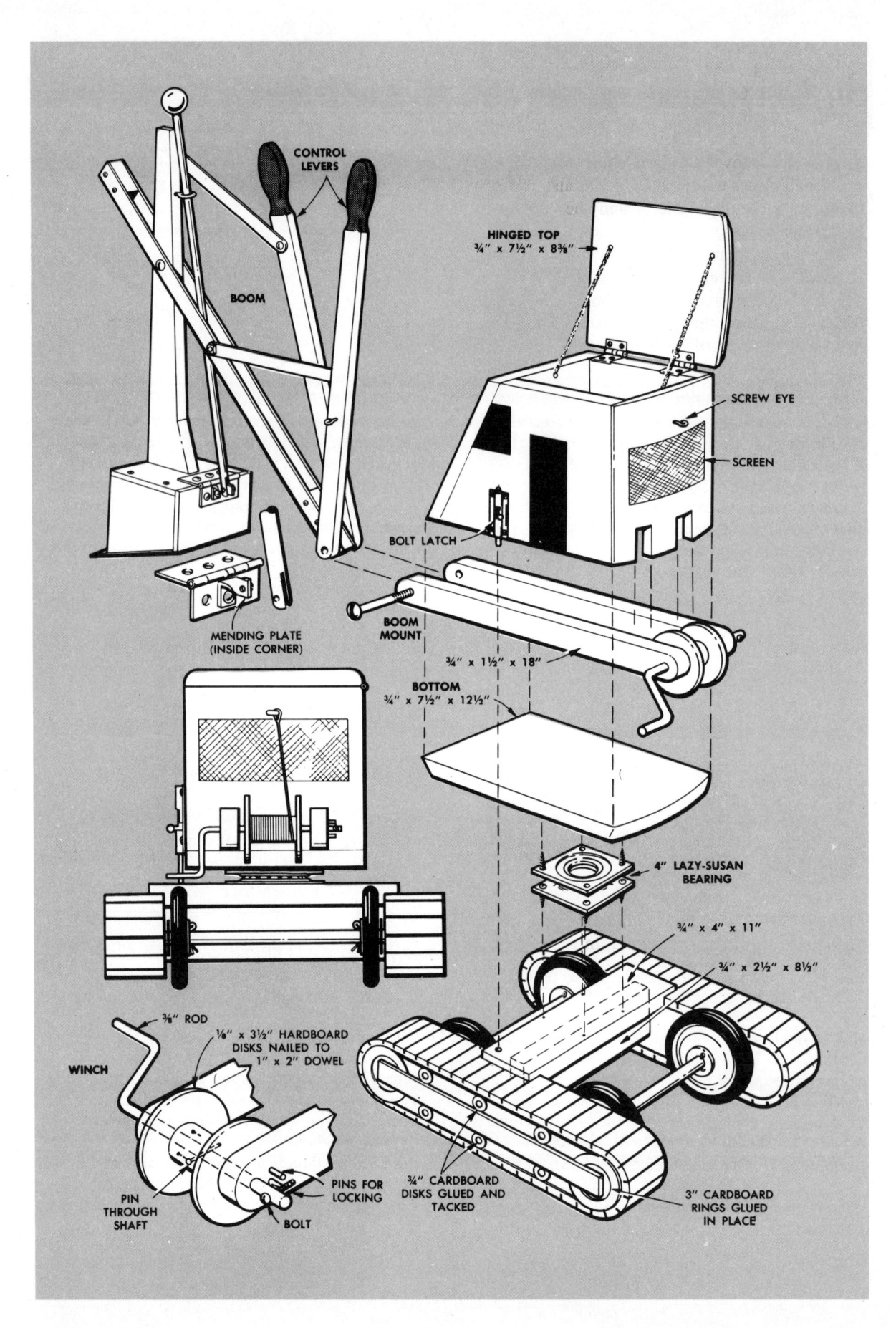

2342

Little digger for junior engineers

BY RON ANDERSON

Junior construction engineers can ride this toy power shovel that operates realistically by using hand controls

■ JUNIOR'S EARTH-MOVING and road-building programs will be greatly extended with this toy power shovel. Comfortably seated on the cab, he pushes himself about and can swivel in any direction. One control lever operates the boom, another the shovel position, while a push rod opens and closes the shovel. There's also a winch to use as a "stump puller," and the cab opens to store valuables.

Dummy traction treads are mounted on two pairs of holders, each pair fitted with spacers. The four pieces having rounded ends are stacked and clamped together so axle holes can be drilled in alignment. Two of these pieces are assembled to a T-shaped crosspiece with waterproof glue and screws. Then the spacers are glued and nailed on and the two outside pieces are attached similarly.

The cleated treads are made from two strips of ⅜-in. white pine. Saw kerfs 5/16 in. deep, and spaced ¾ in., are cut across them. The strips are soaked with water at points where they are to be bent over the rounded ends of the tread holders. The treads are cut out to fit around the ends of the chassis crosspiece, and are attached with waterproof glue and brads, two brads to each cleat. Treads project ¼ in. beyond the outer tread holders.

Ends of the axles come almost flush with the outer surface of the tread holders. Axles are drilled for cotter pins, then slipped through one tread holder, wheels and washers added, then slipped through the other tread holder, after which the cotter pins are installed. Use 5-in. rubber-tired wheels which will project ⅝ in. below the tread holders.

Dummy drive and bearing wheels for treads can be made of cardboard (Bristol board) as shown in the lower right detail on page 2342. They are glued and bradded in place, later painted and then coated with spar varnish to seal out moisture. The bearing wheels also can

2343

shovel, power toy

be cut from tin cans or from polyethylene-plastic food containers. Wooden side plates, projecting over the drive wheels and fitting between the bearing wheels, are nailed on.

A 4-in. standard lazy-susan bearing is screwed to the chassis crosspiece. Later, after cab assembly, the upper plate of the bearing is screwed to the cab bottom, it being possible to drive the screws when the top plate is turned 45 deg. as shown in lower left detail on this page. If you can't get such a bearing, just use two 3-in. metal disks drilled centrally and greased to reduce friction, assembling these on a bolt with large washers under head and nut.

The shovel arm, its two sides, and the control levers are made of ¾-in. wood, while the back, bottom and front are ¼-in. stock. A 1-in. angle bracket, twisted at one end, forms the mending plate on the hinge and connects to a push rod which opens and closes the bottom of the shovel.

The push rod passes through a screw eye which is turned down far enough to provide friction on the rod and prevents the shovel from opening by itself. A ball knob is drilled to fit on the end of the push rod and is pinned to it. Control levers and boom pivot on a bolt that passes through the boom mount, washers being used between the parts.

The boom mount is drilled at both ends and is fastened to the cab bottom with screws, no glue being used. Front and back have two slots that fit over the boom mount. After assembling the cab it is set over the boom mount and on the bottom. Wood screws then are driven through the bottom into the sides. An ordinary door bolt on the cab side locks it to the chassis crosspiece. A screw hook on the cab front engages a screw eye on the boom-control lever to hold the shovel up when it is in traveling position.

The winch is installed on the rear end of the

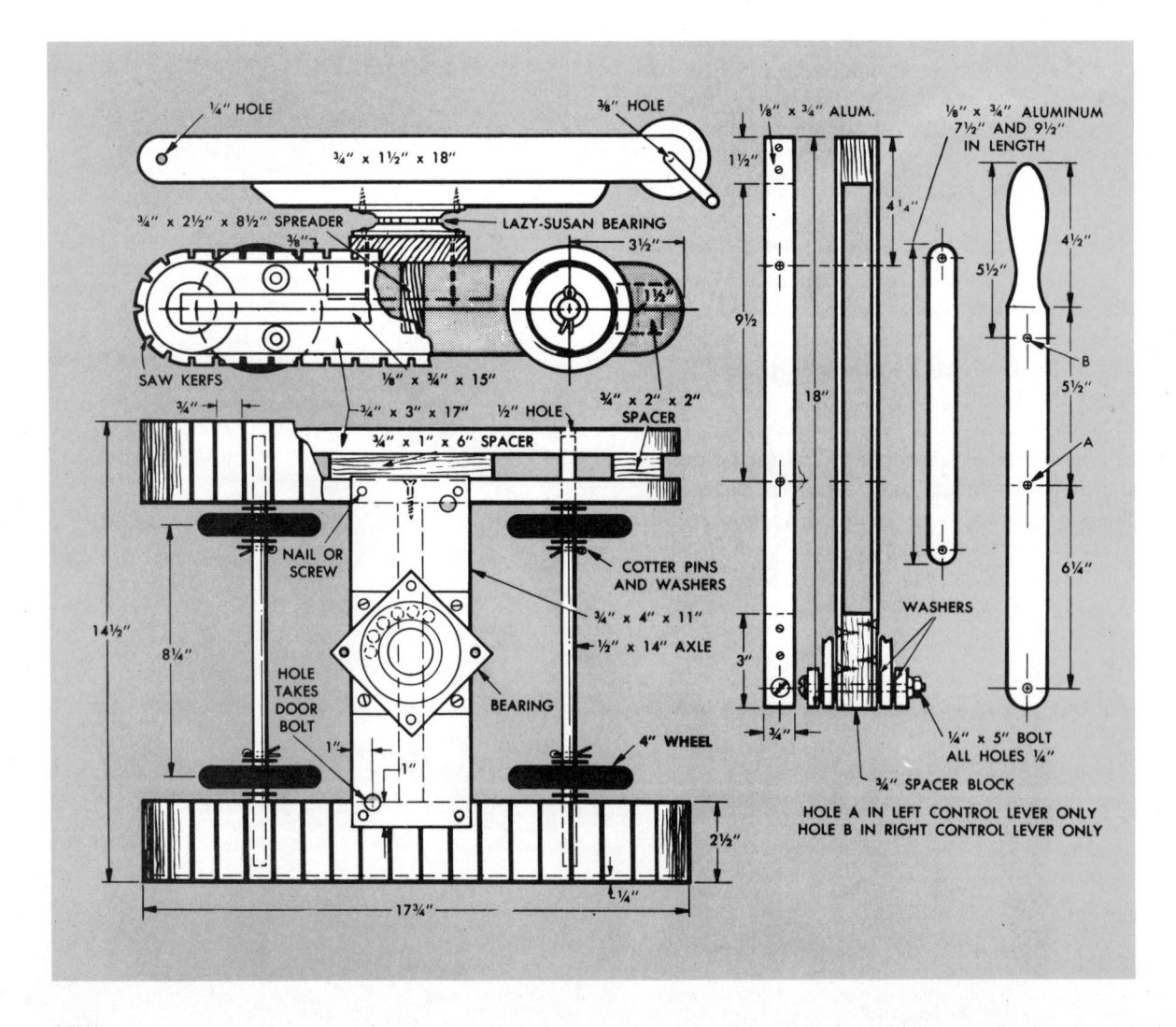

boom mount. There should be enough clearance between the winch drum and the boom mount so the drum can move endwise permitting a bolt at the end of the crank to slide between two pins on the boom mount to lock the winch. Nylon cord is fastened to the drum and is provided with an S-hook made of No. 11-ga. wire, for easy attachment to objects to be pulled. When not in use the cord is wound up on the drum and the S-hook is clipped in a screw eye on the cab.

It is advisable to partly disassemble the unit for painting. The chassis is flat black; the treads and dummy wheels are aluminum and the side plates red. The cab is red as are the handles of the control levers. The rest of the levers are black, as are the doors, windows, boom mount and the ventilating grille, which is cut from ordinary screen and tacked in place.

See also: cannons, toy; duplicator; games, children's; machine gun, toy; magic; toys.

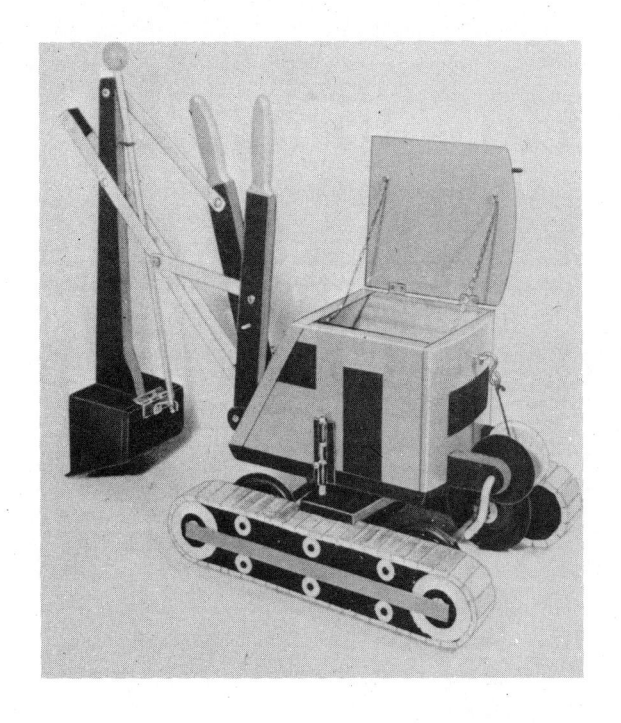

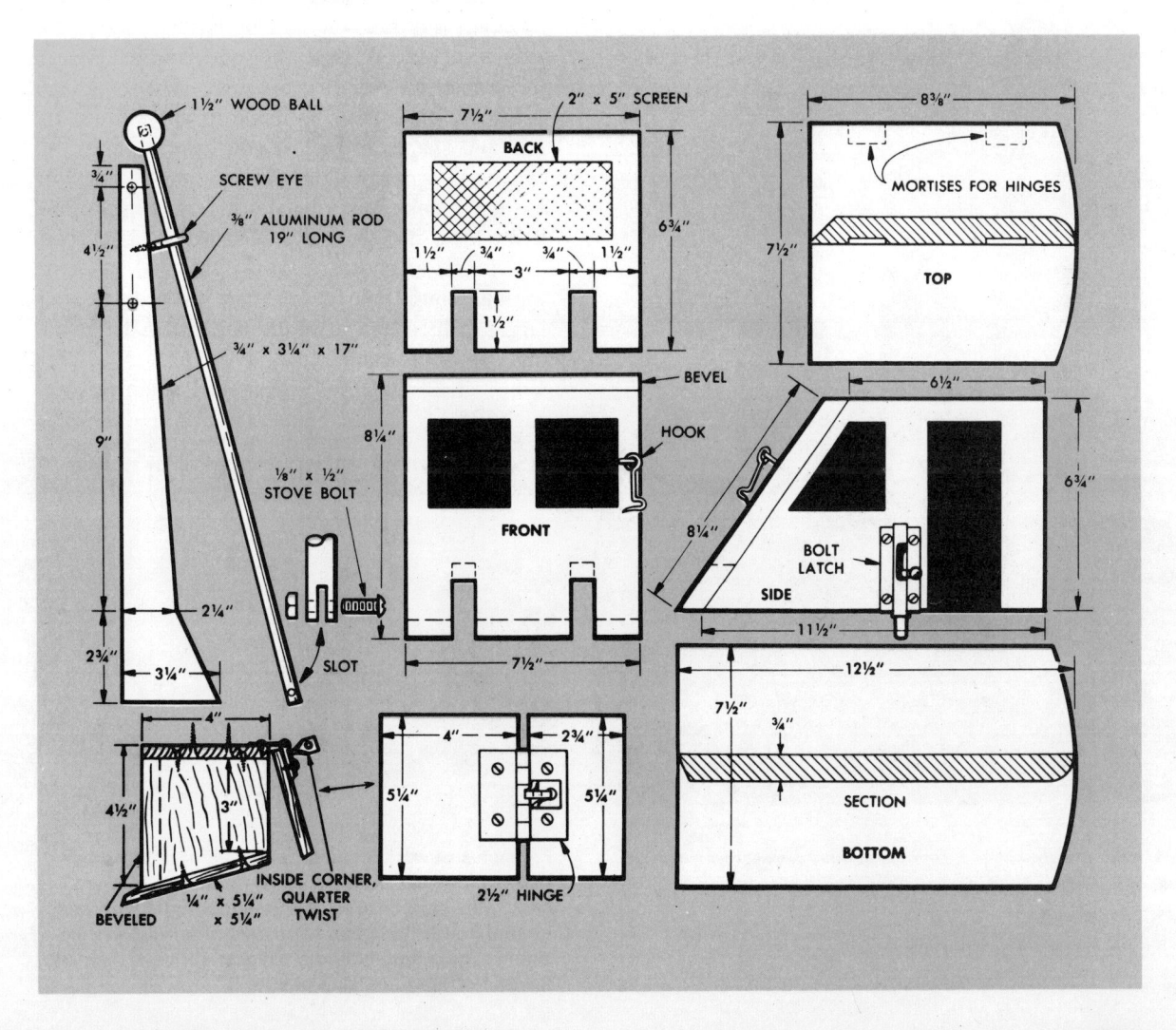

shrink plate

How to make a shrink plate

BY WALTER E. BURTON

There are many times, when you work with metal tubes or shafts, that it would be handy to be able to taper them. Now you can do it

PUTTING THE SQUEEZE on metal with a "swiss-cheese" die is an old trick clockmakers have used for years when they wanted to reduce in size the ends of shafts and tubes. Called a shrink plate, it's nothing more than a block of steel full of tapered holes of different diameters. Here's how it works:

Say you want to slim down the end of a brass tube so it can be joined to another tube in a lap joint. All you do is apply a little oil to the right size hole in the plate, place the tube in it and proceed to shrink the end by either smacking it with a soft-faced mallet or squeezing it between the jaws of a vise.

Shrink plates can be made in any convenient size and shape. In fact, if you have a lathe, you can make a single-hole die by simply chucking a steel blank and taper-boring it. For normal home-shop use the plate need not be hardened. Lay it out as shown above, right, and work up to maximum hole diameter with progressively larger drills. Then ream to final size. After reaming, smooth each hole with abrasive cloth wrapped around the reamer and chamfer them slightly.

See also: drilling; lathe accessories; lathe techniques; punch; strike plate.

Examples of work include (left to right) aluminum body of a center punch shrunk around a hardened shank, the copper tube of an embossing tool shrunk around a steel ball, and two types of ferrule. On the right is the single-hole die used to shrink a disk into the end of the tube lying next to it

shrubs: see landscaping; propagating, shrubs
sickles: see honing
sidewalk cars: see cars, sidewalk

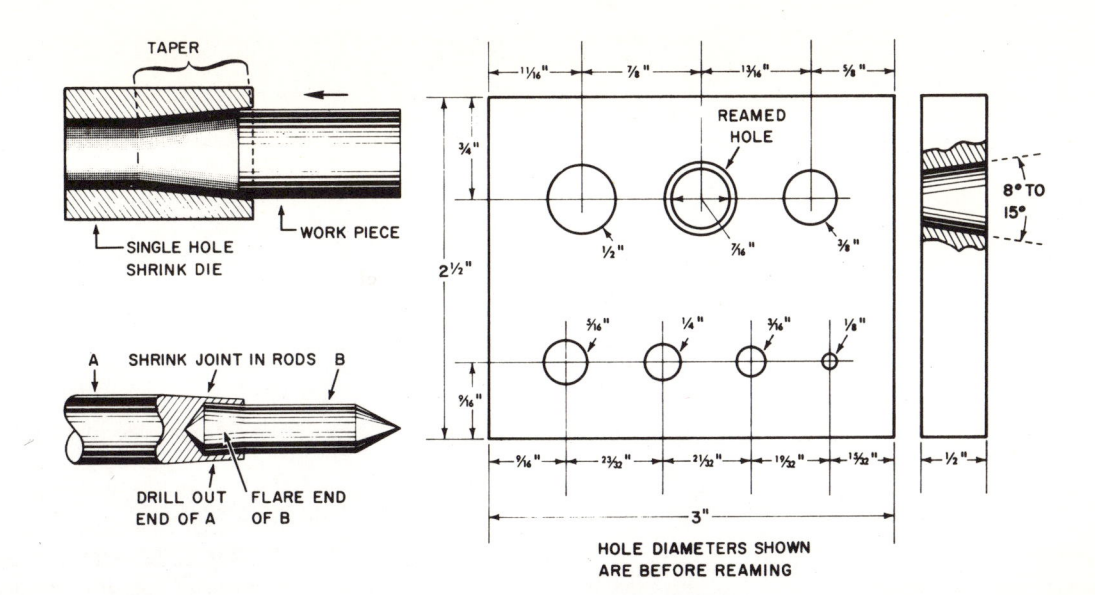

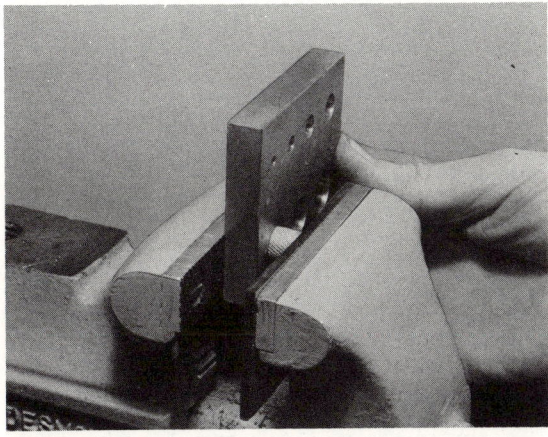

When the workpiece is short, it can be squeezed into the tapered hole by placing both the plate and the work between the jaws of a bench vise. Because of close control of both pressure and alignment, a neat job is the result

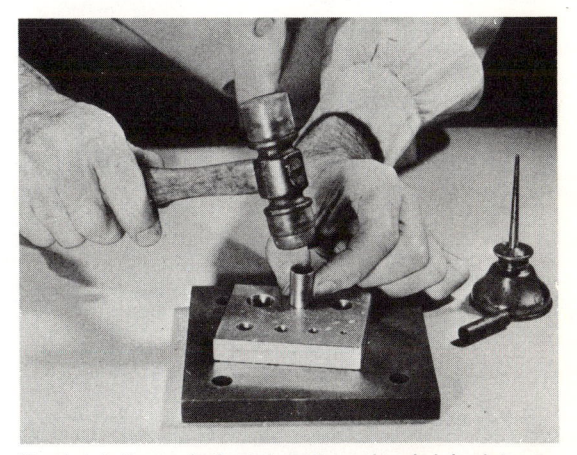

To shrink the end of a tube, place the shrink plate on a solid surface, apply a little light oil to the hole to be used and strike the tube with a soft-faced mallet. The end will be neatly tapered when the tube is removed from the hole

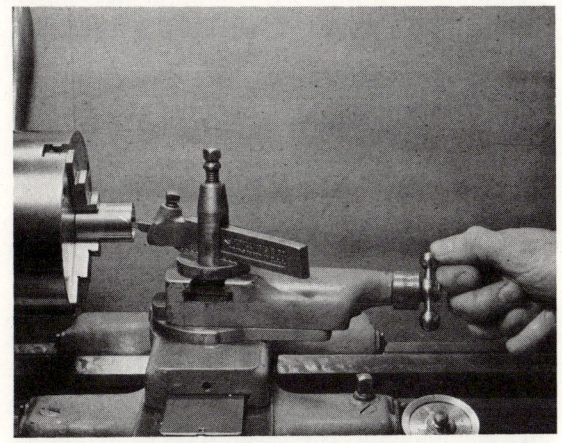

A single-hole die is made by lathe-boring a tapered hole in a cylindrical blank. The taper is formed by feeding the bit with the compound rest set at 5 deg. The taper need not extend the full length of the die. See the drawing at the top of the page

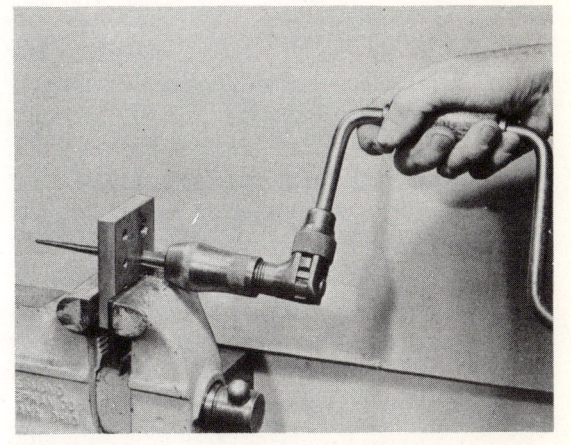

After each hole is drilled with progressively larger drills, it is tapered from top to bottom. Here a brace is used to ream the larger holes. For smaller holes, you can use a taper-pin reamer. Use a cutting oil to lubricate during tapering

2347

siding

Choose the right siding

The ease of installing the new vinyl siding is dramatically illustrated in this photo as it goes over a well-weathered clapboard siding. Furring strips are needed along with window casing sealers

BY RICHARD NUNN

There are lots of smart materials to make your home sparkle like new

THE RANGE of siding materials available to you is so broad you can dress up your home almost any way you wish. For example, in aluminum siding alone there are 15 colors, 7 textures and 12 designs that produce at least 1260 variations. Added to this are designs and textures in plywood, hardboard, vinyl, asbestos-cement, redwood, cedar shakes and shingles, regular wood and fiberglass siding.

Vinyl siding is the newest on the market, and vinyl also is being used to coat wood and metal sidings to increase their durability and decrease maintenance. Vinyl siding is manufactured from a plastic called polyvinyl chloride (PVC). The big features are an end to maintenance and painting. The colors go completely through the material, and only an occasional washing with a mild detergent and water keeps it looking new. Also, it won't dent, scar, corrode, stain or scratch.

The material is manufactured in regular double 4 and 6-in. clapboard designs and single 6 and 8-in. sizes. A vertical 8-in. board is also available; it resembles regular tongue-and-groove siding after it has been applied to the house. Installation of the material is nearly identical to putting on aluminum siding. However, a 3/16-in. gap should be left at the end of each "board" that butts against a stop—such as a corner or window—so the material can expand. The panel should also *hang* on the nails. The nails should never be driven in too tightly since the material will expand. This is also true of aluminum. No special tools are required to install vinyl siding

Wood siding is probably the most common and one of the most attractive siding materials available. Most wood siding has a pattern "built in," through a distinctive cutting method. The common types are drop (or rabbeted) and bevel. Rabbeted drop siding has a groove cut along one edge. The lap of each board over the next lower one is determined by the depth of the rabbet. This material is usually 3/4 in. thick and 6 in. wide.

Rabbeted siding, like bevel siding, should always be applied over sheathing. On walls which are too long for coverage by one board, the butt joints between boards should be made at random, so all joints don't appear in a straight line. Galvanized or aluminum nails should be used; the nails should be driven flush with the

This is the new hardboard siding that has the ruggedness of rough-sawn, deep surfacing of lap siding. The metal corners are prefinished to match it

The end walls of this lakeside home utilize Texture One-Eleven plywood siding on both sides of prefabricated panels framed with 2 x 2-in. lumber

surface. At all corners, the ends of the boards must be butted against a corner board or mitered for a pleasing appearance. Water tends to creep into mitered joints more easily than into tightly butted ones. Metal corners are available; they are preformed to fit over the siding and are fastened on with nails.

Bevel siding has one edge thicker than the other. The board in cross section looks like a wedge. The thin edge is usually 3/16 in. thick; the thick edge varies from 1/2 in. to 3/4 in. The boards are available in 4, 6, 8, 10 and 12-in. widths. In estimating your job, remember that the boards overlap each other, so no board will cover its maximum width.

Lay out your siding job so the bottom of one board will occur at the bottom of the window sill and the bottom of another board will run right over the top of the window frame. This produces a much neater appearance and eliminates cutting.

Horizontal and vertical aluminum siding, which is prefinished in a variety of colors, textures and designs, forms a sidewall that will probably outlast the framework of the building. It is manufactured in Double-Four (two 4-in. panels on one 8-in. siding piece); Double-Five (two 5-in. exposures on one 10-in. siding piece); Dutch-Lap with special contours that produce a Dutch Colonial effect; vertical that is 8 in. flat with no bends or contours, except for interlocking grooves; vertical 10-in. board and batten or V-groove effect; and vertical 12-in. board and batten or V-groove effect. Textures include rough, horizontal wood grains, vertical wood grains, stucco effects, embossed and basketweave effects. The lengths of the "boards" run from 10 to 15 ft.

Plywood siding has many features including beauty, strength, high insulation values, economy and durability. It comes in many grades and surface textures including reverse board and batten (with deep, wide grooves cut into brushed, rough-sawn, coarse-sanded or natural textured surfaces); rough-sawn and kerfed; circular-sawn; brushed; fine-line with fine grooves cut into the surface; striated; medium density overlaid; MDO reverse board and batten, and MDO horizontal lapped.

This material, as thin as 5/16-in., can be applied over plywood and other wall sheathing with studs on either 16 or 24-in. centers. "Sturd-i-wall" construction, where the plywood is applied directly to the studs, is accepted by the Federal Housing Administration and most local building codes. The technique can save as much as 20 percent over a conventional two-layer wall.

Hardboard siding is manufactured in lap siding and panels. The lap variety ranges in size

siding

from 6 to 12 in. and up to 16 ft. in length. It may be applied over sheathed or unsheathed walls with stud spacing not more than 16 in. on center. If you use a hardboard siding with a factory-applied primer, it must be painted within 60 days after installation. You can, however, re-prime it with a quality exterior-grade oil-base primer.

Hardboard panel siding comes in 4 in. widths up to 16 ft. in length. The same general application recommendations for lap siding apply here. For batten strips at the vertical joints you may use either wood or strips of the siding cut to the desired width. Intermediate batten strips may be used for design purposes. Some factory prefinished siding comes with matching plastic or metal snap-on batten strips. The sizes available are 4 x 7 ft., 4 x 8 ft., 4 x 9 ft. and 4 x 10 ft. Thicknesses are ¼, ³⁄₁₆ and ⅛ in. The recommendations above apply only to ¼-in. panels. For panels of other thicknesses, be sure to consult your lumber dealer for recommendations.

Cedar shingles and shakes have been popular as a roofing and siding material for centuries. In the early days of this nation, cedar shakes were split by hand from sections of cedar logs.

For siding, three types are generally used: rebutted-rejoined shingles, machine-grooved shakes and handsplit shakes. Rebutted-rejoined shingles are precision-trimmed for sidewall use, both single-coursed and double-coursed. The edges have been machined to close tolerances, and the butts are trimmed at right angles to the edges. Often these shingles have been face-sanded to provide a smoother surface for finishing. The shingles are sold in cartons, with 56 courses of 18-in. shingles per carton, and 66 courses of 16-in.

Machine-grooved shakes are also called "processed" shakes. They have a striated or grooved face with parallel edges and squared butts. You may apply them double-coursed on exterior walls with an underlay of low-grade shingles or insulation-board sheathing. Two sizes are available—16 and 18 in.—with a weather exposure of 12 and 14 in. They are packed in a carton that provides 100 sq. ft. of covering to these exposures.

Handsplit shakes come in three different types: handsplit and resawn, tapersplit and straightsplit. Generally, the length for all three is 24 in.; however, 18 and 32 in. are sometimes referred to as "standard" sizes. You can buy them in 4-bundle, 5-bundle and 6-bundle squares, depending whether they are packaged in 20-in. or 18-in. "frames." If your home is already shingled and you want to replace a section or one shingle, you often can buy all three in "broken" lots.

When buying this material, keep in mind that it's sold by the "square"—a roofing term meaning that a square will cover 100 sq. ft. of roof, not sidewall. Since the sidewall exposure will usually be greater than a roof, a square will cover more than 100 sq. ft.

Asbestos-cement siding and shingles are durable, attractive and can be applied over any sidewall surface. Because of their physical properties, they lend themselves to areas where the atmosphere is loaded with chemical fumes and smoke. The size most frequently used measures ⁵⁄₃₂ in. thick by 12 in. wide by 24 in. long. The shingles are applied with a 1½-in. lap, require no undercourse, and have an exposure of 10½-in. An asbestos-cement 4 x 8-ft. panel is also available, along with clapboard or wide siding board. In design, they are made in a straight vertical pattern—similar to striated plywood—in a wood-grain pattern and smooth. Colors are available and they're impregnated throughout the product.

Fiberglass stone and brick is another recent development in the siding field. The material comes in sheet form—usually 2 x 4-ft. pieces—and it can be nailed directly to sheathing or furring strips on existing homes. It's basically made from fiberglass—plus additives—so it is resistant to the weather, chemicals, etc. Only an occasional hosing down with water is required to keep it looking like new. On one brand, Roxite, the edges are lapped and nailed. After the panels are up, a special caulking compound is provided so the joints can be "tuckpointed." This operation is done with a regular caulking gun. The "mortar" is then smoothed with a tapered piece of scrap wood. A similar item in the same line is "premortared" so the caulking operation isn't necessary. Other siding includes simulated brick and field stone. It, too, is easy to install over sheathing or existing siding with furring strips and nails.

Corrugated metal siding—steel and aluminum—is manufactured in two styles: 1¼-in. pitch and 2½-in. pitch. Both have a mill finish or a stucco-embossed finish. All styles, widths and thicknesses are available in lengths of 6, 7, 8, 9, 10, 11 and 12 ft.

Fiberglass panels are available in sheet form—both flat and corrugated—for siding jobs such as patio enclosures and windscreens. Many colors are available.

See also: building; finishes, urethane; nails; remodeling, exterior; sheathing.

Use the right nail for exterior siding

It's a matter of choosing a nonrusting nail and the proper design in head, shank and point

■ IF YOU'RE CONTEMPLATING an exterior remodeling job involving natural wood siding, such as redwood, it's important that you familiarize yourself with the special nailing procedures involved.

Never use a nail that will rust for exterior work (and this includes cement-coated nails). Stick with aluminum or stainless steel, if possible. Hot-dipped galvanized nails are sometimes satisfactory, but you may find that the galvanizing flakes off when you drive them, and if this happens, you're likely to get those ugly black corrosion stains.

As for the head design, there are three types commonly used with natural wood siding. A regular siding nail, which is the best choice for most work, has a slightly tapered head which can be either driven flush or countersunk. If you're definitely planning on countersinking, a casing-head nail is probably just as good. Finishing nails are best for blind-nailing tongue-and-groove siding.

Shank design is also important. The standard smooth, round shank has sufficient holding power for most applications. If you're bothered by nails loosening, however, replace with the spiral or annular-grooved type.

Even the point is important. Regular diamond-pointed nails are easy to drive and have excellent withdrawal resistance. On the other hand, a needle point or chisel point drives like a tiny wedge, and this is more likely to result in splitting. A large manufacturer of redwood siding recommends the use of special siding nails that have thin, grooved shanks for improved holding power and blunt points to prevent splitting.

When you're nailing short lengths or ends, which are particularly vulnerable to splitting, predrill the holes before driving nails.

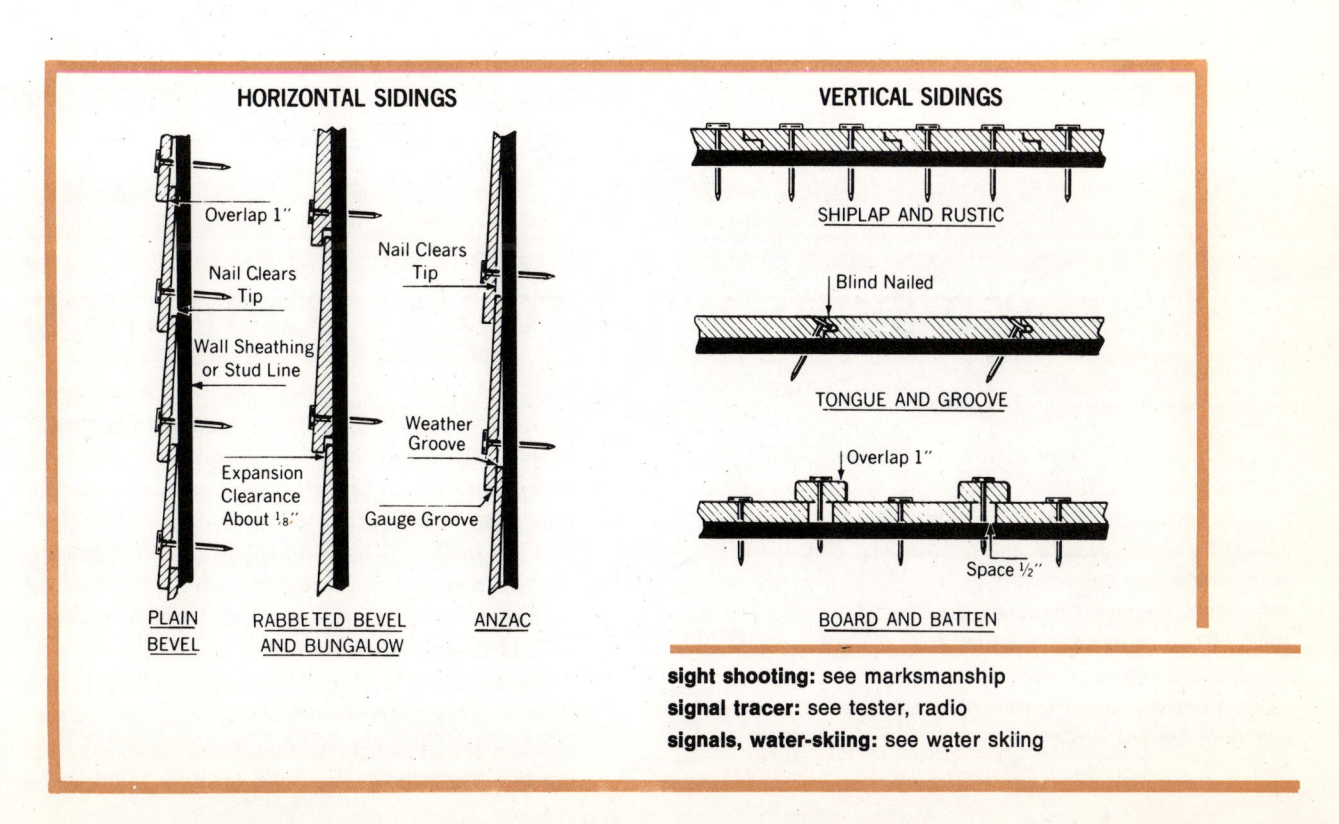

HORIZONTAL SIDINGS

- PLAIN BEVEL — Overlap 1", Nail Clears Tip, Wall Sheathing or Stud Line, Expansion Clearance About 1/8"
- RABBETED BEVEL AND BUNGALOW
- ANZAC — Nail Clears Tip, Weather Groove, Gauge Groove

VERTICAL SIDINGS

- SHIPLAP AND RUSTIC
- TONGUE AND GROOVE — Blind Nailed
- BOARD AND BATTEN — Overlap 1", Space 1/2"

sight shooting: see marksmanship
signal tracer: see tester, radio
signals, water-skiing: see water skiing

Carving signs with router templates

BY RAY SHOBERG

silicon cells: see solar motors
silver soldering: see bandsaws, blades
sink, children's: see kitchen, play
sites, home: see home sites
skate sharpener: see ice-skate sharpener
ski boat: see boats, buying

ALL OF US have had some occasion to hand-letter a sign, but most of us are shy about it, except in an emergency. A sign is such a public thing, deliberately calling attention to itself—and to any lack of skill on the part of its creator. Yet we couldn't live without signs—and it's expensive and often inconvenient to seek professional help each time we need one.

Here, at last, is a foolproof technique for making truly professional signs—and you never touch a lettering brush. You don't even have to lay out the letters: it's done for you, automati-

Doors can stay in place for routing, saving the time of removal and avoiding the less-attractive separate signboard. Since veneer on flush doors is thin, make a very shallow cut

Picture outlines such as those above and on page 2352 require special templates. But all lettering can be done with the five templates shown in the Project-a-Plans on page 2495

cally, by an ingenious set of router templates held in a simple frame. Five of them, used in various combinations, let you rout every letter in the alphabet—and all the numbers, too. Yet these templates are easy to make, using the Project-a-Plans on page 2495.

And the signs you end up with are something you'll display with pride. The painted letters are "carved" into the surface, as in signs you've seen in National Parks. One reason this style of signs is so popular in tough maintenance areas is that it lasts forever. Weather can't erase it, and even if the paint wears away, the letters are still readable.

The sketches on page 2355 show how the system works. An adjustable frame holds the

signs

A template tip to fit your router must be purchased and attached to the base with two screws. The tip guides the cutter neatly along template slots

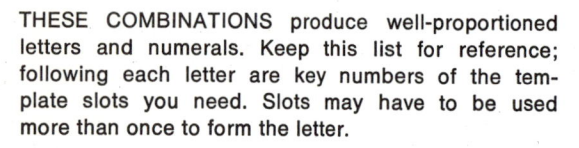

Project each slide directly onto a plywood template blank on which the sizing square has been drawn, and with an awl, punch the exact center of every cross

THESE COMBINATIONS produce well-proportioned letters and numerals. Keep this list for reference; following each letter are key numbers of the template slots you need. Slots may have to be used more than once to form the letter.

A—5,11	S—13
B—1,14	T—1,2
C—4	U—2,12
D—1,8	V—5
E—1,2,3	W—5
F—1,2,3	X—6
G—4,11,12	Y—2,10
H—1,3	Z—2,6
I—1	0—12
J—2,4	1—1
K—1,10,16	2—2,8,13
L—1,2	3—13
M—1,7	4—1,11,16
N—1,6	5—2,3,13
O—12	6—4,13
P—1,14	7—2,6
Q—12,17	8—13
R—1,10,14	9—4,13

templates while you're routing; it's secured to the face of the work by C-clamps or small brads. The length of the rabbeted rails and the sheet-metal strips can be adapted to the size templates you plan to use. The hold-down clamps are secured by screws which can be moved to different holes in the rails as the work progresses, to avoid shifting the frame itself. For all the frame assembly, use sheet-metal screws with pan heads thin enough to let the router pass over them.

It's not difficult to make accurate templates once you've clipped out the paper patterns and rubbed a little vegetable oil on both front and back to render them transparent. Since the templates must be square (so they can be used in four positions and flipped over for four more) we've designed the Project-a-Plans for use in super-slide mounts, rather than regular 35-mm mounts with smaller, rectangular windows. Super-slide mounts are available at your photo dealers in several forms. If you use the inexpensive fold-and-seal cardboard type, you'll have to trim the color frame around our Project-a-Plans somewhat so they'll set within the cement seal-stripe on the inside face of the mount. Despite the larger window, these mounts have the same 2 x 2-in. outer dimension as 35s, so they'll fit any standard projector.

Decide what size letters you want, then cut five identical template squares from plywood, half again as large as the letter height (for example, an 8-in. letter needs a 12-in. square). Letters less than 4 in. high, however, still require a 6-in. square—the minimum size that will support the base of the average router.

Now, mount one of the squares on the wall and aim your projector at it. Move the projector back and forth until the white image exactly covers the square. Be sure the lens axis is perpendicular to the plywood, or distorted templates will result. Once you have the projector set up, don't move it when you're ready for the next square. Instead, mount that square in place of the one already marked and insert a new slide.

While the image is projected on the plywood, mark the exact centers of all the crosses. To distinguish between the marks *within* a slot to be cut and those *outside,* circle the first type and make an x through the others.

When you've laid out all five squares, clamp a scrap board to the back of each to prevent splintering while you drill. Choose a bit to produce a hole that will pass the template router tip you've purchased, and drill through the plywood at each circled spot. Lines drawn tangent to the edge of these holes and joined with arcs scribed from the cross marks complete the layout. (If you happen to need a slot width of 1½ in. for 8-in. letters, or ¾ in. for 4-in. letters—or any other combination in the same proportions—you can trace the slots directly from the projection. Where this is not practical, lay out as described and then remount the plywood square in front of the projector and throw the image onto it once again, as a check. Your layout slots will be narrower or wider than the projected image but the lines should be parallel.)

Now use a jig or coping saw to remove the slot areas and sand or file the edges to be sure the template tip moves freely through the full length of each slot.

Cut a ⅜-in.-deep groove around all four edges of the template to take the hold-down clamps. These clamps can be made from corner irons, such as those used to repair storm windows. Make the frame and clamps first, and use them to position the blanks for projection.

You can achieve a variety of effects by using

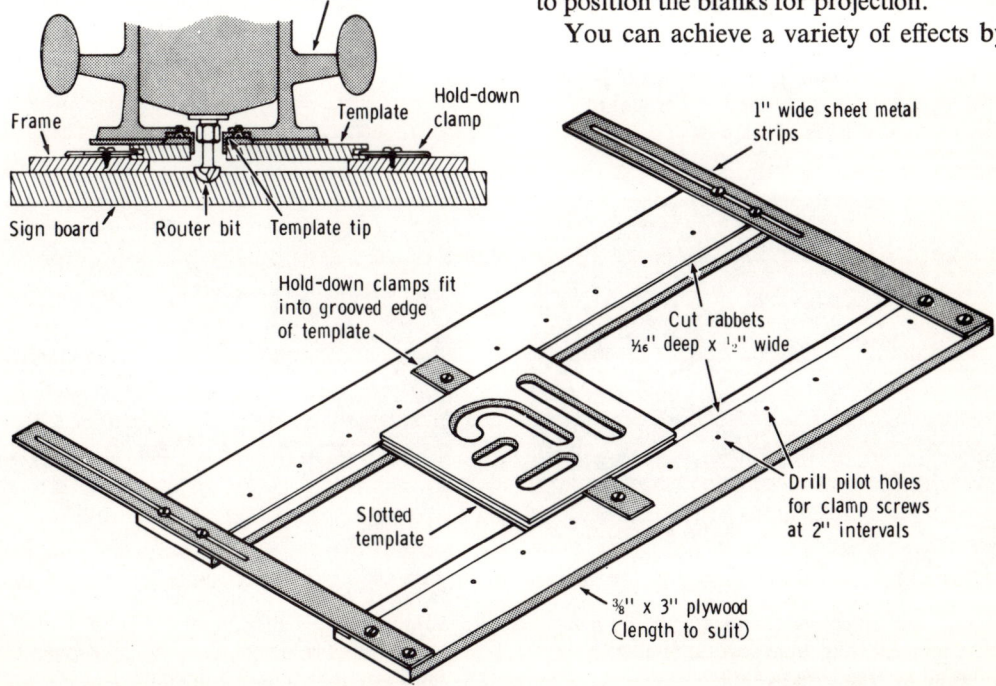

Swing a compass from the crosses outside the slot areas. The other crosses are centers for drilling. Connect the compass arcs and edges of the holes

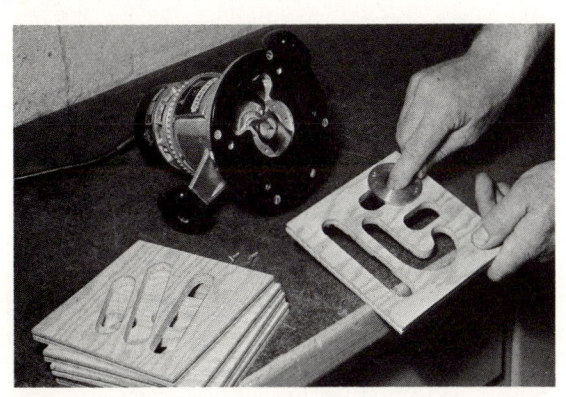

After sawing all cutouts, insert the template tip in each slot and move it from end to end to be sure it will slide without binding or excess play

2355

signs

Spacing between letters isn't automatic. For the best appearance, lay out the words first by tracing through the templates. Check spacing before routing

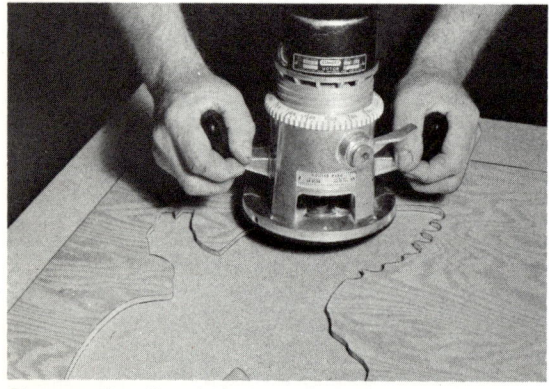

Shapes other than letters require only a simple "silhouette" template cut into plywood or hardboard. Sketch only the outer lines of the design

After routing, coat all recessed areas with any good exterior enamel, spraying from several angles to be certain that all surfaces are coated

router bits of different shapes and sizes. And for the signboard, you can use plywood, chipboard, rough-sawn or planed lumber—or even plexiglas and other plastics. Often you can rout directly into doors or wooden wall panels.

Smooth bare-wood surfaces are easiest to finish, however, as shown in the bottom photos on this page. It's a simple matter of coating the routed surface, then sanding the surface back to bare wood and brushing on a sealer or exterior varnish. If you use dark-brown paint, the letters will appear to be burned into the wood with a branding iron. If you prefer a painted background with letters in a contrasting color, paint the background first; the recessed letters are still much easier to paint than surface letters.

For decorative designs, such as emblems or silhouettes, you can create special templates by photographing a sketch of the design on a 35-mm transparency. This slide will be your own Project-a-Plans.

After working with the lettering templates awhile, you may want to make several additional ones which combine two or more of our slot layouts into one continuous slot—thereby eliminating some of the template shifting. One word of caution before the shavings start to fly: it's a good idea to first lay out all the lettering in pencil, by tracing through the template. This not only gives you practice in selecting which slots you'll need for a given letter (as listed in the chart on page 2354)—it may also spare you the plight of the well-known gent who got to the edge of his "PLAN AHEAD" sign to find he'd left no room for the "D."

See also: alphabets; drafting equipment; routing.

FOR PROJECT-A-PLANS SEE PAGE 2495

Surplus paint is sanded off the surface of the sign when dry. This leaves a clean-edged paint filler in all depressions you have routed

2356

clever ideas

Next time you cut a strip of sheet metal lengthwise with tinsnips, use the tinner's trick of rolling the sheet loosely before making the cut. There's less distortion of the metal along the cut and less tendency of the metal to curl. Not only that but the sheet is easier to handle and you're less likely to injure your fingers along the cut edges. The trick is especially helpful when you are cutting a long strip.

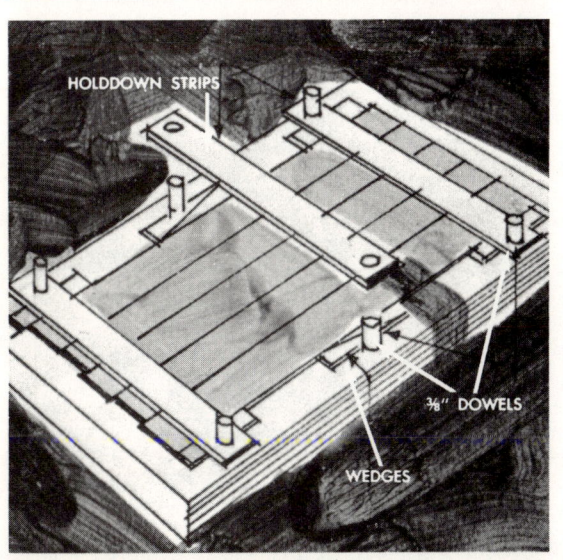

Modelmakers and others who occasionally have need to edge-glue a number of strips of thin stock can put this wedge clamp to good use. It's designed to prevent buckling of the edge-glued strips when clamping pressure is exerted. The detail tells the whole story of its construction and you can make it any reasonable size to suit the purpose. Use a piece of ¾-in. plywood for the base, cutting it about 1½ in. larger each way than the panel. Make wedges of hardwood of the same thickness as the stock to be glued. The hold-downs should be of ½ or ¾-in. hardwood for greater stiffness.

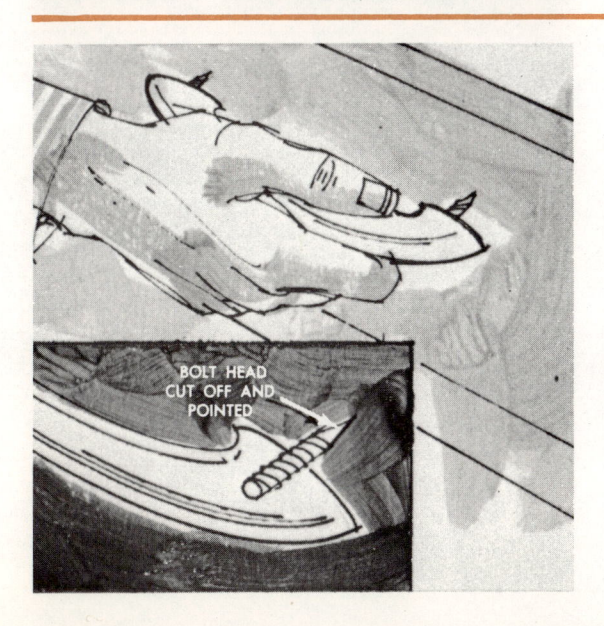

Say you have the problem of locating and spacing screw holes for a number of identical drawer pulls. This must be done accurately, and you can do it by using one of the drawer pulls as a marker. Turn out the regular screws and then locate two ordinary screws, or stove-bolts, of the same thread size. Cut the heads off the screws and grind the cut ends to sharp points. Turn these altered screws into the tapped holes in the drawer pull and there's your marker.

skiing

Ski parallel in one day

BY STUART JAMES

Soaring through an effortless turn, Shortee ski inventor Clif Taylor leads two of his pupils through a series of downhill turns

With a pair of Shortee skis and three simple movements, anyone can learn to ski like an expert

skiing, water: see water skiing
skimmer filter: see filters, swimming pool
skimmer, sand: see sand skimmer

2358

■ "THE TROUBLE with the short ski," says one critic, "is that you can't get the speed you get from a long ski." Another critic complains that the short ski is not good for deep powder.

Despite the critics and detractors, the ranks of Shortee skiers grows each year. When I finally joined them, I had fun on skis for the first time. Frankly, I'm not interested in racing speed on skis. As for deep powder, unless you ski the Rockies or Sierra Nevadas you'll hardly ever see it. But if you do, the 4-ft. Shortee will soar through it.

Inventor, prophet and promoter of the Shortee ski is professional skier Clif Taylor. When an instructor of U.S. Army ski troops in World War II, Taylor conceived the short ski as a method of teaching proficiency on skis in the shortest possible time.

I went to Brattleboro, Vt., to meet Taylor and try out his system. My first surprise was that initial practice began indoors. I was given a rectangular piece of heavy cardboard upon which was printed a pair of skis only 30 in. long. I stood on this cardboard and faced a large piece of paper on which was printed a half-moon-shaped diagram. With this device I was to learn the three basic movements that comprise the Taylor Method—foot turns, leg turns, and hip turns.

I stood relaxed, knees bent slightly, feet flat on the cardboard. I faced the center line on the diagram sheet. With my arms slightly outstretched for balance, I turned both feet to the right, making the movement from the ankle. Back to the center line, then to the left. It was jerky and awkward at first, but after a few times I had adjusted the weight on the cardboard so that it moved smoothly, and then I made the foot turns to a counted rhythm.

leg turns easier

Leg turns are easier. The entire movement is made by the leg below the knee. Since you have more power, the movement of the cardboard is more pronounced and the rhythm more easily attained.

The hip turn is executed by a full turn of the legs from the hip. The movement is much the same as one would execute for sliding sideways on ice.

When I had achieved a degree of good rhythm in these three movements, we turned on some dance music and I kept time to the music, mixing up the different movements.

If this seems too easy to transfer directly to

Three basic turns can be learned at home with a piece of heavy cardboard. Stand on the cardboard (above) in a relaxed position with your knees slightly flexed. Turn both feet (below) for the foot turn. The leg turn, executed by only the leg below the knee, moves the skis in a little wider arc than the foot turn. The hip turn (a power turn for a sudden stop or a long turn) utilizes the full leg from the hip

2359

skiing

The foot turn is a simple maneuver. You traverse slightly to left of the fall line. Your body (A) faces downhill at all times. Stand directly over the skis with your knees slightly flexed. As you turn your foot at the ankle (B), the tips of the skis automatically come to the right (C). Pivot is made on the balls of feet (D). Full sweep of ski tips from left to right (E) is only about 12 in. Repeat maneuver in the opposite direction to maintain desired speed and control

the ski slope, then you're feeling just as I did the next day when I snapped the bindings on a pair of real Shortees at Hogback Ski Area near Brattleboro. I had been a real hotshot on a smooth carpet. A ski slope would be different.

But we didn't go on a ski slope. "It's always best to start on flat ground," Clif explained. "Walk on the skis. Tramp around. Make turns. Try some skating. You'll see how easy they are to handle."

"How about ski poles?" I asked.

"You won't need them. You can use them later if you want to, but in the beginning it is best to keep the hands free and the arms swinging to get the feeling of a natural body rhythm."

I walked and skated around, and I practiced jumping straight into the air and making a full turn. The small skis were easy to handle, and I was reminded of the first time I headed for the novice area on a pair of 7-ft. skis. I made it about 50 ft. from the ski shop and then ended up in a mess of skis, poles and legs that took three persons to untangle.

The first official instruction was to stand in one place on level ground, then repeat the foot turn exercises I had practiced the night before. It was more difficult.

keep heels down

"Don't lean forward," Clif said. "Just relax and stand over the skis. The weight is on the balls of your feet, and keep your heels down."

For the next 10 minutes I stood in position and went through the three basic movements, making a butterfly pattern in the snow. Then we moved on to a gentle slope.

"Always start on a nice easy slope," Clif said. "This is particularly important for the person who is teaching himself."

I went down the slope. I made a series of foot turns, counting aloud to maintain the rhythm. I stopped at the bottom, walked back up and repeated the maneuver. As before, it was jerky and erratic at first, but I very quickly learned that when I turned my foot the ski turned, and then I gradually worked up a sense of timing that resulted in a relatively smooth pattern.

I practiced for a half hour and then Clif said, "Okay, let's go up." We took the T-bar to the top of the novice slope.

"Do you always go up on the slope this fast with a beginner?" I asked.

"It's the best way to learn," Clif said. "All of the technique of skiing boils down to making the skis turn. When you turn the skis at will you

Smooth and rhythmic, the leg turn is like dancing down the slope. The lower leg turns from the knee, and the greater power makes it a longer and more graceful turn than the foot turn. It slows you, but it is the common maneuver for relaxed, linked turns downhill

Spectacular sweeping turns and sudden sliding stops are executed with the hip turn. With your body always facing downhill, the entire hip is rotated in the direction you want to turn. The body twists below the waist, and the upper body remains faced toward the direction of the descent

have control over your downhill flight, and that's all there is to it."

I was still a bit skeptical, and the first time I tried to stop on a fast descent I fell back on long-ski technique. I weighted the downhill ski, unweighted with an upward movement, then weighted again with a full hip thrust. Instead of stopping I spun completely around.

"Now do you believe they're easy to turn?" Clif asked, chuckling. "You don't need all that power. A little unweighting will make the turns easier to execute, but all you need is a slight downward pressure of the knees. You can also unweight by an upward motion, but the downward knee pressure is smoother and you can make quicker turns without any loss of control."

I followed directions and immediately began making effortless linked turns. The body always faces downhill, with the hips and legs handling all turns.

"If you're skiing relaxed and naturally," said Clif, "you don't need a lot of rules about reverse shoulder and leaning out from the hill. You know that you can direct the skis or come to a stop, so you're not caught up in a feeling of fear. In this frame of mind you just think ahead to what you want to do, where you want to go, and the body automatically reacts in the proper way."

I felt the usual tightening sensation when we moved over to a slope covered with moguls (bumps). Like most intermediate skiers I had suffered my share of bruises from tangling with moguls and I wasn't keen on a repeat performance. With the Shortees, however, they added to the fun. You have such complete control over the small skis that you can use the bumps like an expert, sliding up the side to allow the contour to make your turn, then slipping into a trough, zipping down, then up over the top and sliding down the opposite side, using the next rise to lift you and turn.

"From now on it's just a matter of practice," Clif said. "You should use those skis until they feel as familiar on your feet as your shoes. That's when you'll begin to ski instinctively. When you're on ice you'll automatically seek more control and you'll lean more forward to use the edges. In soft snow you'll just automatically move your weight back to keep the fronts up."

I spent another three days at Hogback, skiing every slope they had, learning and enjoying every minute of it. Then I went up to Killington to try the expert slopes on a king-sized mountain. I had a few tense moments on a steep, icy slope, but I mastered that on a second try and sailed down with the greatest of ease.

There's no doubt about it. With the Shortee skis and Clif Taylor's three basic exercises— you can ski in a day.

See also: driving, snow; sleds; snow fort; toboggan.

skin diving

Hitch a ride on this scuba sea tow

BY RICHARD HANSON

■ COSTING LESS THAN $25 or so, this simple tow is basically just a 12 x 24-in. stainless-steel aircraft oxygen tank containing a ⅙-hp. motor and a 12-v. battery. No machining is required. You can assemble the whole thing with common tools, plus a small amount of welding.

The sea tow will run for several hours on a single charge, and has a speed of 2–3 mph which can be increased or decreased by varying the pitch of the homemade prop. To keep costs down, many common materials are used in the construction. For instance, handles are made from 1-in. conduit; an automobile horn button serves as the switch and the stuffing box is assembled from easily obtainable plumbing fittings.

Begin by cutting the end off the tank, using

A surplus oxygen tank and a ⅙-hp. motor, which is also available through surplus outlets, are the main components of the sea tow. Powered by a 12-v. battery, it will run for hours on a single charge

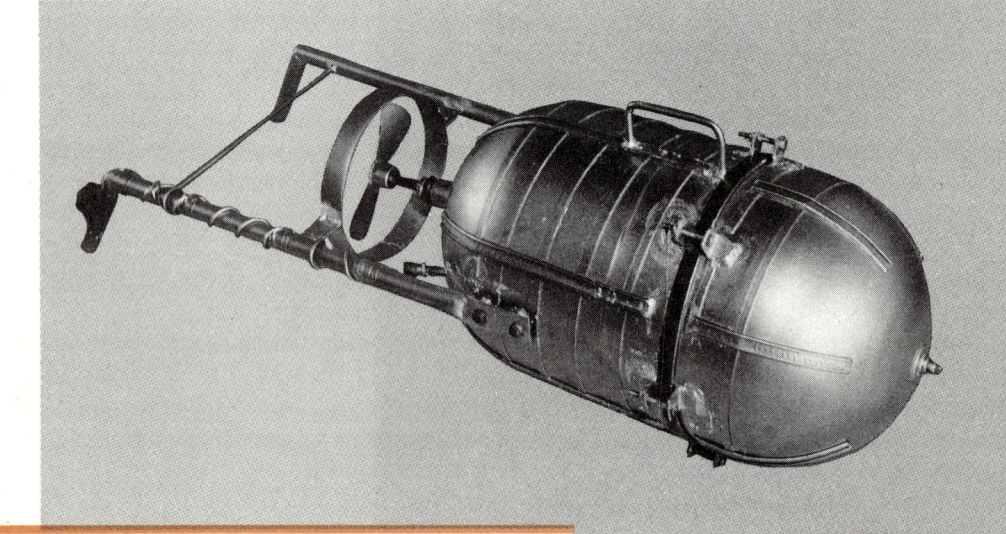

ski sled: see sleds
ski, water: see water skiing
skittles: see games, adult
slalom skiing: see water skiing

2362

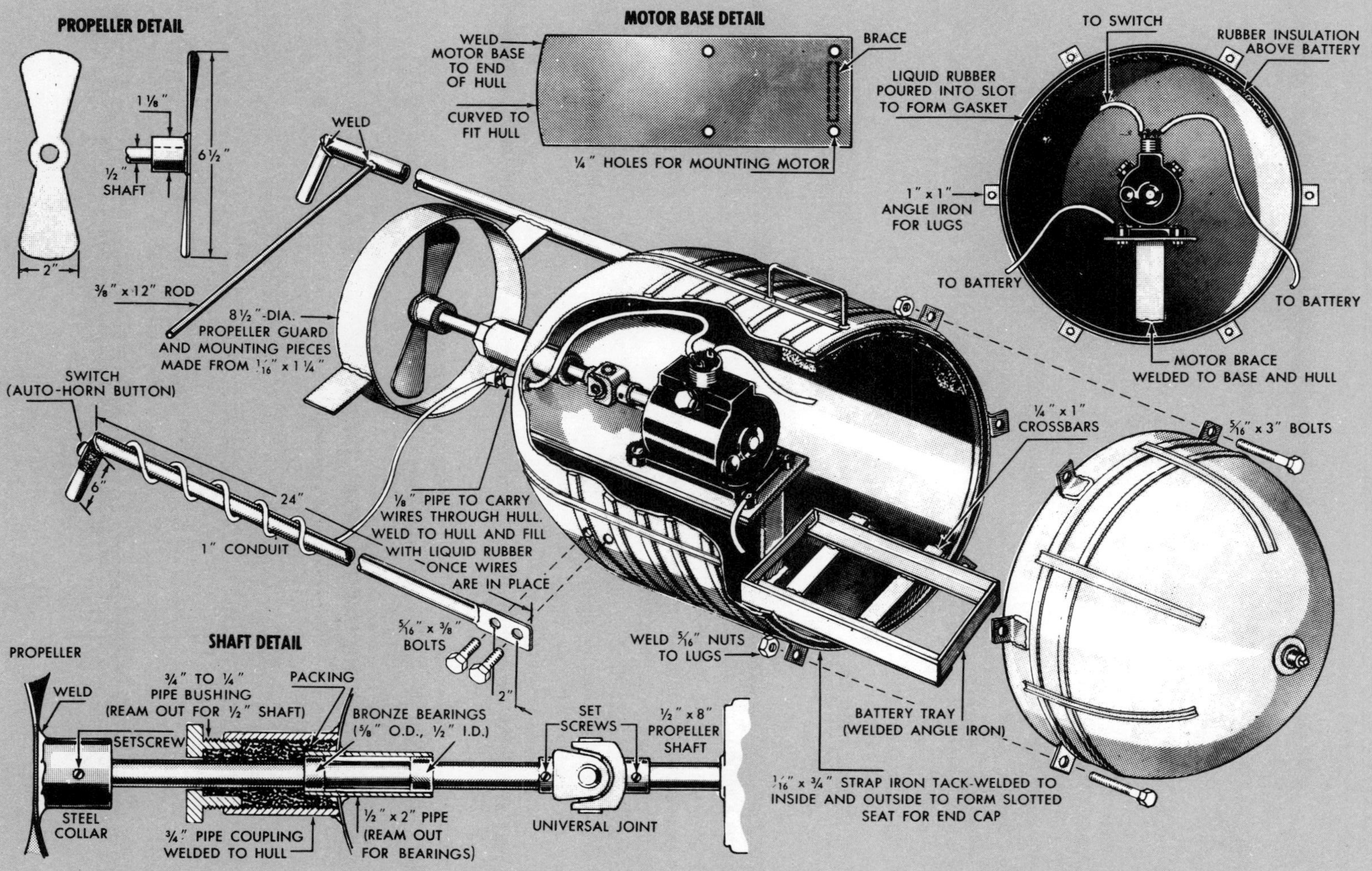
PROPELLER DETAIL
1 1/8"
1/2" SHAFT
6 1/2"
2"
MOTOR BASE DETAIL
WELD MOTOR BASE TO END OF HULL
CURVED TO FIT HULL
BRACE
1/4" HOLES FOR MOUNTING MOTOR
TO SWITCH
RUBBER INSULATION ABOVE BATTERY
LIQUID RUBBER POURED INTO SLOT TO FORM GASKET
1" x 1" ANGLE IRON FOR LUGS
TO BATTERY
TO BATTERY
MOTOR BRACE WELDED TO BASE AND HULL
WELD
3/8" x 12" ROD
8 1/2"-DIA. PROPELLER GUARD AND MOUNTING PIECES MADE FROM 1/16" x 1 1/4"
SWITCH (AUTO-HORN BUTTON)
6"
24"
1" CONDUIT
1/8" PIPE TO CARRY WIRES THROUGH HULL. WELD TO HULL AND FILL WITH LIQUID RUBBER ONCE WIRES ARE IN PLACE
5/16" x 3/8" BOLTS
2"
1/4" x 1" CROSSBARS
5/16" x 3" BOLTS
WELD 5/16" NUTS TO LUGS
BATTERY TRAY (WELDED ANGLE IRON)
1/16" x 3/4" STRAP IRON TACK-WELDED TO INSIDE AND OUTSIDE TO FORM SLOTTED SEAT FOR END CAP
SHAFT DETAIL
PROPELLER
WELD
3/4" TO 1/4" PIPE BUSHING (REAM OUT FOR 1/2" SHAFT)
PACKING
SETSCREW
BRONZE BEARINGS (5/8" O.D., 1/2" I.D.)
SET SCREWS
1/2" x 8" PROPELLER SHAFT
STEEL COLLAR
3/4" PIPE COUPLING WELDED TO HULL
1/2" x 2" PIPE (REAM OUT FOR BEARINGS)
UNIVERSAL JOINT

skin diving

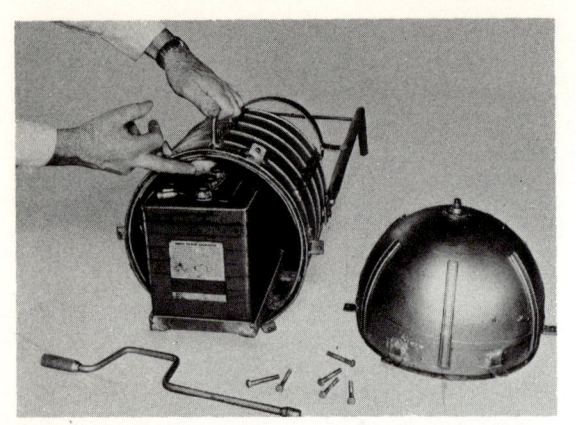

A sheet of rubber mounted over the battery prevents accidentally bumping terminals on hull during removal. Carrying handle is made from 3/8-in. stock

Place spacers under the motor if this is necessary to achieve correct alignment. Locate the battery tray as close as possible to 1/8-in. motor base

sea tow, continued

either a hacksaw or a saber saw with a metal-cutting blade. Grind off the bands about ¾-in. back from both sides of the cut, so that you can install the two iron bands which form a grooved seat for the end cap. Next, pour liquid rubber into this groove to act as a gasket.

Place the battery base as close as possible to the motor base. To prevent the terminals from touching the tank when removing the battery, cut a small sheet of rubber from a discarded inner tube and use adhesive to mount this on the inside of the tank over the terminals. If it's an automobile battery, secure all wires to terminals with small hose clamps, and be sure to use spillproof caps. Ideally, the battery should weigh about 40 lbs., since this will allow you to add extra ballast to balance the unit for easier guiding.

The horn-button switch should be mounted on two 3/16-in. nuts welded to the handle. Run one wire up around the handle and through the 1/8-in. pipe to a motor terminal, then seal this through-hull fitting by filling with liquid rubber. A short length of wire from the other switch terminal should be grounded to the handle at the switch base. Cover the switch and handle with a loosely wound layer of plastic electrical tape, and brush several coats of liquid rubber over this taped section to make the switch watertight yet operable.

A word of caution: When charging or discharging, a battery produces highly explosive hydrogen gas, so double-check all hull connections to make sure everything is sealed tightly, and don't smoke near the unit. Wait an hour before installing the battery after charging.

See also: swimming pools; underwater camera cases; water skiing.

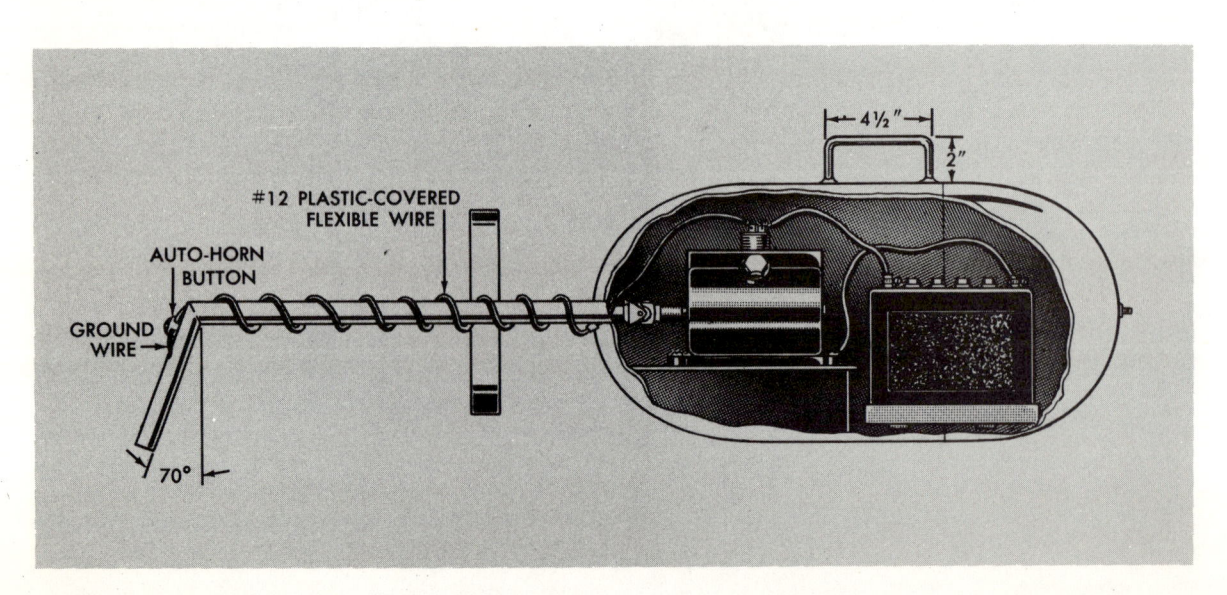

slate floors

■ APRIL SHOWERS GIVE RISE to something less pleasant than May flowers: they bring much mud to be tracked indoors. Many homes do not have practical entryways. Often the front door opens right onto the living-room carpet and this can result in a constant cleaning problem as water drips from raincoats and umbrellas, and mud is tracked in.

The elegant solution is to slate the floor of the entry. Whether it is a small alcove (shown at the left) or a stair "hall" (below) a slate floor can transform it into a separate area that's not only practical, but actually gives the feeling of a larger living room.

At first glance, the job looks like one for a professional. But replacing the finish flooring with slate requires no specialized skills on your part. Instructions on how to go about it are given on the next three pages.

Lay a slate floor in your entry

Mud, snow and water are not so hard to fight when you have this entry. Here's how

sled, aqua: see water skiing
sled, river: see riverboat

2365

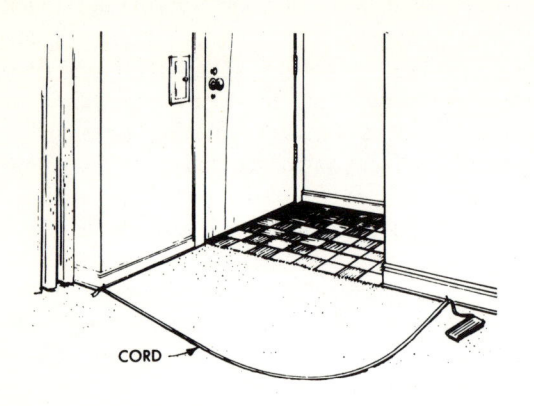

slate floors

STEP ONE: Tack or tape a length of heavy cord between the baseboard points to which your slate floor will extend. Adjust the cord to various free-form shapes until you establish a graceful limit line, and mark it on the carpet—or other surface—with chalk. If you have wall-to-wall carpeting, cut along this line with scissors and bind the cut edge with iron-on tape to prevent unraveling, unless you eventually intend to cap the edge with a flexible carpet bar. In this event, remove the tacks and roll the carpet and pad back, marking the cutting line directly on the finish flooring—or subflooring—instead of the rug. Subflooring may be plywood.

STEP TWO: If your hardwood floor is nailed directly to the subfloor, use a portable circular saw, set to just the thickness of the finish flooring—usually ¾ in. Though the blade should be sharp, don't use your best new one since you are likely to hit an occasional nail, especially on the diagonal cuts. Or use a special nail-cutting blade. In order to cut and remove flooring near the walls, you'll have to pry off the base shoe. A circular saw will work only on the straight-line cuts, of course.

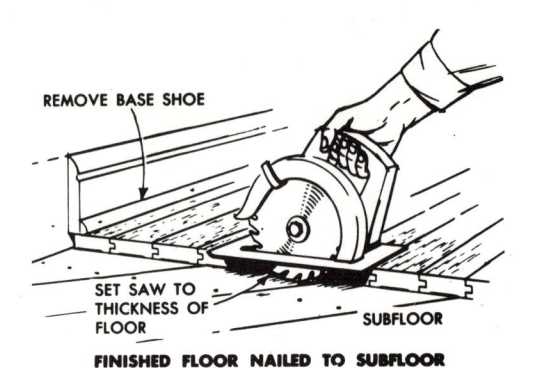

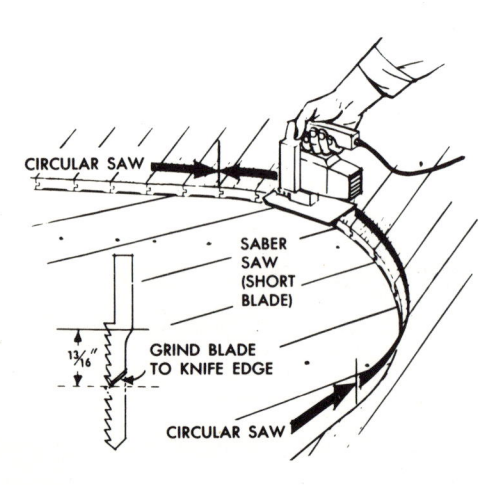

STEP THREE: Curved cuts must be made with a saber saw, but you'll have to shorten the blade, as shown at the left, if the finish floor is nailed directly to the subflooring. Adjust the saw to the lowest point of the stroke, then mark off down the blade to the exact thickness of the finish floor. Grind off the blade to a knife edge and lower it into the kerf of one of the circular-saw cuts, extending the cut around the curved section of the limit line. Then pry up the waste pieces and pull the nails.

ALTERNATE STEP A: Sometimes your hardwood floor "floats" on furring strips to accommodate electrical conduit—or where application is over a concrete slab. In such cases, the space beneath will probably let you use an unmodified blade in the saber saw. This speeds up the cutting, so you may want to use this saw for the straight cuts as well. Even so, take it slow and easy; you're still likely to hit a nail or two. Pry up and discard the waste flooring and furring. Battens used to protect the electrical conduit aren't needed, as the conduit will be buried in cement. You also will have to remove the base shoe for this—and perhaps the baseboard.

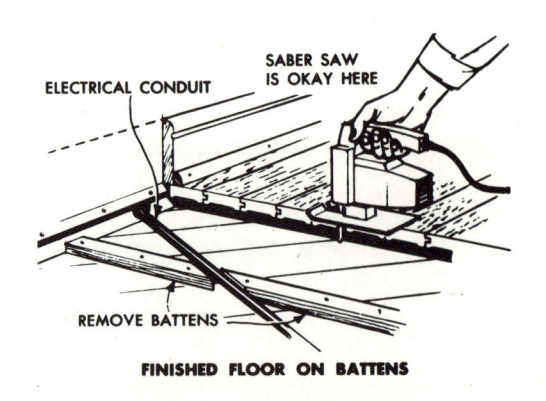

ALTERNATE STEP B: Cut through the furring and battens at the limit line and pry them out. Cut short lengths of furring to slip under the trimmed ends of any flooring strips that project far enough beyond their last uncut support to be in danger of springing down under weight. Whether the floor is laid directly on the subfloor or is floating, as shown here, the cut ends of the finish flooring strips must be covered with a thin plastic sheeting (such as a dry-cleaner's bag) to prevent moisture in the mortar bed from seeping into the grain and causing water stains in the flooring. It isn't a bad idea to paint-prime the edges of the flooring for moisture protection.

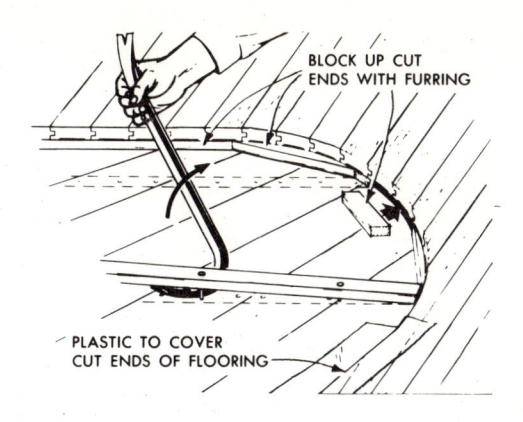

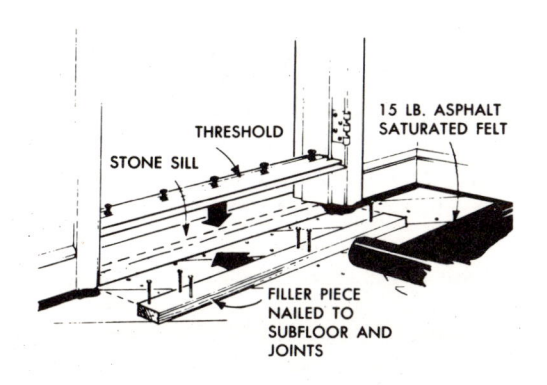

STEP FOUR: The threshold is often attached directly to the finish flooring and may have to be pried up before the trimmed-off pieces can be removed from beneath it. This will leave a gap between the interior trim and the exposed subfloor, so cut and nail in a filler strip to take up the space, as shown. The subfloor should be covered with a layer of building paper before these various gap-fillers are installed. Drive screws through the threshold into the filler strip. They should be countersunk flush with the top surface of the threshold.

STEP FIVE: Use slate ¼ or ¾ in. thick, in either irregular shapes or cut rectangles. To assure the best pattern for the space available, order half again as much slate as needed. You can usually return uncut extras. Slate is sold by weight; enough for 25 sq. ft. runs from $12 to $16. Place the largest pieces first; then fill in with smaller ones. For cutting, use a masonry blade in your circular saw; wear protective goggles. When finished, lift out the pieces and recreate the pattern on the floor nearby.

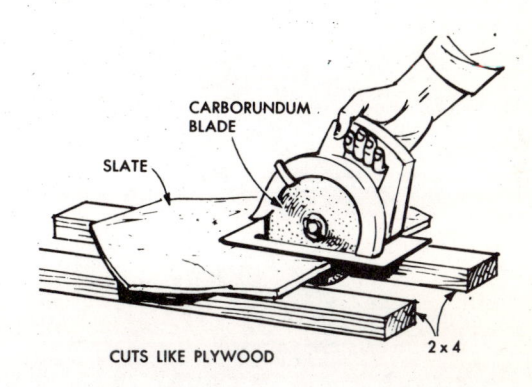

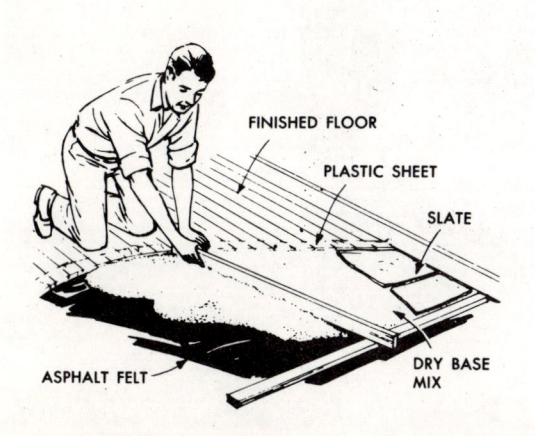

STEP SIX: Mix two parts No. 1 sand to one part cement and add only enough water to make the mixture appear as wet sand. It should form a firm ball when squeezed in the hand. Spread the mixture to a level about ¼ in. from the surface of the finish floor and tamp it down with a scrap piece of 2 x 4 or brick. On a large area, lay spaced wooden strips of the same thickness you want for the mixture layer, then ride the ends of the leveling straightedge on these as shown. When one section is filled level, proceed to the adjacent area and use the strips in the same manner as before. Flow the mixture into the space the strips occupied.

slate floors

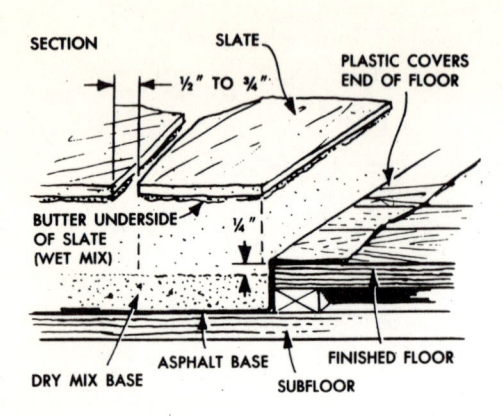

STEP SEVEN: Replace the slate, as positioned originally. Work each piece back and forth until it's bedded and level with the wood top floor. Use a carpenter's level. Mix another concrete batch, this time a soupy 3 parts fine sand to 2 parts cement. Carefully pick up one slate at a time and butter the back with wet mix. Moisten the area the piece came from by squeezing a wet sponge above it, then replace the slate, taking care to retain the proper spacings for neat grout lines. Use a putty knife to apply the wet mix.

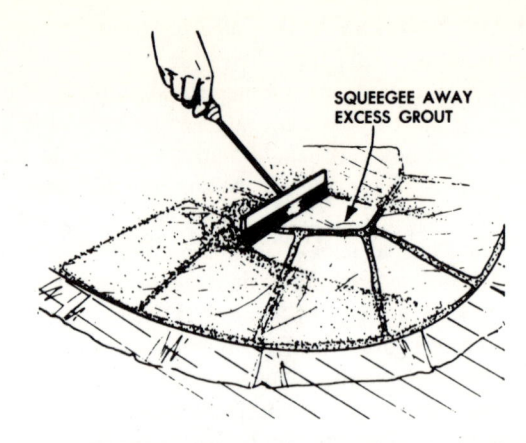

STEP EIGHT: When all the slate is back in place, mix a small soupy batch for grouting, adding lime to whiten to the desired shade. Work this into the gaps and around the edges of the outside pieces. Let it set about two hours. Then, with a window squeegee, remove as much dry grout as possible. Finish the job with a wet sponge. The slate surface should be free of grout.

See also: floors; floor finishing; floor polisher; tile, floor.

After eight hours, clean off remaining grout by scrubbing with burlap and sawdust. A week later, flow on a coat of silicone sealer, rub dry in half-hour. Slate can be waxed

Tob-sled

BY JAMES SIMACK and GORDON HOFFMAN

■ HALF TOBOGGAN AND HALF SLED, this "tob-sled" offers the best of both to give you the ride of your life. Its three conduit runners give it incredible speed, and its upturned nose lets it plane swiftly over deep, packed snow.

Bending the upturned ends of the runners is easy with a pipe bender, which you can rent. Getting all three alike is important. After bending the first one, use it as a pattern for the other two.

The three runners are ganged together at the front and the rear with flat-steel crossbraces. Then, each runner is attached to the plywood bottom with six sheet-metal screws, using the ¼-in. holes in the plywood to spot the ⅛-in. pilot holes in the conduit runners.

The rest of the work goes easily. The plywood edges are covered with aluminum trim, a sheet-metal snow shield is added to the runners at the front and the ropes are entwined through four sash handles attached to each side.

See also: parade floats; skiing; snow fort; toboggan.

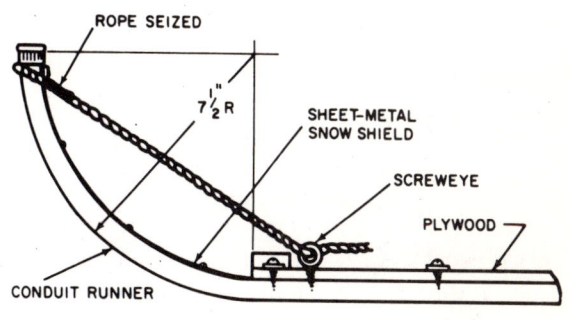

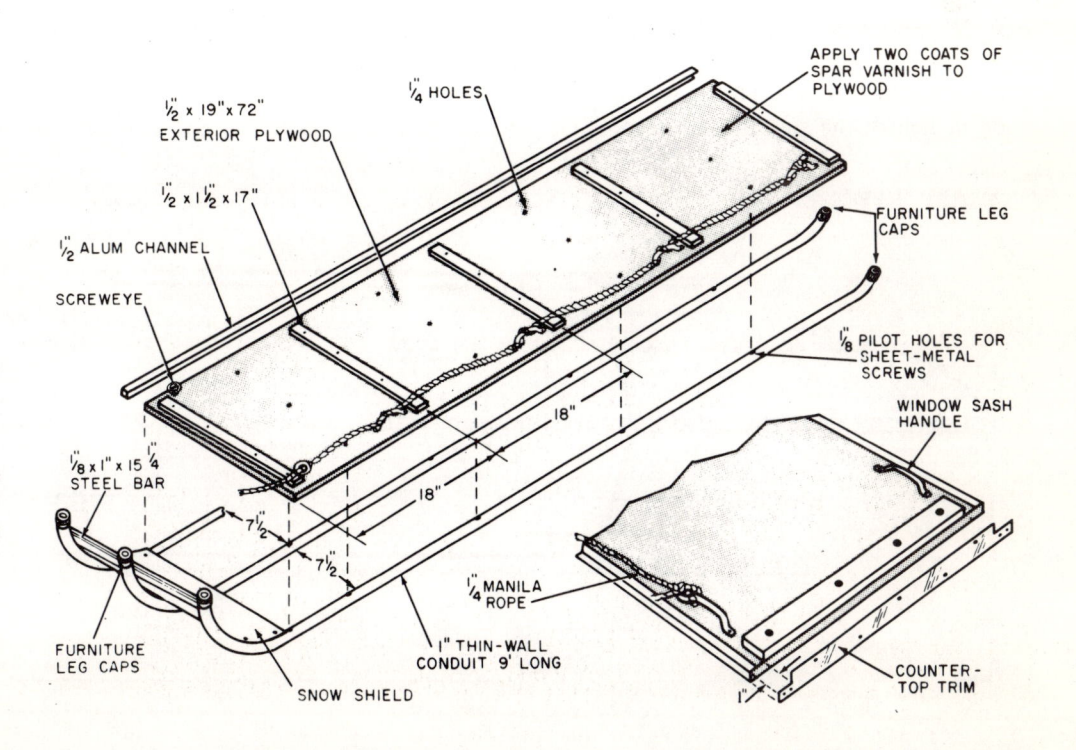

sleds

Ski sled with outriggers

BY H. B. DABKOWSKI

■ STEEL-RUNNER SLEDS are no match for this unusual speedster. It's made of plywood, marine or exterior. You'll need ½ in. for the seat, runners and spreaders, ¼ in. for the skis. The pull-apart drawing shows how the parts interlock with half-lapped slots. The cut-out areas are made to lighten the sled but are something you can skip. Use a waterproof glue and #6-1½-in. flathead wood screws to assemble the parts.

The ski runners won't give you any trouble if you start at the curved end. Shape the ends according to the plan view and cut the strips extra long. Now, with the sled upside down and the help of an extra pair of hands, fasten the tip of the ski to the curved section of the runner, using glue and several screws placed 1 in. apart. If you have a C-clamp, use it too. Next wring out a hot towel and place it along the bend. As the wood becomes pliable, pull the ski down a little more and add another screw. Once past the curve of the runner, space the remaining screws a foot or so apart. After painting, varnish the skis.

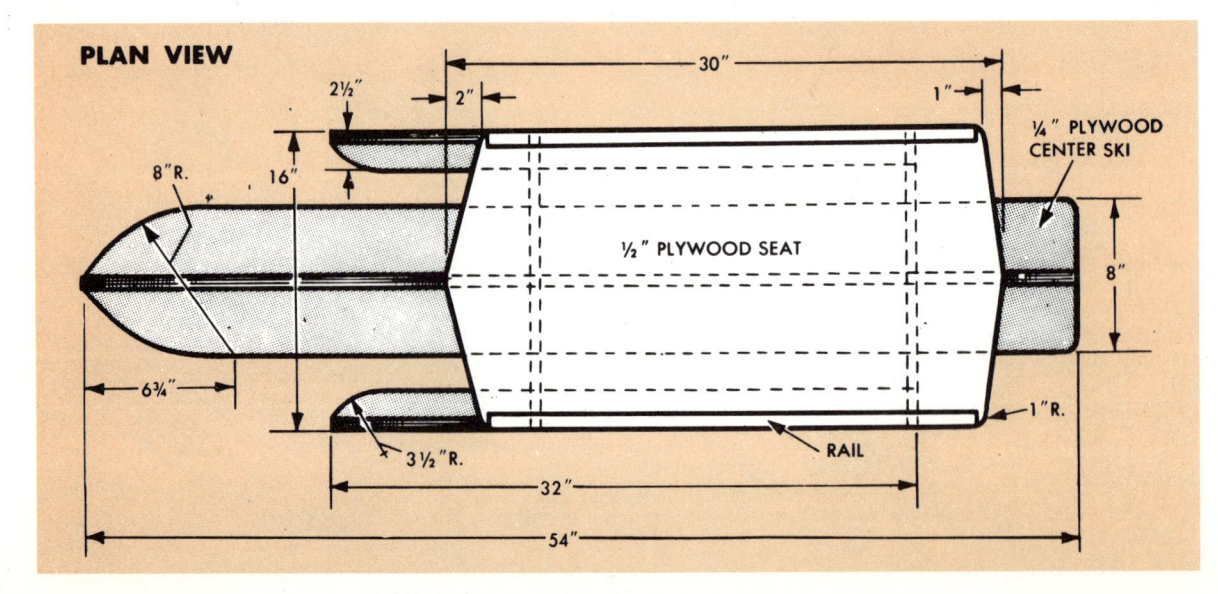

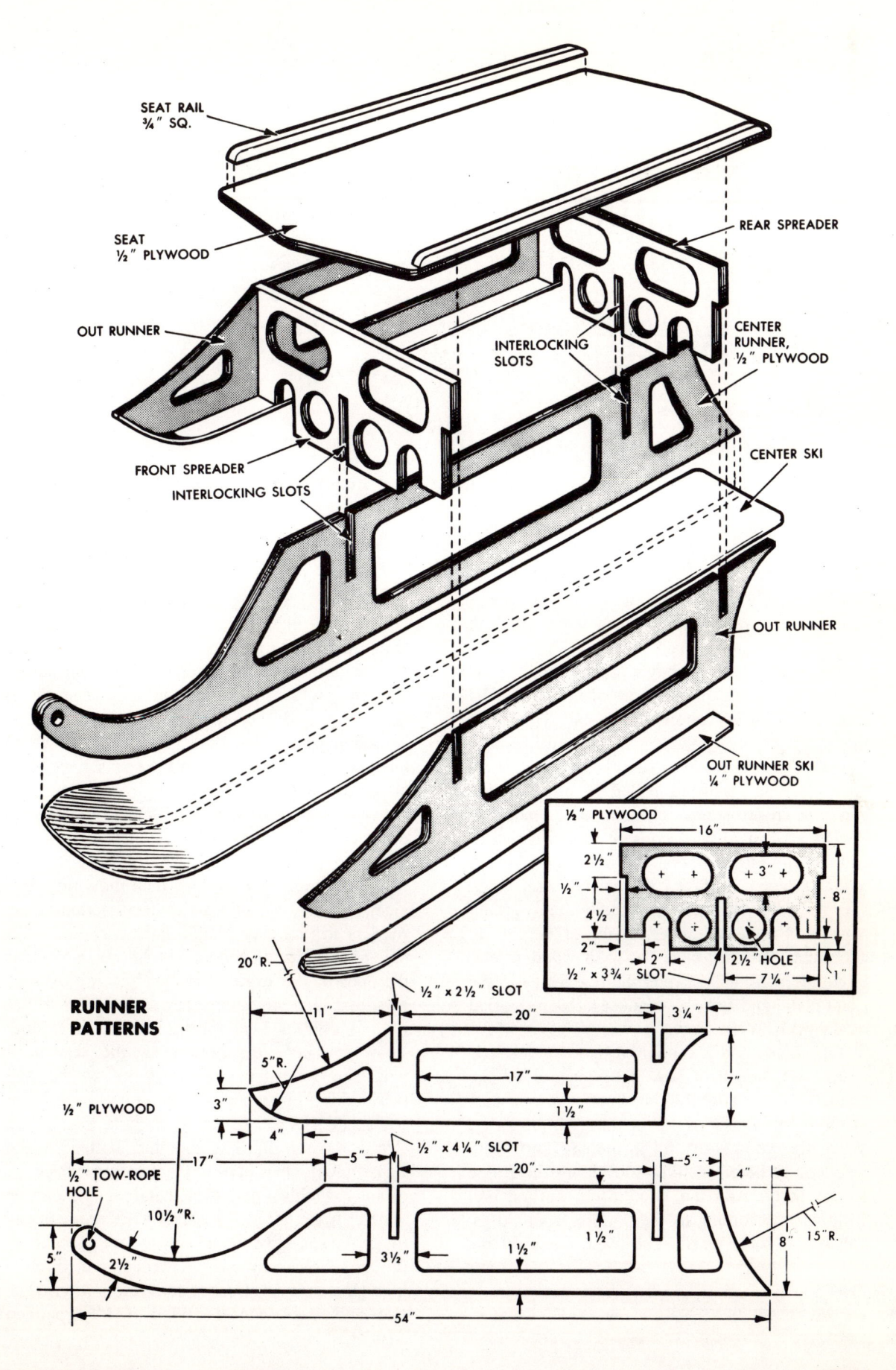

- SEAT RAIL ¾" SQ.
- SEAT ½" PLYWOOD
- REAR SPREADER
- OUT RUNNER
- INTERLOCKING SLOTS
- CENTER RUNNER, ½" PLYWOOD
- FRONT SPREADER
- INTERLOCKING SLOTS
- CENTER SKI
- OUT RUNNER
- OUT RUNNER SKI ¼" PLYWOOD

½" PLYWOOD — 16" — 2½" — ½" — 3" — 8" — 4½" — 2" — ½" × 3¾" SLOT — 2" — 2½" HOLE — 7¼" — 1"

RUNNER PATTERNS

½" PLYWOOD

20" R. — 11" — ½" × 2½" SLOT — 20" — 3¼" — 5" R. — 17" — 7" — 3" — 4" — 1½"

½" TOW-ROPE HOLE — 17" — 5" — ½" × 4¼" SLOT — 20" — 5" — 4" — 10½" R. — 5" — 2½" — 3½" — 1½" — 1½" — 8" — 15" R. — 54"

2371

sleds

Here comes the snow boat

BY RON ANDERSON

Small fry can have fun with this tobogganlike sled.
Because it's light, it's easy to pull and steer

■ SMALL AND LIGHT ENOUGH for small fry to pull up a snow-covered hill, this steerable tobogganlike sled will provide them with thrilling rides in deep or packed snow. With its twin rudders and tiller it is truly a "snow boat."

Start by cutting out the sides of the body. The four 1 x 2 cross battens are installed between the sides at the points indicated, using flat-headed nails. The seat is simply an 8 x 12½-in. piece of ¼-in. plywood nailed in place to the two rear cross battens. The seat back measures ¾ x 12 x 14 in. in size and is glued and nailed to ends of the side members. The bottom is covered with a sheet of 30-ga. galvanized steel, bent sharply at the ends to fit over the body, front and back, and nailed in place. Strips of ⅛ x ¾-in. aluminum, fastened with flat-head wood screws in countersunk holes, cover the nail heads in the sheet metal and serve as runners to keep the sled on course over the snow.

The short hood is supported by a frame made of a 24-in. length of ¾ x 2-in. pine. Bend the frame to shape after making a series of saw cuts at the points indicated and soaking in hot water. When the wood is dry fill in the saw kerfs with wood putty before nailing and gluing the frame to the body. Add the hood itself, cutting and bending it according to the pattern from 30-ga. galvanized sheet metal. The icicle effect on the hood is created by using white enamel paint, together with a masking tape pattern.

The most interesting feature of the snow boat is its twin-rudder steering mechanism which does double duty as a stabilizer on the steep slides. The two rudders are made of ¾-in. pine cut to the shape and size indicated. Strips of ⅛-in. aluminum are attached to the bottom edges of the rudders with countersunk wood screws. The aluminum strips not only strengthen the rudders but also serve as runners. The rudders are mounted on 6-in. strap hinges which, in turn, are bolted to a pair of 2½-in. butt hinges screwed to the back of the seat. This dual mounting provides both lateral and up-and-down action of the rudders so that they remain in firm contact with the snow under all terrain conditions. Note that the ends of the strap hinges are given a 90-deg. twist and then linked together with a piece of flat iron. A pair of 3-in. springs hooked to a large screw eye near the bottom of the seat back maintains a constant downward pull to keep the twin rudders in contact with the snow.

The tiller is a 2-ft. length of ½-in. thin-walled electrical conduit, flattened and bolted to the right rudder, then bent to clear the seat back. A rubber crutch tip or bicycle handbar grip can be added. After thorough sanding to remove any rough edges, give your snow boat a coat of primer followed by one or two coats of durable high-gloss enamel. Do not paint the bottom. The seat and back can be fitted with a padded cushion.

sled, sports: see sports boat
sleeper, car-top: see car-top sleeper

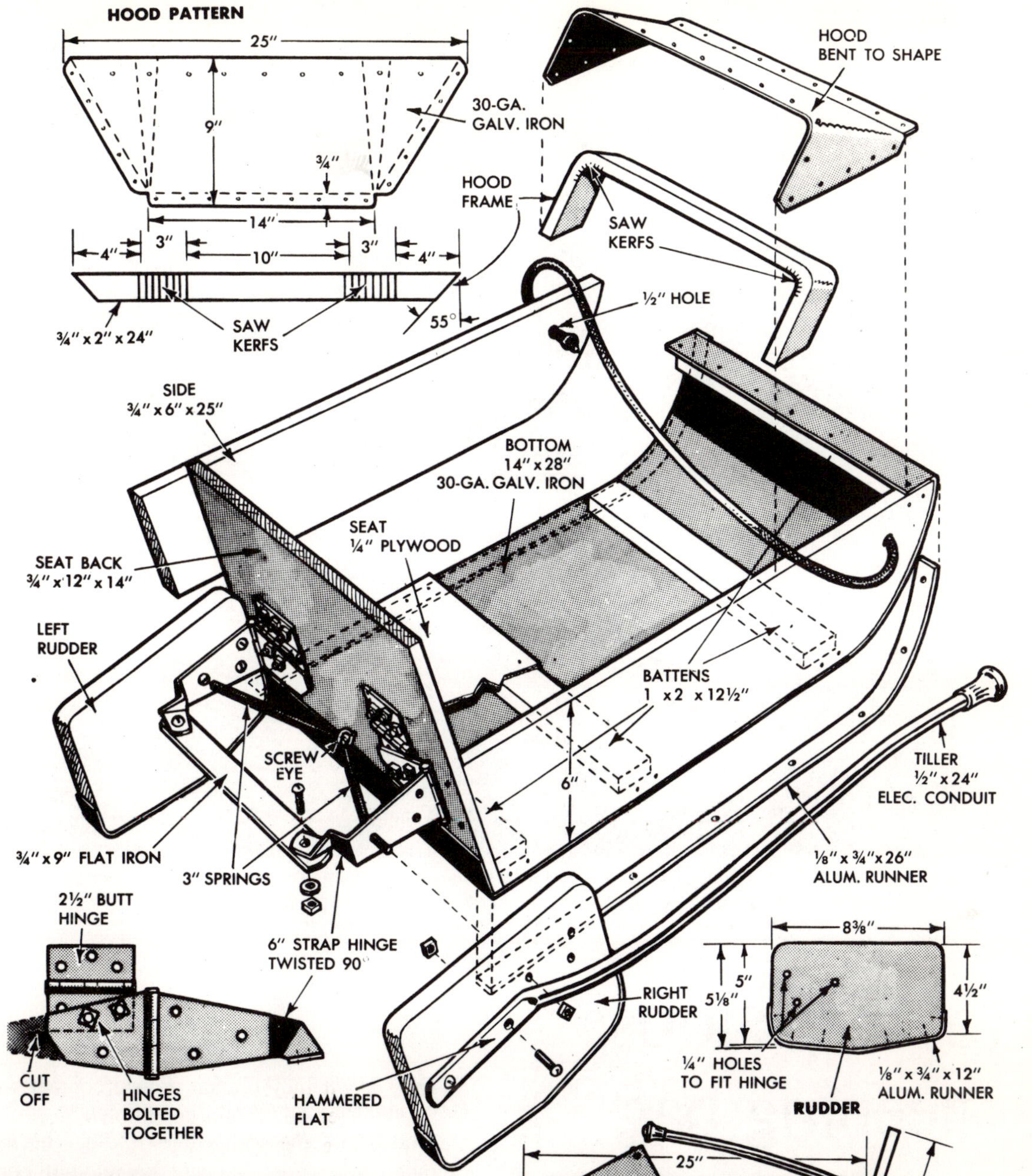
HOOD PATTERN
25"
9"
30-GA.
GALV. IRON
3/4"
14"
4"
3"
10"
3"
4"
SAW
KERFS
3/4" x 2" x 24"
55°
HOOD
FRAME
HOOD
BENT TO SHAPE
SAW
KERFS
1/2" HOLE
SIDE
3/4" x 6" x 25"
BOTTOM
14" x 28"
30-GA. GALV. IRON
SEAT
1/4" PLYWOOD
SEAT BACK
3/4" x 12" x 14"
LEFT
RUDDER
BATTENS
1 x 2 x 12 1/2"
SCREW
EYE
6"
TILLER
1/2" x 24"
ELEC. CONDUIT
3/4" x 9" FLAT IRON
3" SPRINGS
1/8" x 3/4" x 26"
ALUM. RUNNER
2 1/2" BUTT
HINGE
6" STRAP HINGE
TWISTED 90°
CUT
OFF
HINGES
BOLTED
TOGETHER
HAMMERED
FLAT
RIGHT
RUDDER
8 3/8"
5"
5 1/8"
4 1/2"
1/4" HOLES
TO FIT HINGE
1/8" x 3/4" x 12"
ALUM. RUNNER
RUDDER

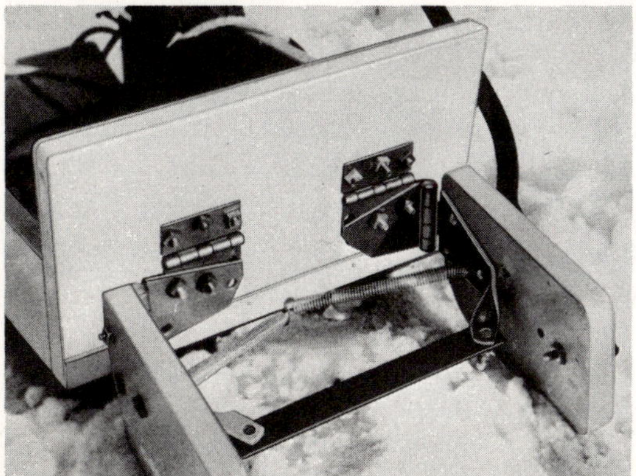

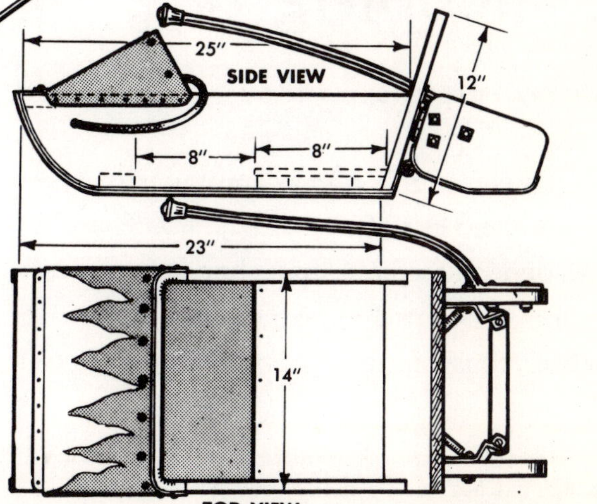
25"
SIDE VIEW
12"
8"
8"
23"
14"
TOP VIEW

sleeping bags

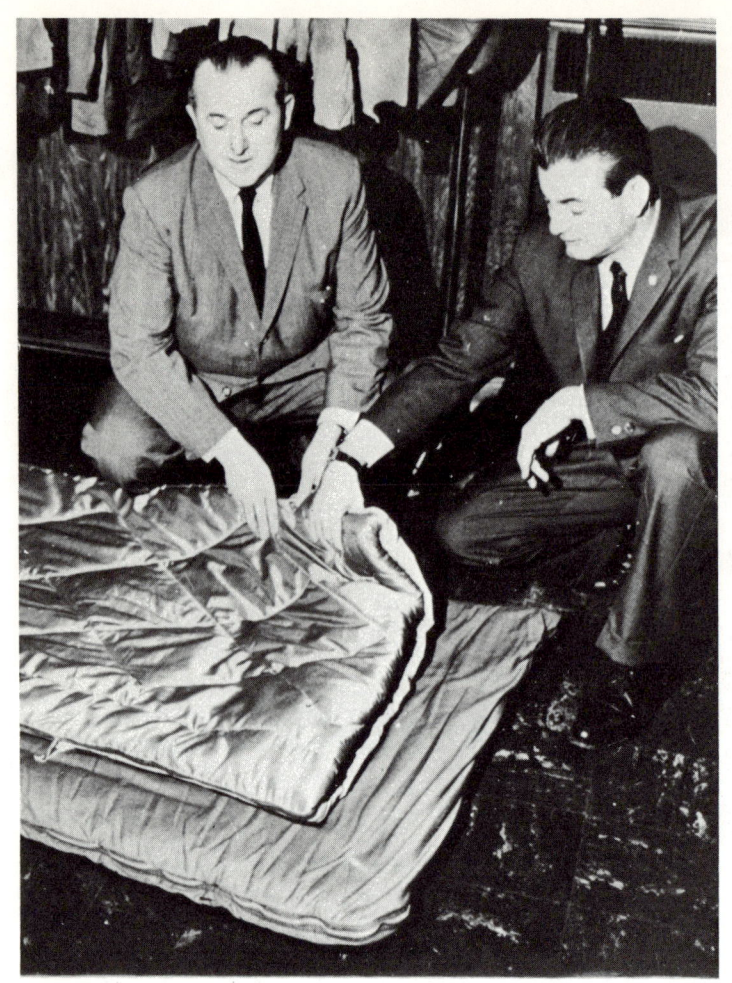

An oversize bag (left photo) gives you 6 in. more in length and width for big men and restless sleepers. Note how small the regular size is in the photo. The shell fabric (right photo) should have a high thread count—more threads per sq. in. The lower high-count fabric shown is the best

How to choose a sleeping bag

BY PATRICK K. SNOOK

If you're going on a camping trip, how well you sleep at night will depend on the sleeping bag you choose. Here are some tips on making the best selection, considering both comfort and price

---

slide projection cabinet: see projection cabinet

2374

■ No CAMPING TRIP is a success if you can't sleep comfortably. And the difference between sleeping snug and warm or spending the night cramped and miserable will be in your choice of sleeping bags. Here's how to select the right one:

The major factors to consider in buying a sleeping bag are, in order of importance: filler and fabric, size and shape, construction and accessories. By far the most important is the amount and type of insulating material that keeps you comfortable.

The oldest filler materials are eider duck and goose down—and all the advances of modern science have failed to equal them. Down is light, warm and durable—it will weigh half as much and take up only a third as much space as its nearest competitor. But there are drawbacks.

A rolled size of down bag (left), compared to a synthetic-filled bag of equal comfort rating

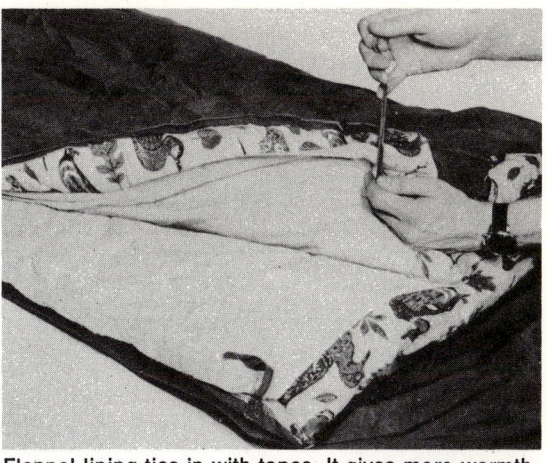

Flannel lining ties in with tapes. It gives more warmth, and removes easily so that you can clean and air it

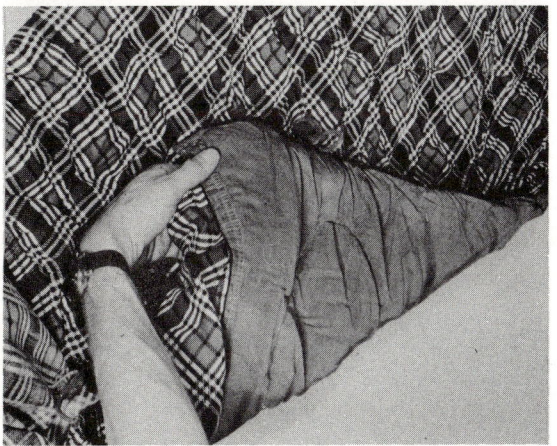

A compromise bag has a waterproof bottom, but the top is only water-repellent for ventilation

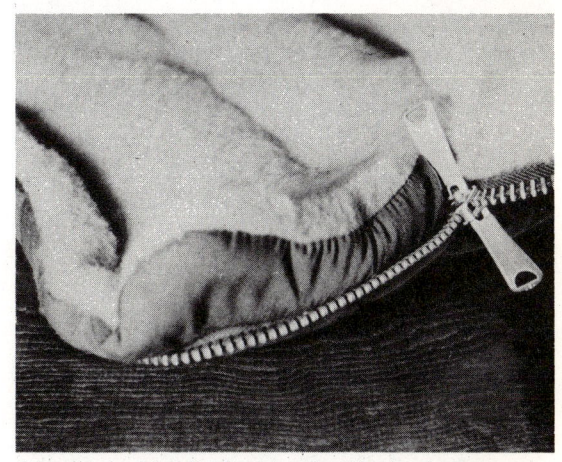

A heavy double-tab zipper makes the best closure. A draft tab covers inside of the zipper for warmth

Down is expensive (about twice the cost of synthetic fillers of equal insulating capacity), sometimes hard to find, subject to moth, rodent, and mildew damage, and slow drying. Also, some campers are allergic to feathers, and down is feathers.

A good substitute for expensive down is a batting made from specially crimped *polyester* fiber designed for sleeping bags and insulated clothing. Another good synthetic is a similar filler made of *acetate* fiber, which has a slightly lower insulating quality. Therefore a bag must be bigger and heavier, but the price makes it attractive.

Both synthetic fibers are nonallergenic and not dusty, and are also moth-, rodent- and mildew-resistant, and quick-drying. If you aren't worried about size and weight in packing, and don't need to be insulated below 10 deg., they'll do the job at a great saving.

Some of the other fillers used are synthetic pile linings, clipped feather ends, clipped synthetic fiber ends, kapok, wool, cotton, and many other materials. While none of them equals the big three for insulating ability, all have a great price advantage. If you don't need the insulation, they're okay. Remember, too warm a bag is uncomfortable also.

Sleeping bags are rated for the lowest temperature at which they'll keep the *average* sleeper comfortable. That rating depends on the type and amount of filler in the bag, and most good manufacturers list the rating of each bag. All of them must list the amount and type of filler on the Federal bedding label ("Do Not Remove This Tag"). By comparing the amount and type

2375

sleeping bags

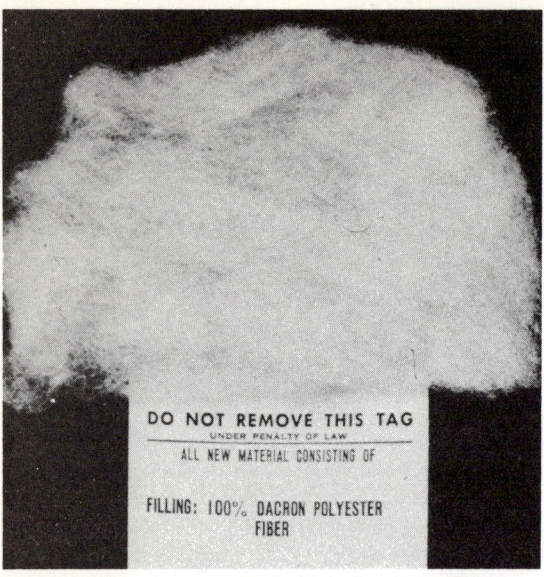

Polyester fiber is a good substitute for down. The trade name varies, but the tag always will list material as polyester filler after the trade name

Combinations of synthetic fillers, often from cut ends, don't equal virgin filler for warmth, but they make a good budget bag for warmer camps

choosing a sleeping bag, continued

Stitching patterns insure even distribution of the filler. Overlapping V-tubes are the best for down. Diamond and loop stitch are the best for synthetics

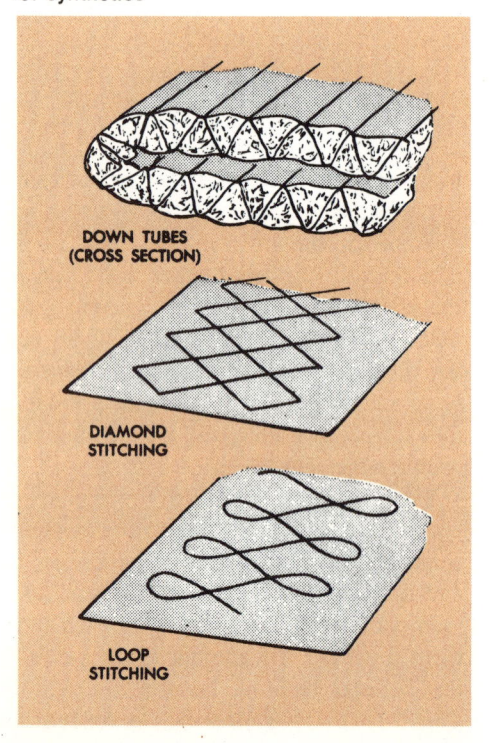

DOWN TUBES (CROSS SECTION)

DIAMOND STITCHING

LOOP STITCHING

of filler against a rated bag, you can approximate the rating of any bag, and it's your best bet as a buyer's guide to comfort.

Consumer bags are rated from 50 to 10 deg. Heavy-duty arctic models can take you down to 30 below, but they're expensive professional models. Buy the rating you'll need, and remember, if you like an extra blanket at home, get a bag rated a bit lower than you think you'll need.

The shell (outer) fabric should be tough, lightweight, and water repellent—not waterproof. A water*proof* bag will trap your body moisture inside, and you'll wake up wet and cold. If you're concerned about ground moisture, use a ground cloth or tarp, and don't attempt to sleep outside in the rain. Get a fabric with a high thread count (more threads per sq. in.) and get at least a percentage of synthetic material for durability. The shell material is also listed on the bedding label.

Size and style of your bag are up to you. The formfitting "mummy" style bags are lightest and least bulky, but many campers don't like their zipped-in feeling. The square bag, or sleeping robe if it unzips clear around, will be more like your bed at home. Many robe-styles can be zipped together to make double bags, and the full opening zipper makes them easy to air and clean.

The average adult bag will measure about 32 by 76 in., *finish* size. If you're over 6 ft. or more

Pure goose down can't be equalled for warmth or for light weight. Despite fragile nature of individual feathers, they are quite durable

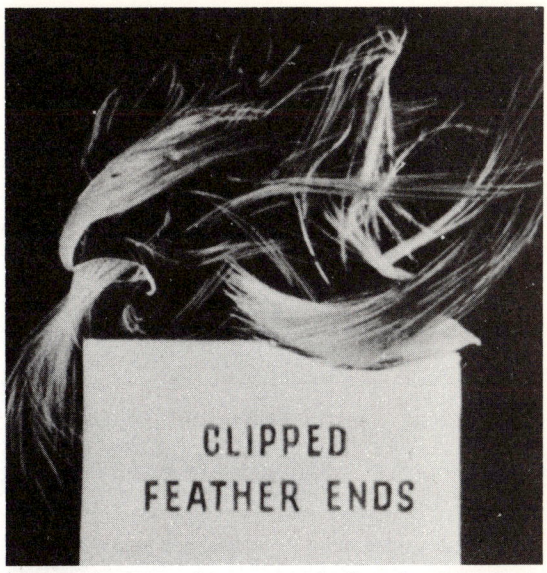

Clipped feather ends, a poor substitute for down, don't have the insulating quality or resiliency of the real thing. Check the tag

A close second among synthetics is acetate fiber filler. The "Do Not Remove This Tag" is for the dealer. You can take it off your bag

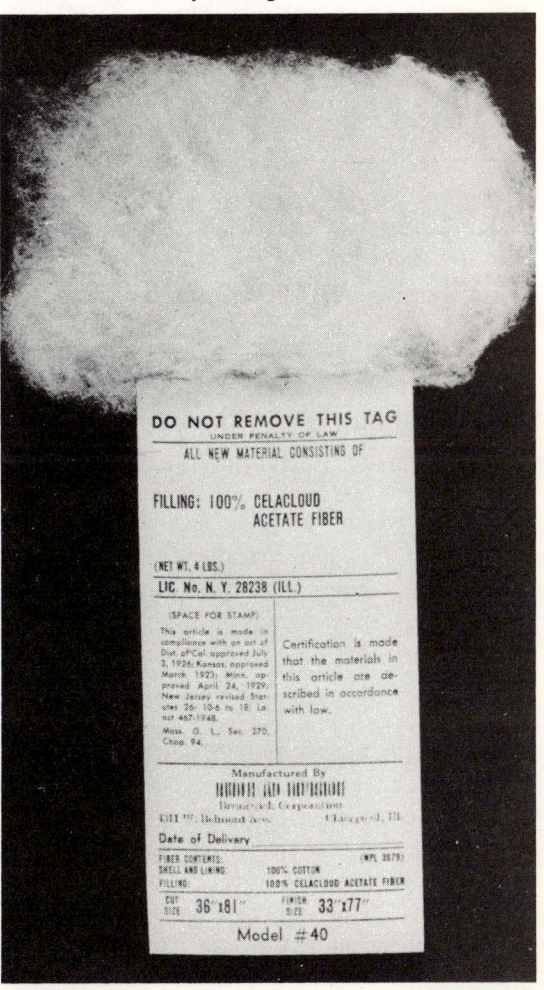

than 40 in. around the middle, or a restless sleeper, you'll like the oversize bag, around 40 by 82. You can get smaller-than-adult bags for kids, but if you buy good bags, they'll outgrow them before they wear them out. Better go full size. If rolled size is important to your packing plans, remember that bags are rolled loosely on the shelves, and ask for a chance to roll it tight for comparison.

Construction features that mark a good sleeping bag are easy to spot. Look for a high-grade, heavy-duty zipper with pull tabs inside and out. Snaps don't make good closures. Look for a "draft tab" inside the zipper, to keep out cold air and keep the cold metal off your skin. Check for heavy thread and double stitching in the seams. Quilting pattern marks quality; look for V-tubes in a down bag, and a diamond or cross-stitch in synthetics. Loopstitching is less desirable, but less expensive. Look for a liner for extra warmth and wear, and for easy cleaning, and for cloth tie tabs to hold it. Head canopies aren't really much use, but the canopy makes a wrapper when rolled, and that's essential for long shell wear. An air-mattress pocket is good, but only if the bag is big enough so the inflated mattress won't crowd you. If you'll be camping out in very cold weather, a head-and-shoulder hood is a good idea.

See also: boots; camping; clothing; packs, camping; trailers.

slide projectors

Sound track for your slides

BY BYRON G. WELS

Using your tape recorder, you can give your slide shows a professional touch, with narration, music, dialogue and sound effects. Best of all, slides will advance automatically while you enjoy the show with guests

■ TURN THE LIGHTS DOWN, turn on the tape recorder, and your first slide is projected on the screen. From there on, you sit back and enjoy the show with your guests. Slides change automatically, timed with a prerecorded tape narration and background music.

The key to such a system is a small plastic "sandwich" on which two brass spacers, ¼ x ⅜ in. long, are mounted as shown above. Connect these spacers to the switch circuit of an automatic slide projector as in the drawing.

With your slides in proper sequence for projecting, add the narration and music to a tape recording. Whenever you want to change a slide, apply a strip of aluminum foil tape (arrow in photo) to the *shiny* uncoated side of your recorded tape. Then, with the switch mechanism connected to the slide projector, when you play the tape the aluminum "cue" strips close the circuit and change the slide.

The "switch" can be mounted to your tape recorder with epoxy cement if you plan to use it often. If not, use transparent mending tape. Thread the recording tape through the head and around the switch on its way to the take-up reel.

See also: cameras, used; darkrooms; hobby workspace; photography; projection cabinet; tape recorders; testers, photo.

clever ideas

When painting or varnishing removable shelves in a bookcase or closet, there's no need to wait for one side to dry before painting the other. Drive a couple of nails part way in both ends of each shelf. Then, at the time of painting, rest the board by the nails between two sawhorses or other supports. Paint the ends, both edges and one face and flip it over.

Surfacing the steps of your stepladder with closely spaced droplets of plastic rubber is a clever way of providing a nonslip footing. First be sure that the wood is dry and free of oil and then simply squeeze out a drop at a time about 1 in. apart. When dry, the nodules will provide an excellent rubber tread which prevents accidents.

With a key it's not so bad, but when trying to open a glove compartment by pressing the lock alone, there's nothing to get hold of. You can make it a lot easier to open the compartment in your car by adding a handle. And by picking out a fancy cabinet pull, it looks like part of the original equipment. Just drill two small holes through the door.

You won't run the risk of smearing the address on a package label when sticking it down if you apply pressure by rolling rather than stroking your fingers across it. The handiest thing for this is a pencil. Simply roll it over the label with the palm of the hand. Pressure from the pencil will also assure a well stuck label which won't pull off.

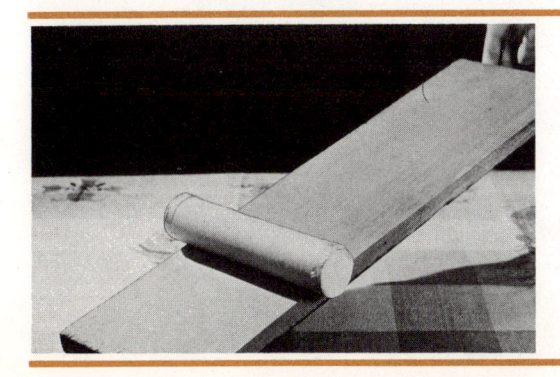

Pour an inch of sand or salt in a short length of mailing tube and cap both ends. Stand it on end, then roll it down an inclined board. You'd expect it to roll off the end of the board, but it doesn't. It slows down, even stops dead in its tracks. How come? As long as the sand stays in the end of the tube, the tube rolls freely, but as the sand shifts and levels out, the center of gravity changes.

Compound slide rest for a wood lathe

BY WALTER E. BURTON

Have you wished you could do metal turning? This accessory lets you do it on your wood lathe. Furthermore, you don't need special metalworking equipment to make the slide rest

■ WHEN YOU ADD a compound slide rest to a wood-turning lathe, you expand the tool's abilities to include reasonably precise machining of metals, plastics, hardwoods—any turnable material.

The lathe does not need altering unless you must change pulleys or add a jack shaft to produce spindle speeds low enough for metal turning. You'll probably also want to add a chuck or two of the type used to hold metal rods, tubes and rings—say one universal (3-jaw) chuck and one independent 4-jaw type.

The compound slide rest shown in use on the facing page was designed to be built in a shop that presently has no metal-working lathe. It's not as complicated as a quick glance at the drawings on the following pages might suggest. The basic materials needed will include:

One plate of ⅜-in. steel and three plates of ¼-in. steel (keyed A, J, K and S on the drawings); four ⅝-in.-square steel bars for the lower slide rails (E and F); four ⅜-in.-square steel bars for the upper slide rails (L and P); strips of ⅛-in.-thick brass in 5⁄16-in. and ¾-in. widths, for the gibs and their retaining plates (I and O); eight end supports of ¼-in. steel (B and C, G and H, M and N, Q and R); pieces of the same stock, to form the tool-post slot; enough ⅜-16 threaded rod (the type sold in local hardware stores) to make one 6-in. and one 10-in.

2 Upside-down assembly of cross-slide sections assures accuracy. After rails F are joined to end supports and plate J, use assembly as spacing cradle for rails E. Slip paper between gib and rail before clamping to drill for bolts and pins at the right

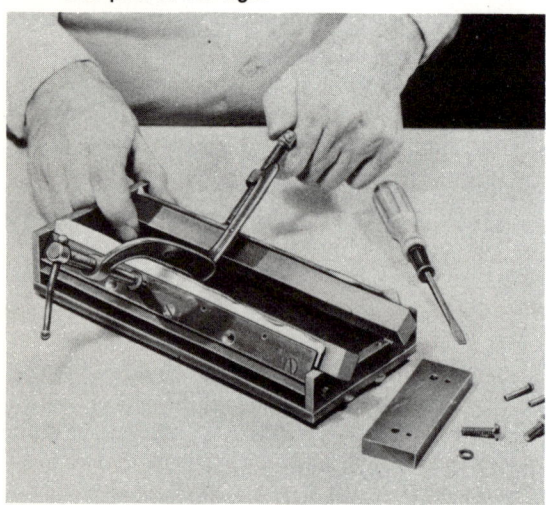

3 To make a curved slot in plate J, secure plate K to it with a pivot bolt and drill a series of overlapping holes through the locking bolt hole, while K is pivoted about 100 deg. Then file away jagged edges and file a hex nut to fit the slot as shown on page 2383

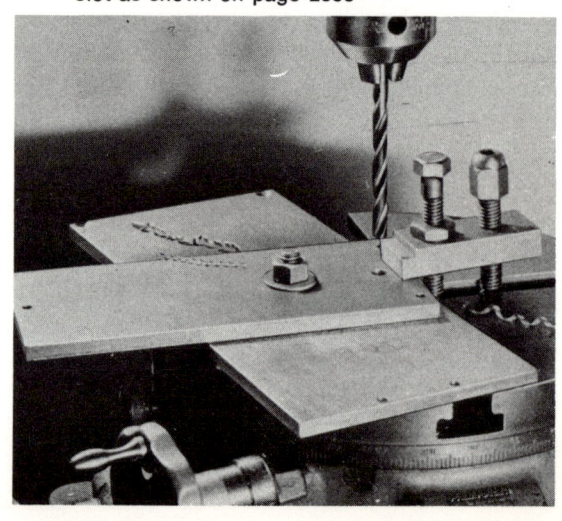

slides, drawer: see hardware

1 Drill rails for bolts and pins, using predrilled end supports as templates

feed screw; and two brass blocks, each ¾-in. to 1-in. square and about 1 in. long, for feed-screw nuts, which are stationary.

Start with the cross slide. This half of the assembly consists of two rail-and-plate sections. The bottom (fixed) section bolts to the lathe bed; the top (sliding) section moves crosswise to the lathe bed—as for facing cuts—and serves as a mount for the pivoting compound slide. The gibs, attached to the rails of the sliding section, are adjustable to control any play that may develop.

It's important that rails are mounted exactly parallel to each other and to the plate on which their end supports are mounted. Assemble the top section first, clamping the rails in position and using the predrilled end supports for boring templates, as in Fig. 1. Note that the gib-retaining plates are already attached to the rails. A V-block makes a good clamping support. After these rails are secured, use them as a form for clamping the lower, fixed rails while the latter are drilled for the bolts and pins that fasten them to their end supports (Fig. 2). Before applying

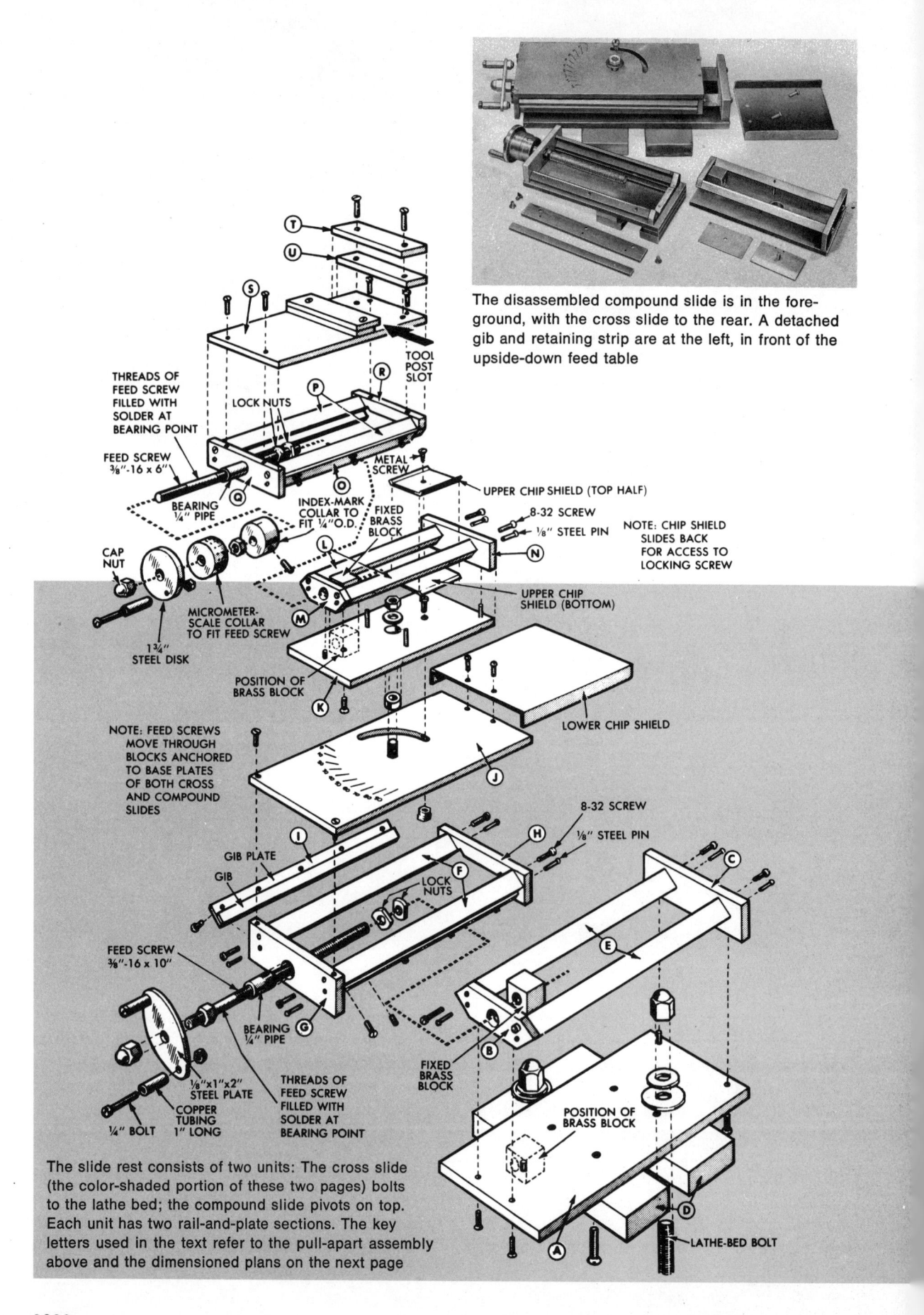

slide rest, lathe

The disassembled compound slide is in the foreground, with the cross slide to the rear. A detached gib and retaining strip are at the left, in front of the upside-down feed table

THREADS OF FEED SCREW FILLED WITH SOLDER AT BEARING POINT

LOCK NUTS

TOOL POST SLOT

FEED SCREW ⅜"-16 x 6"

BEARING ¼" PIPE

METAL SCREW

UPPER CHIP SHIELD (TOP HALF)

8-32 SCREW

⅛" STEEL PIN

NOTE: CHIP SHIELD SLIDES BACK FOR ACCESS TO LOCKING SCREW

CAP NUT

INDEX-MARK COLLAR TO FIT ¼" O.D.

FIXED BRASS BLOCK

MICROMETER-SCALE COLLAR TO FIT FEED SCREW

UPPER CHIP SHIELD (BOTTOM)

1¾" STEEL DISK

POSITION OF BRASS BLOCK

LOWER CHIP SHIELD

NOTE: FEED SCREWS MOVE THROUGH BLOCKS ANCHORED TO BASE PLATES OF BOTH CROSS AND COMPOUND SLIDES

8-32 SCREW

⅛" STEEL PIN

GIB PLATE

GIB

LOCK NUTS

FEED SCREW ⅜"-16 x 10"

BEARING ¼" PIPE

⅛"x1"x2" STEEL PLATE

COPPER TUBING 1" LONG

¼" BOLT

THREADS OF FEED SCREW FILLED WITH SOLDER AT BEARING POINT

FIXED BRASS BLOCK

POSITION OF BRASS BLOCK

LATHE-BED BOLT

The slide rest consists of two units: The cross slide (the color-shaded portion of these two pages) bolts to the lathe bed; the compound slide pivots on top. Each unit has two rail-and-plate sections. The key letters used in the text refer to the pull-apart assembly above and the dimensioned plans on the next page

2382

2383

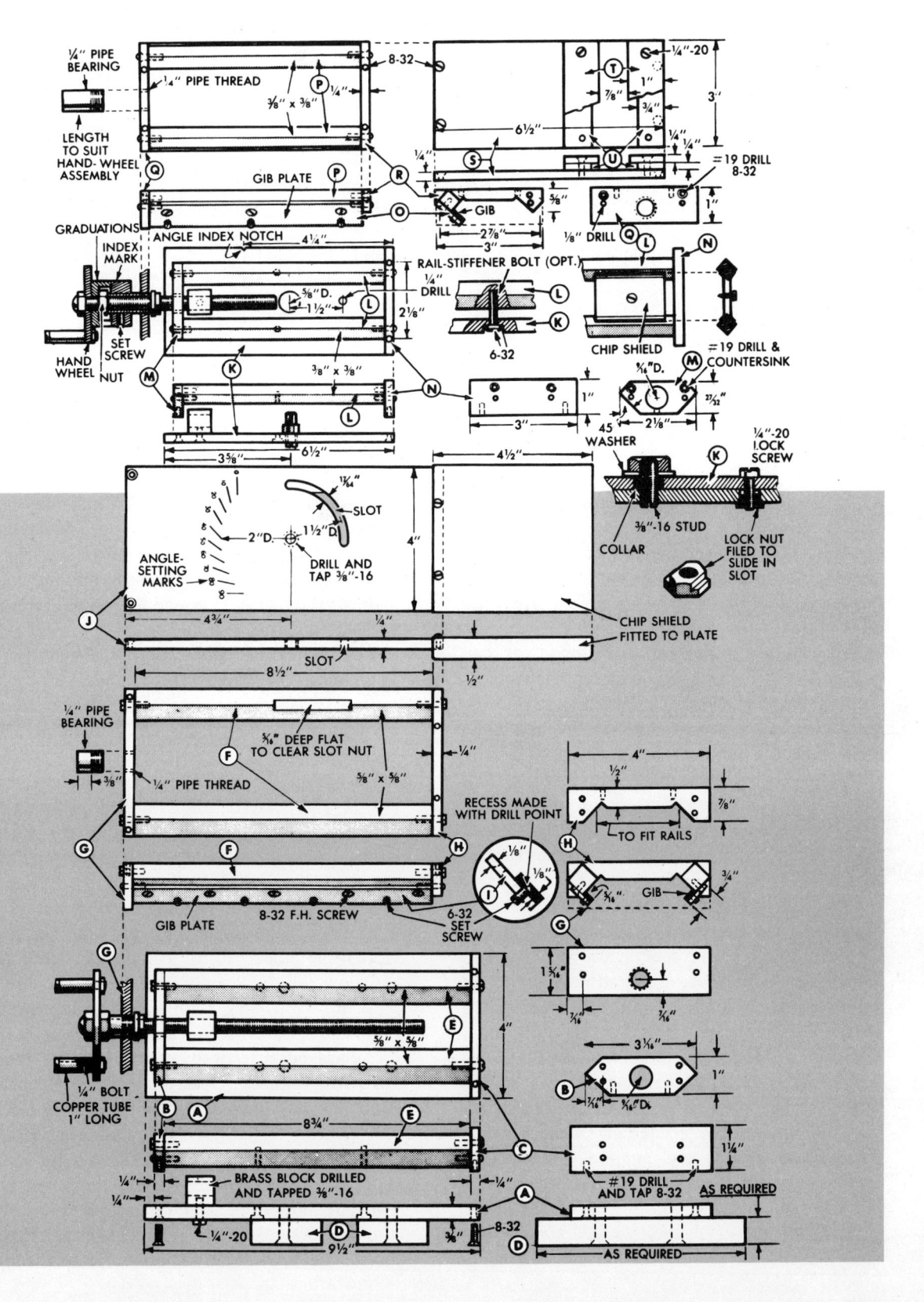

slide rest, lathe

4 Scribe a scale into the face of plate J, after making an index notch on the edge of plate K. Set the compound slide at accurate angles with a protractor, tapping lightly with a hammer and clamp tight. Use the square edge of the protractor to guide the scriber. To use the scale, be sure the cross slide is clamped at right angles to the headstock axis

compound slide rest, continued

the clamps, place a strip of fairly heavy paper between each gib and its retaining strip, to provide clearance for easier assembly. Gib setscrews will take up the slack when the unit is in use. At each point where a setscrew touches a gib, drill a recess about 1/16-in. deep and not much wider than the screw tip. These prevent lateral shifting. Position the screws to provide access when the rail sections are assembled.

You can use either two 8-32 bolts, or one bolt plus a 1/8-in. steel pin, to fasten each rail to each end support. When predrilling the supports, use a No. 29 (tap-size) drill for the bolt hole; then, after the supports have served as boring templates, enlarge these holes with a No. 19 bit. Bolt heads are countersunk.

To prepare the bearing for the 10-in. feed screw, ream out a piece of 1/4-in. iron or brass pipe until it's round and smooth. Take pains to see that the end of this pipe is square with end support G when screwed tight. Drill and thread the brass block so the feed screw is parallel to the top and bottom plates A and J. At the point where the screw rotates within the pipe bearing, coat it with solder or babbitt to fill the threads and increase the diameter. Then file until the screw rotates snugly inside the bearing. Two thin nuts, jammed together behind this soldered section, ride against the inside end of the bearing. The central hole in end support B should be large enough for these nuts to turn inside it.

In the photos and drawings, different hand controls are shown on the two feed screws. The choice between a two-handled crank or a hand-wheel is not critical, unless you plan to add micrometer scales.

Making the compound slide. This—the pivoting half of the accessory—is of the same basic construction as the cross slide, but on a smaller scale. As shown in Fig. 3, its bottom plate (K) pivots on plate J of the cross slide, for angular settings. The pivot stud is threaded into plate J and passes through a bushing press-fitted in plate K; it protrudes enough to permit the use of a washer and nut.

The completed unit shown was built for an 11-in. lathe. The top surface of the tool-post-slot strips (T) should be about 1 in. below the center line of the lathe headstock spindle. Thus, overall height of the accessory shown is about 4½ in. from the lathe bed. The two mounting blocks (D) can be dimensioned to bring the toolpost slot to the proper height for various lathes. These blocks are simply 2-in. wide steel bars or strips bolted to the bottom of plate A; length and spacing should be whatever is required for secure fastening with lathe-bed bolts.

Test the unit by turning an easy material such as wood. Oil any moving parts, and be sure all bolts are tight. Adjust gib screws to take up any play in the slides. At first, the feed screws may turn hard because of slide tightness and roughness. Rails not equipped with gibs (which add stiffness) may have a tendency to spring. In the unit shown, rail-stiffening bolts were installed midpoint on the fixed rails of the compound slide. They can be seen in the photo on page 2382, and are given as an optional detail.

If there's excessive chatter when turning metal, check the unit for play. Grasp the tool-

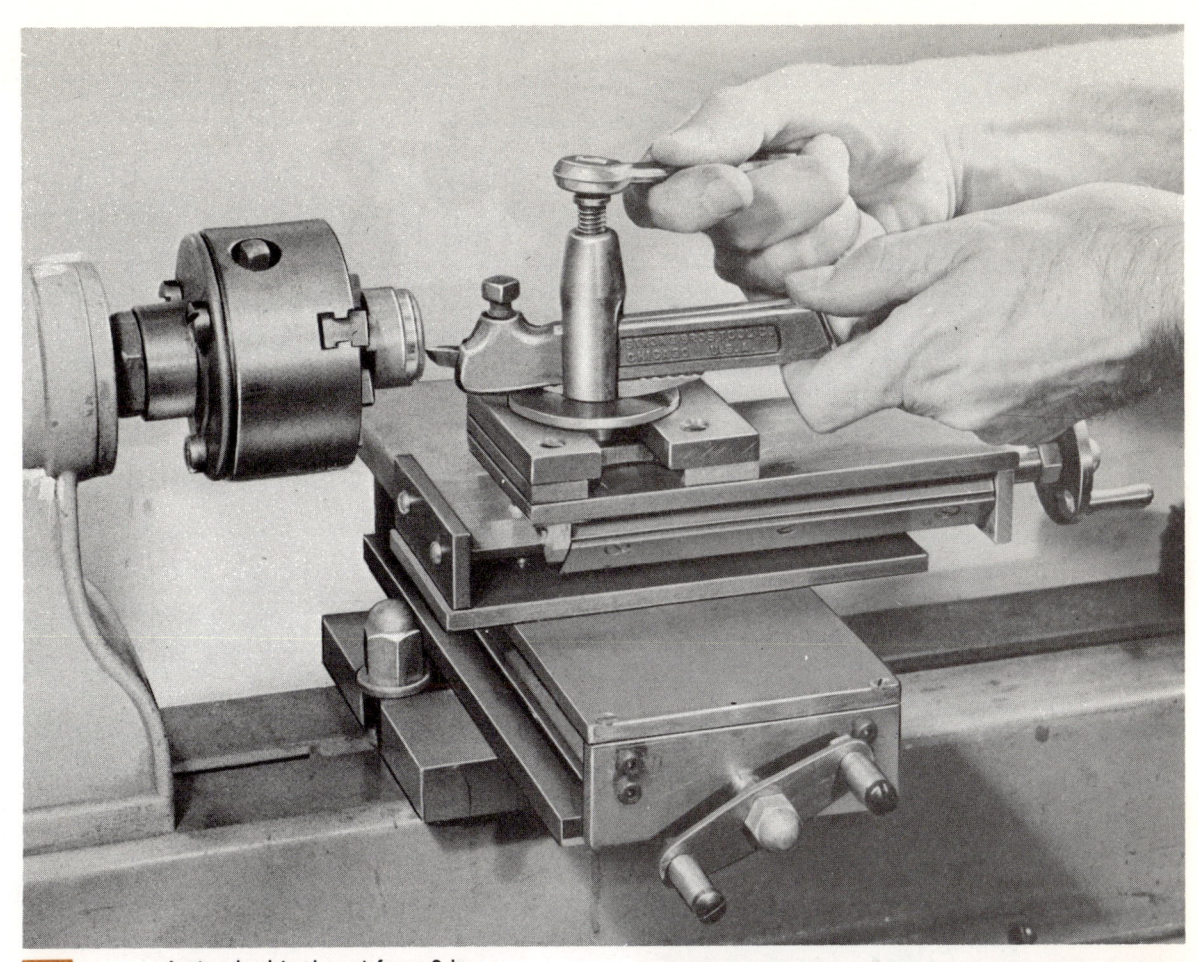

5 A standard tool post for a 9-in. metal-turning lathe clamps regular toolholder. Point of the bit normally should be on the center line of the lathe spindle. Much work requires no micrometer collars on feed screws, but they are easily added, as shown at the right

post and try to rock it in various directions. If chatter persists once play has been removed, you may have to lower the spindle speed. Wood lathes often have a minimum speed that is too high for large-diameter metal turning.

You can do a lot of turning without feeling the need for the angular scale shown in Fig. 4, or for micrometer collars on each screw to gauge-feed in small fractions of an inch. These features may be added later. The collar shown (Fig. 5) is 1¼ in. diameter and ½ in. long. Its matching index ring, setscrewed to the bearing pipe, is about the same size. Each turn of the screw moves the tool 1/16 (or .0625) inch. Since the micrometer collar is divided into 125 equal spaces, each division indicates a tool movement of .0005 in.—two divisions, .001.

One way to graduate the collar: clamp it in the lathe chuck, wrap a strip of paper around the chuck body and trim it to exact circumference. Remove this band, divide the circumference into 125 equal parts, tape it around the chuck again, and provide a fixed pointer for the division lines. Use a pointed tool in the compound slide rest to scribe equivalent lines on the face of the collar.

See also: belt sander; grinding; lathe accessories; lathe techniques; routing; saber saws.

2385

sliding doors

Bypassing window-doors provide a room with a vista view, plus convenient access to patio

How to hang sliding doors

---
sliding mount, camera: see tripods
sliding screens: see remodeling
sliding work holder: see bench saws
sling psychrometers: see humidifiers; psychrometer

■ TRACK HARDWARE has given a new "swing" to doors. They now can be in pairs, or ganged together in groups. No longer are doors limited to old-fashioned swinging in and out.

Available in kits, track hardware is a cinch for the do-it-yourselfer to install. In many cases, the hinges don't have to be mortised, automatic alignment makes the doors easy to adjust and a screwdriver, drill and hammer are about all you need to install them once you have the opening framed. In fact, you can purchase bifold doors, for example, in sets in which the doors are already hinged and the pivots in place to make them require even fewer tools to hang.

Of the three types—bypass, bifold and multifold—bifold doors are preferred for wardrobe closets. Folding open in pairs, they provide full access to the closet, whereas bypassing doors

The rough opening should be at least ¼ in. oversize to provide clearance for shimming and plumbing the frame. Below, after the panel is set, the door is swung inward to rest in the corresponding bottom rack

How to hang BYPASS DOORS

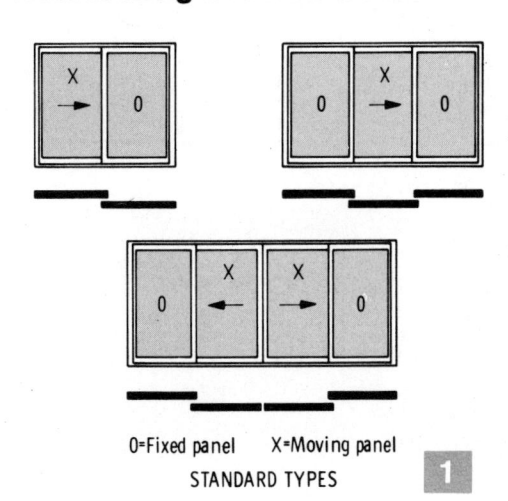

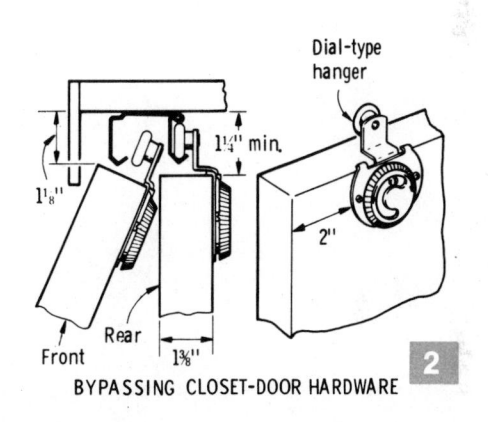

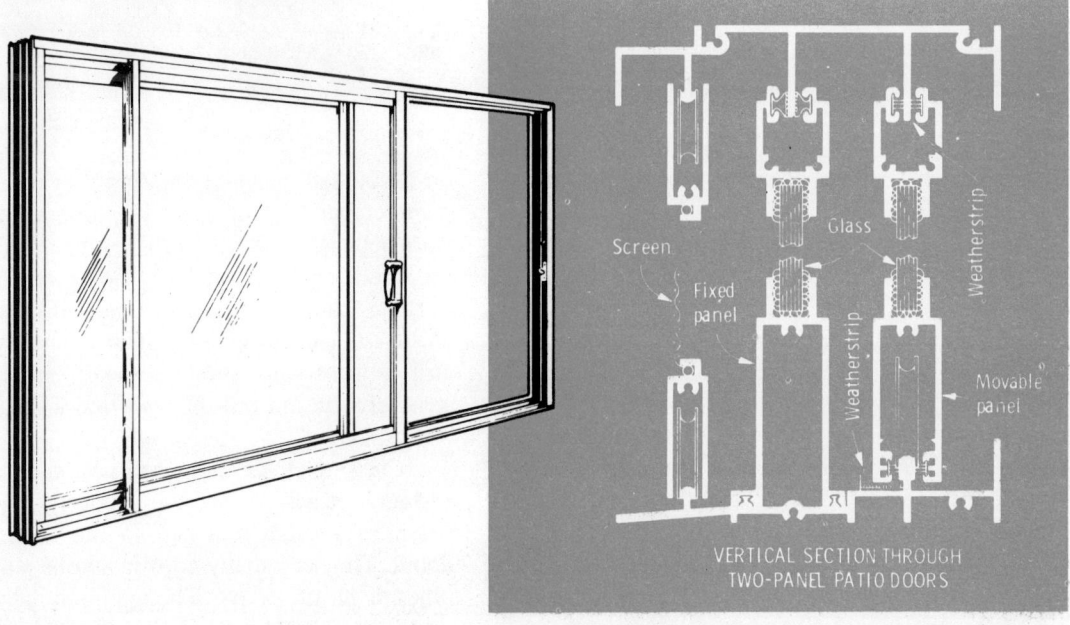

O=Fixed panel   X=Moving panel
STANDARD TYPES **1**

BYPASSING CLOSET-DOOR HARDWARE **2**

VERTICAL SECTION THROUGH TWO-PANEL PATIO DOORS

2387

sliding doors

How to hang BIFOLD DOORS

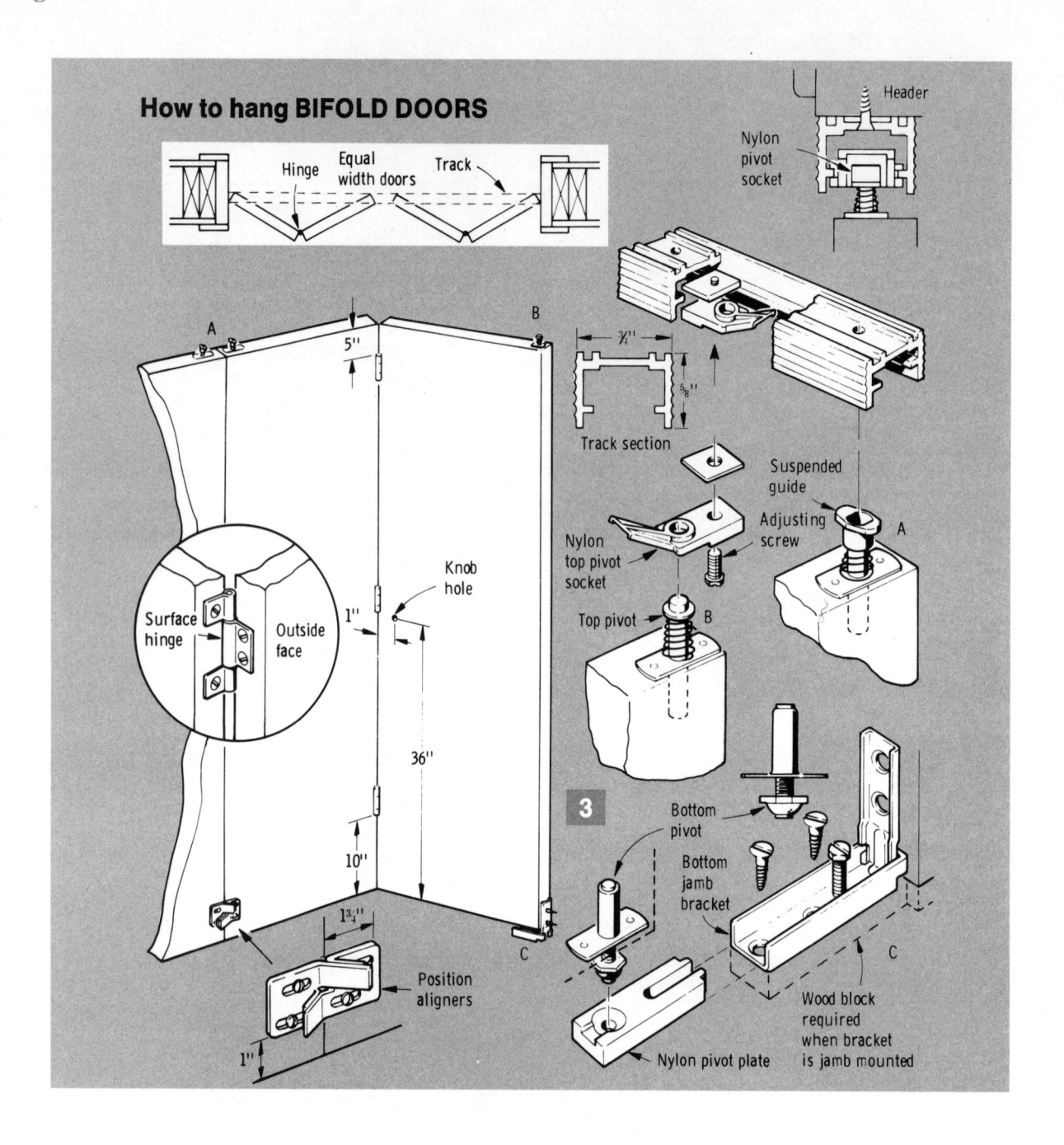

have the disadvantage of always blocking half the opening.

You'll find bypassing doors widely used where the passageway leads to a patio. Here they're glass, of course, supported in heavy aluminum frames and available for two, three or four-panel installations as shown in Fig. 1. A typical vertical cross section through a two-panel Stanley door is shown on page 2387. As in all similar installations, one or more panels is fixed. Here the inner panel is movable and bypasses the fixed outer one. A third panel, a screen, bypasses the fixed panel.

While bypassing patio doors are designed for do-it-yourself installation, they're ordered as a complete unit. You don't buy doors and hardware separately as you do when hanging bypassing doors on a closet. Patio doors are available in three frame depths, 3⅝, 4¹³⁄₁₆ and 6 in. and in single or ⅝-in. insulating glass. Double weatherstripping around the perimeter makes them weathertight and meeting rails mesh neatly without sticking.

Bypassing closet doors roll past each other on a double track as shown. Hangers fitted with nylon rollers are attached to the backs of the doors. They're usually adjustable one way or another to get the doors to hang plumb once they're

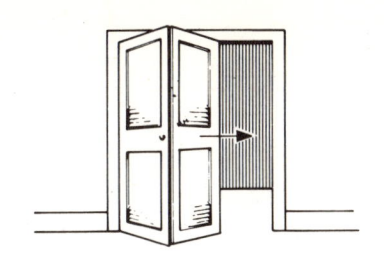

TWO-PANEL BIFOLD DOORS

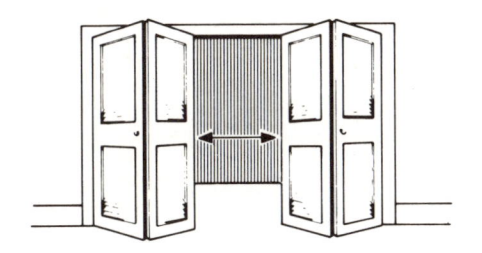

FOUR-PANEL BIFOLD DOORS

Two-door bifolds can be used on a divided "his-and-her" closet, or can be used in pairs, left, to create a four-panel door for a single closet. The doors run on an overhead track

up. Hangers are made to accommodate both ¾ and 1⅜-in.-thick doors by simply switching them, the front ones being placed in the rear track and the rear ones in the front track. The rear door is hung first then the front door, by tilting. Bypassing doors are kept from rubbing at the bottom by an adjustable nylon floor guide which is screwed in place and adjusted to provide 1/16-in. clearance.

Closet doors, bypassing or otherwise, come in standard sizes and you have to take this into account when framing the opening. As a rule of thumb, the width of the finished opening must be twice that of the doors minus 1 in. This provides for a 1-in. overlap at the center. As for height, the finished opening should be door height plus 1½ in. so you have ¼-in. clearance at the bottom and 1¼ in. at the top for track and hangers. The 1¼-in. clearance is required for Stanley's No. 2850 kit which features dial-adjustment hangers, but this will vary with the particular hardware used.

Louvered bifold doors are popular for closets, and both lumberyards and mail-order houses sell such doors in 12, 15 and 18-in. widths, 1⅛ and 1⅜ in. thick. The doors are installed in either two or four-panel combinations and are hung in pairs to fold to one or both sides of the opening. Again the opening must be framed to suit the doors. Two-panel doors require a finished opening of 24, 30 and 36 in.; four-panel doors require a finished opening of 48, 60 and 72 in. Bifold hardware is sold in two and four-door kits. In some, the track is in two lengths, in others, one.

There are many different kits available, but all work similarly. Fig. 3 shows a typical set. Pivots in the doors engage a track at the top and sockets at the bottom, and are installed either in holes drilled in the doors or attached to the backs. Doors are hinged in pairs with the hinge barrels facing to the rear. Spring-loaded or rubber snubbers keep the doors shut when closed and interlocking guides attached to the rear sides of the doors keep them in alignment at the bottom. No floor guide is needed.

Multifold doors, often called accordion doors, differ from bifolds in that they fold flat in a zigzag manner and can be ganged together in a series of panels to form a floor-to-ceiling divider wall. The panels can all be hung in a single group to fold and collect against one wall, or hitched together in two groups of different numbers to fold and collect against both walls. In each case, the doors occupy small space when folded flat against the wall. Tension springs on the door tops keep them aligned when shut and closely stacked when open.

Maximum-width door for home installation is 24 in. Minimum thickness is 1 in.; maximum,

sliding doors

How to hang MULTIFOLD DOORS

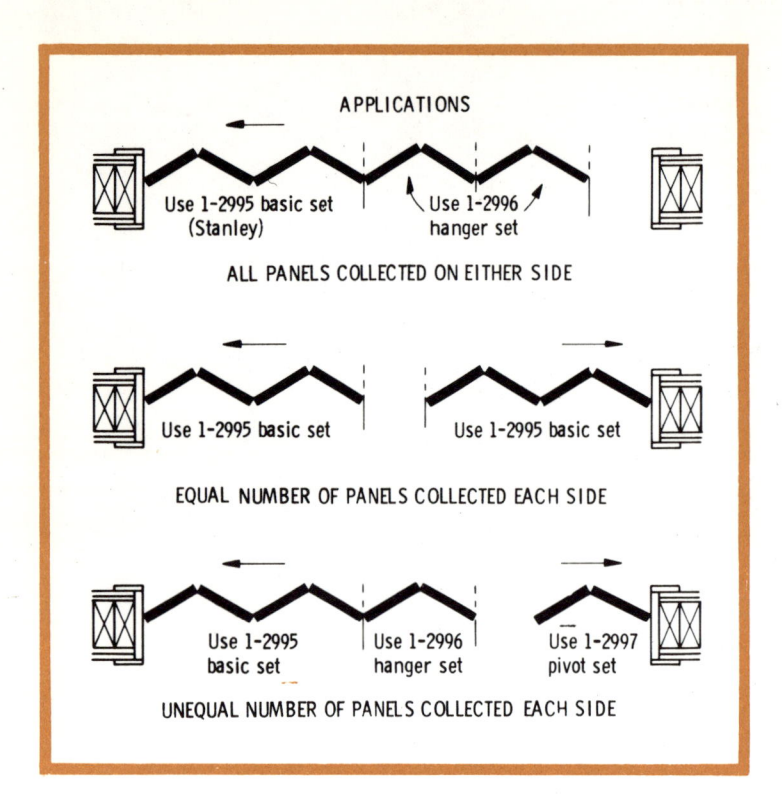

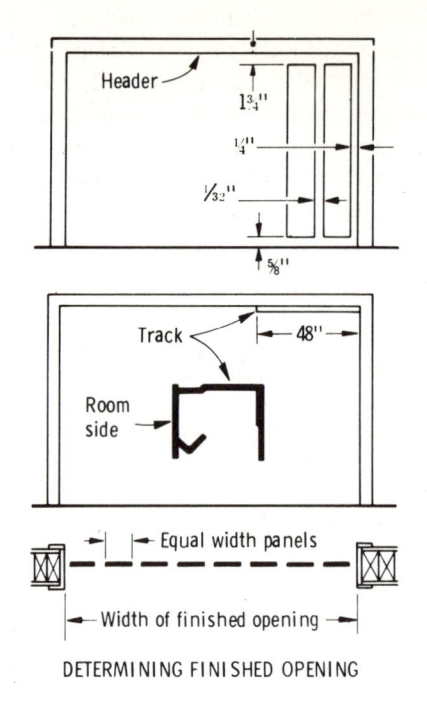

APPLICATIONS

Use 1-2995 basic set (Stanley) — Use 1-2996 hanger set
ALL PANELS COLLECTED ON EITHER SIDE

Use 1-2995 basic set — Use 1-2995 basic set
EQUAL NUMBER OF PANELS COLLECTED EACH SIDE

Use 1-2995 basic set — Use 1-2996 hanger set — Use 1-2997 pivot set
UNEQUAL NUMBER OF PANELS COLLECTED EACH SIDE

Header — 1 3/4", 1/4", 1/32", 5/8"

Track — 48", Room side

Equal width panels — Width of finished opening
DETERMINING FINISHED OPENING

As in the detail, right, swivel roller hangers are mounted flush with the side and end of the doors. One hanger is required for each pair of doors, as is shown in the detail directly below

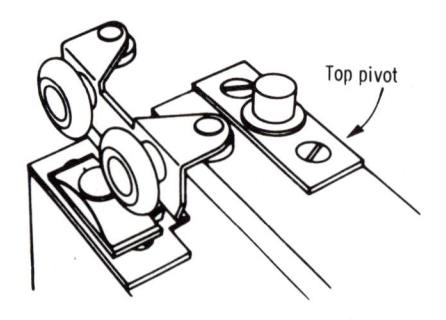

Top pivot

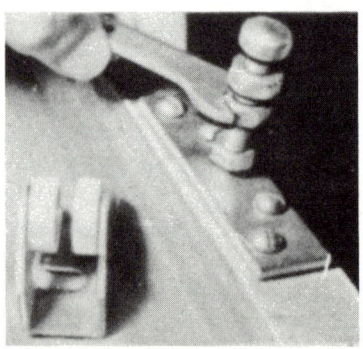

Above, the hanger bolt is screwed in position by turning the fixed adjusting nut with a wrench. Below, be sure the hanger carrier is aligned with the door surface. This is important. Otherwise the door is almost sure to bind unduly

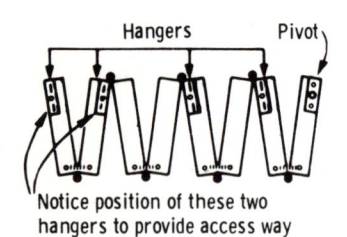

Hangers — Pivot
Notice position of these two hangers to provide access way

In those installations where all the doors are hinged together, only one top pivot is usually required for the job. Notice especially the locations of the two door hangers at the opposite end of the detail drawing

The spring-and-stud fixtures are screwed to each pair of doors at the ends opposite the hangers. The springs apply a constant tension to keep the doors properly aligned for smooth operation

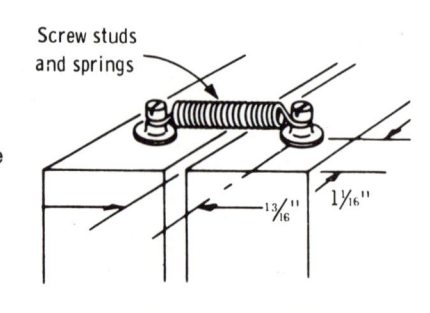

Screw studs and springs — 13/16", 1 1/16"

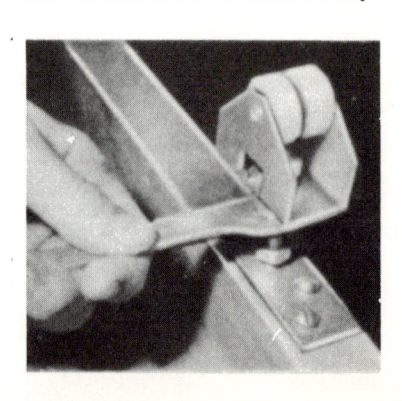

2390

1¾ in. However, standard 1⅜ x 18-in. flush doors are a good average size to consider. While butt hinges are furnished with the kit hardware, continuous hinges make a far neater installation.

Multifold track comes in 2 and 4-ft. sections to suit the size of the opening, whether it is a full room or a doorway. Top and bottom pivots support the starter door or doors, and these are installed after you have one section of track screwed in place. Then the doors, one by one, are all hung in this one section of track before the rest of the sections are added end to end. The hinges, of course, would all have been fitted beforehand and removed while placing the doors in the track.

While there is multifold hardware that's designed to support doors weighing up to 35 lbs., you can buy heavy-duty, multifold hardware to support doors weighing as much as 175 lbs. Here the track is I-beam or channel shape and comes in 16-ft. lengths.

See also: building; hardware; remodeling; patios.

How to hang HEAVY-DUTY MULTIFOLD DOORS

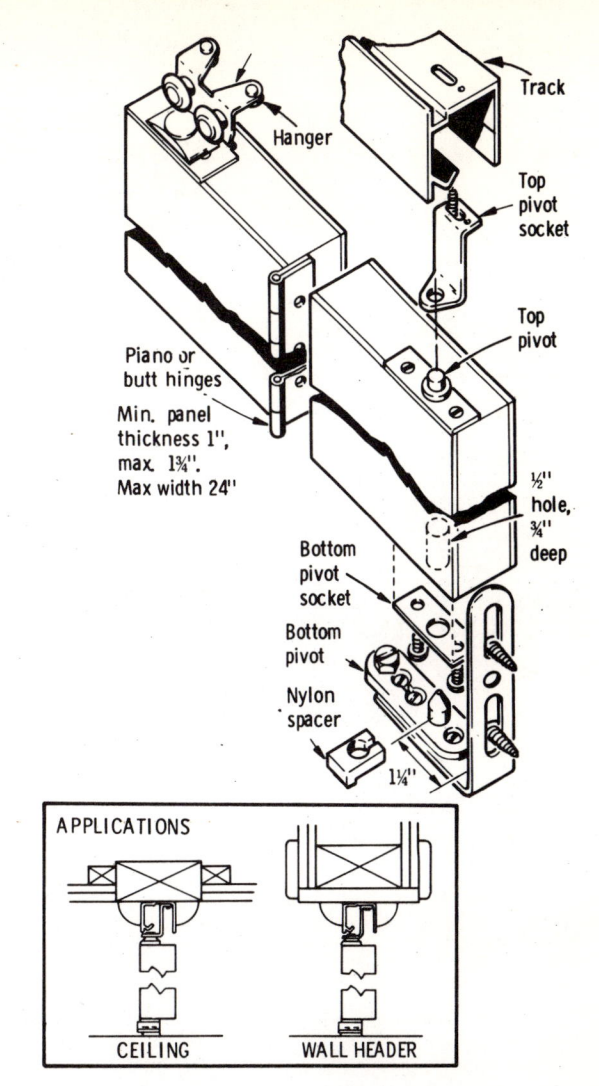

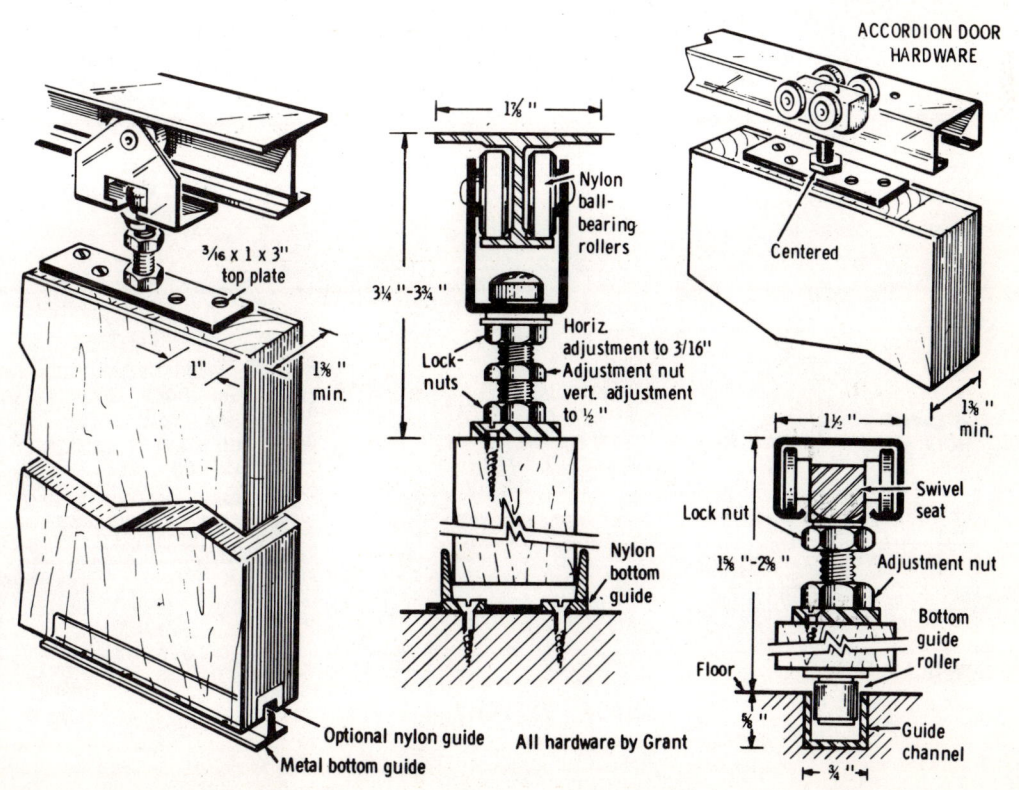

slitting saws

Pee-wee saws make hard jobs easy

BY WALTER E. BURTON

These midget circular blades, better known as slitting and slotting saws, make play of tricky shop projects

■ IF YOU DON'T have a screw-slotting cutter or some other midget circular saw in your shop, the chances are that, no matter what craft activity is most appealing to you—from jewelry craftsmanship to model-making—you probably are doing a lot of things the hard way.

In case you've never used one, a screw-slotting cutter is a midget circular saw designed as a milling cutter for slotting screw heads. With a little ingenuity, however, you can devise dozens of other ways of putting it to good use. In addition, there are many similar saws made for all-around use by the craftsman. The term "slitting saw" sometimes is applied generally to screw-slotting cutters and similar small circular saws.

In the home shop, such cutters can be used in a drill press, lathe and milling machine. Some craftsmen use them in portable electric drills and small hand grinders, though it's not easy to produce smooth, straight cuts with a hand-held tool mainly because of the instability of such an arrangement.

Pee-wee saws come in a wide range of thicknesses and diameters. For the model-maker, and the jewelry craftsman who wants to slit chain links or saw coiled wire into rings, there are blades as thin as .006. For all-around work in metal, wood and other materials, a more practical thickness is .032 or so.

Diameters most likely to interest the craftsman range from less than ½ in. to 2¾ in. or perhaps slightly larger. Various mounting-hole sizes are available. In operations such as precision wood cutting, the larger diameters are desirable since they can handle thicker material. (The photos here show a tiny .008 saw 9/16 in. in

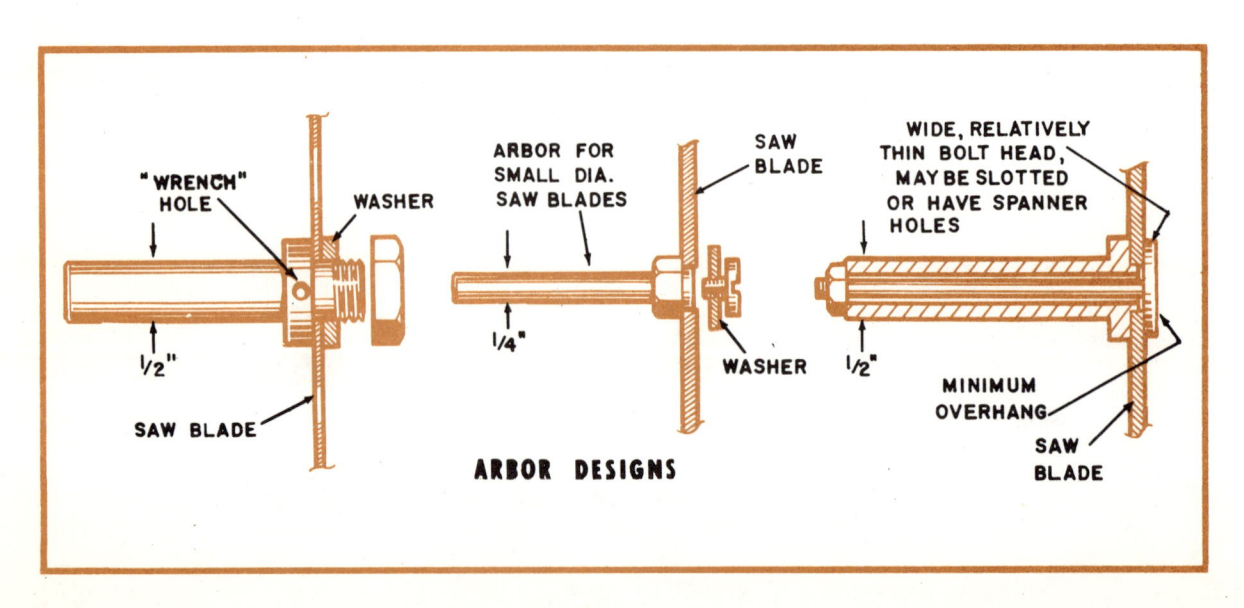

ARBOR DESIGNS

Slitting and slotting saws come in a number of different diameters and thicknesses with various mounting-hole sizes. Perfect for precision cutting jobs, they normally should be run at fairly slow speeds

Avoid the ever-present danger of overheating. When sawing metal, it's good to lubricate with sulphurized cutting oil. It's also a good idea to stop the saw occasionally and allow it to cool

Cutting square tubing to precise lengths is easy with this .032 saw mounted on a milling machine. For angle cuts of such metal, you can tilt either the vise or the material on which you're working

Straight-sided openings can be cut precisely square with a slotting saw in a milling machine. To do it, nail the material on which you are working through a scrap area to a vise-held wooden block

The original purpose of a slotting saw makes it a useful drill-press accessory. Here it's mounted on an arbor to cut a driver slot in a headless screw that is held horizontally in a vise

Using the same setup as shown at left, except that the work is held vertically, you can cut short sections from brass tubing. Drive a wooden plug into the tubing to prevent crushing in the vise

2393

slitting saws

pee-wee saws, continued

Only .008 thick, this remarkably tiny saw used on a small lathe neatly slits the metal ring that has been clamped on the toolpost. Cylindrical bushings are slit in the same way

Model builders can find many uses for these thin and smooth-cutting saws. This bench-lathe setup produces splinterless veneer strips. To do this job, just set up the saw and feed the wood past it

When you plan to cut bars, the stock must be clamped squarely to the saw and the vise properly aligned. Spacers support the work until it is held firmly in place by the vise jaws

diameter, and two .032 cutters in diameters of 2 in. and 2½ in.)

For milling-machine use, the cutter can be mounted on the regular arbor supported by an overarm, or on a short arbor gripped in a collet. Likewise, for use in a drill press or lathe, saws usually are provided with shanks by mounting them on arbors.

A useful arbor for the larger-diameter saws has a ½-in. shank 2 to 3 in. long. Saws should, of course, be clamped securely on their arbors and should rotate with uniform contact of teeth against work.

While the photos show only a few of the possible uses for slotting cutters, they should suggest many more. For larger equipment than that usually found in the shop, metal-slitting saws can be obtained in diameters from 2 in. to 8 in., and thicknesses from 1/32 in. to 3/16 in. One type has taper-ground sides with the greater thickness at the teeth; another is toothed for side chip clearance.

Usually, these small saws should be run at fairly low speeds. If run fast, especially when cutting certain metals or wood, they may overheat.

In metal-sawing, it is desirable to use a cutting lubricant, such as sulphurized cutting oil. And to keep chips from jamming the cutter, especially if it is a little dull, a piece of soft wood touched occasionally against the saw will help.

See also: bench saws; circular saw blades; radial-arm saws; saber saws.

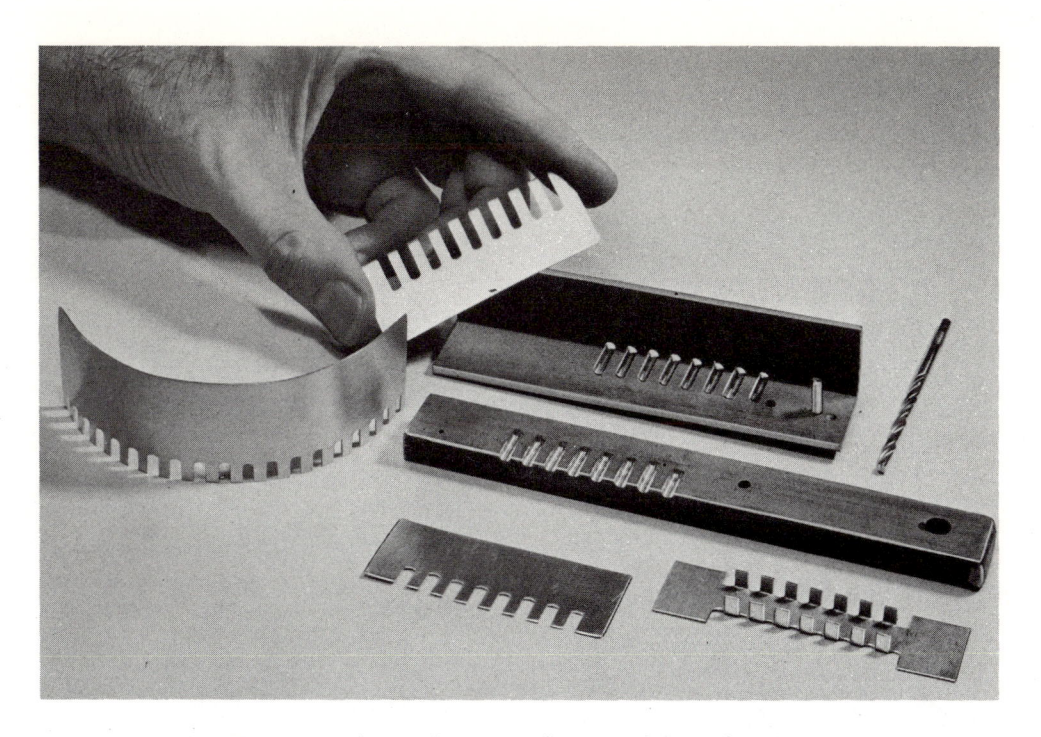

Metal slotting with a twist drill

BY WALTER E. BURTON

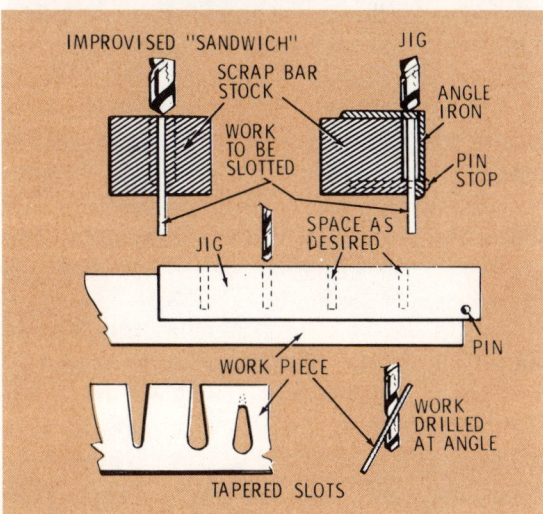

■ LOOKING more like the product of a stamping machine, the above samples actually are the work of a twist drill. The simplest way to slot a piece of sheet metal by drilling is to sandwich it between two pieces of scrap metal and drill a hole into the edge of the sheet, so that the bit—of greater diameter than the sheet thickness, cuts equally into each scrap piece.

To do this requires a jig made from a piece of angle iron and bar stock. First, remove any inside radius (fillet) from the angle iron so that the bar and work will fit snugly inside. Then install a pin in the bar or angle to engage a hole in the other part, so the jig halves can be assembled in alignment for each slotting job. Place the metal to be slotted between the bar and inner surface of the angle iron and clamp the entire assembly in a vise. The holes are drilled through the angle iron and edgewise into a scrap of sheet stock to the required depth. When all the holes are drilled, the jig is completed and ready for repetitive slotting.

See also: drilling; sheet metal; slitting saws.

slotting saws: see slitting saws
small boats: see boat handling

smelting furnace

Here's the completed furnace set up ready for use. The burners have separate gas valves to provide precise adjustment of the flame. A single valve controls the air supply from the vacuum cleaner. Although not pictured, the molding flask should be placed near the furnace

Gas-fired smelting furnace

BY E. R. HAAN

■ WITH THIS SMALL FURNACE you can melt down aluminum, brass and copper; preheat small, thick pieces of iron and steel for brazing or forging; caseharden soft steel; make up alloys and bake vitreous enamels on metals. You can use either LP or city gas. The cost runs from $25 up.

The refractory lining: Build the refractory lining inside a sheet-metal can from 11½ to 14 in. in diameter, and from 14 to 17 in. high. Drill and ream two ¾-in. holes diametrically opposite each other as indicated. Then cut 5 pieces of firebrick to the sizes given for the furnace floor. To cut firebrick neatly you score it all around at a marked line by tapping with a sharp cold chisel to form a groove 1/16 to ⅛ in. deep and then break with a heavier blow. The refractory lining consists of ganister and pieces of firebrick. Ganister is a mixture of equal parts of pulverized firebrick and either prepared refractory cement or fire clay. The mixture should have the consistency of rather stiff mortar. If you use prepared cement, you will need two 1-gal. cans. If you use fire clay, you add water sparingly. Pieces of firebrick usually can be had at little or no cost from a brickyard. Pulverize these with a hammer.

Cover the bottom of the can with ganister about 1¼ in. deep, and tamp it down to eliminate air pockets. Place the 5 pieces of firebrick in the positions shown, press them down into the ganister so that their top surfaces will be level ¼ in. below the holes in the sides of the can. Press ganister into the spaces between the pieces of firebrick to come 1 in. from their tops.

Next, make the cylindrical inner form of sheet metal. This is 7 in. in diameter for a can of 11½ to 12 in. in diameter so the lining will not be less than 2¼ in. thick. The inner form is 8 in. in diameter for a 12 to 14-in. can. Hammer the seam moderately tight so that it can be pried open for removal of the form. Drill and ream

---

smoke barbecue barrel: see barbecues
snow driving: see driving, snow
snowflakes: see Christmas decorations

two ¾-in. holes diametrically opposite each other and ¼ in. above the bottom edge. Place the form centrally on the furnace floor so the holes are in line with those in the can, and push an 18-in. length of ⅜-in. pipe through all the holes.

Now you build up the lining. Set 8 to 12 lengths of wire or old hacksaw blades vertically at the center of the lining for reinforcement. Tamp the ganister into all voids and in good contact with the can, inner form and pieces of firebrick. After the lining has dried overnight, turn out the pipe and remove the form. Then let the lining cure for three days.

Burner details: The ⅜-in. nipples of each burner should come ¼ to ⅜ in. inside the surface of the lining. A similar amount of clearance is allowed between the reducers and the outside of the furnace. The brass half unions fitting the tees are the kind used to attach ⅜-in. copper tubing with compression nuts. Enlarge the inner part of the hole at the beveled end with an ¹¹⁄₃₂-in. drill to a depth of ¼ in. To do this you mount the fitting at a true perpendicular in a drill vise and do the drilling on a drill press.

Tap the enlarged portion of the hole with a

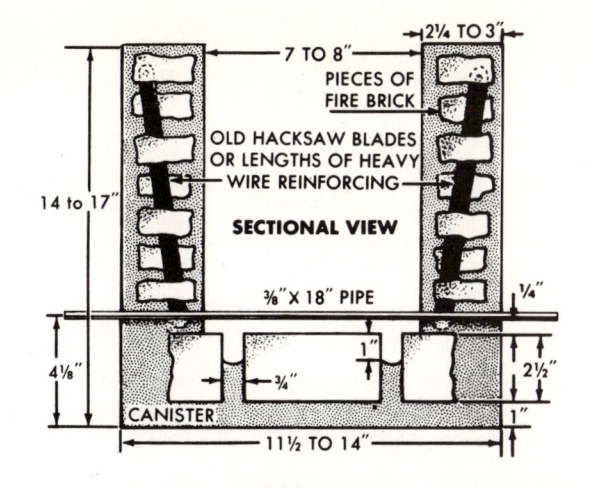

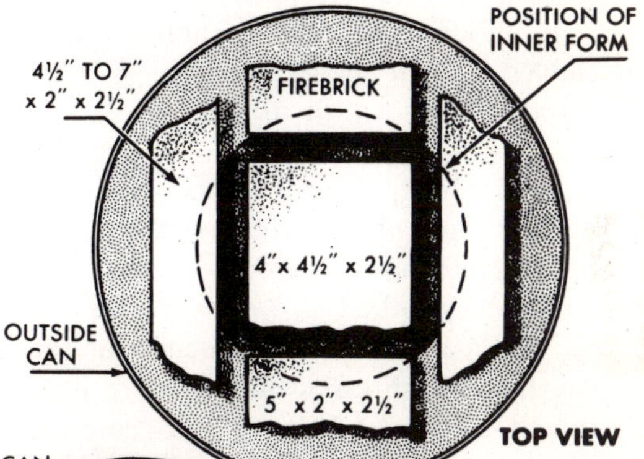

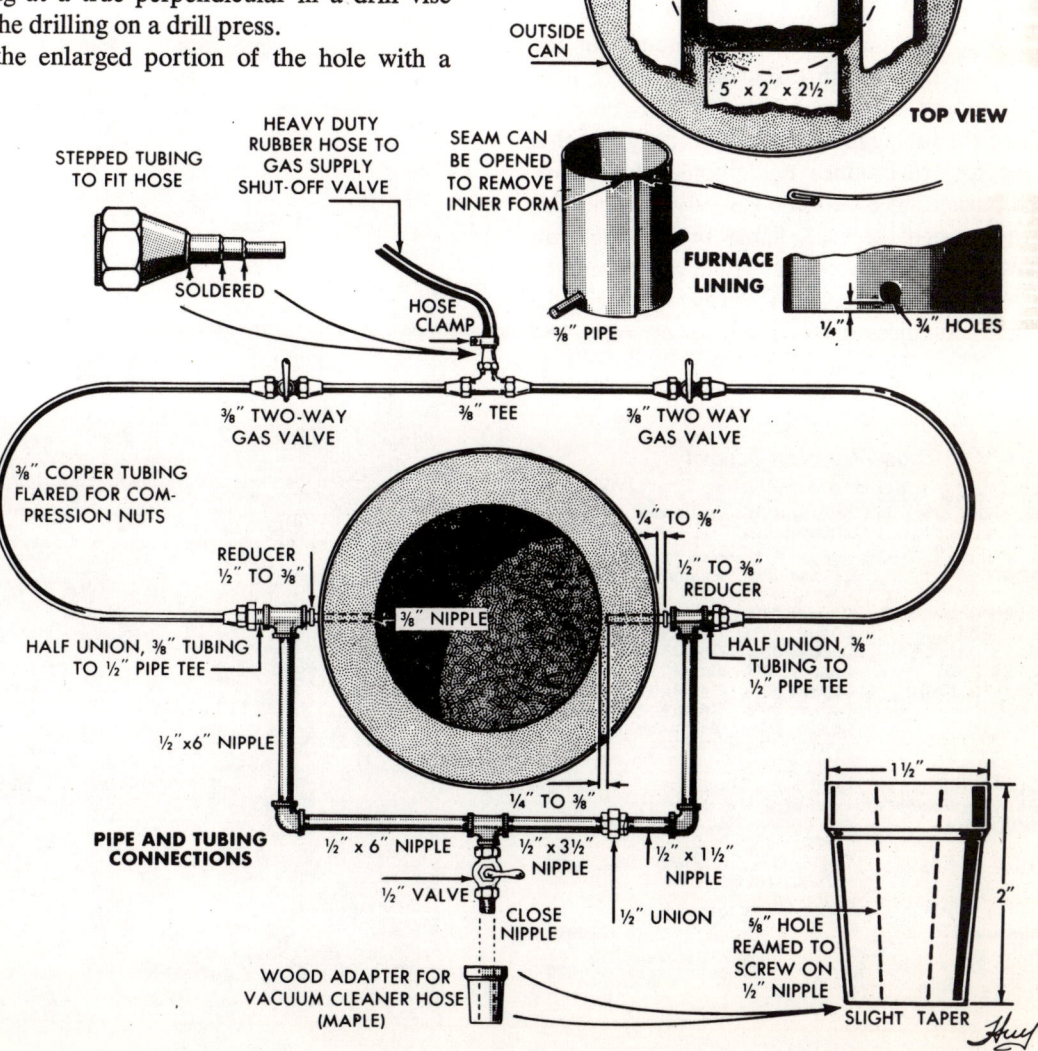

smelting furnace

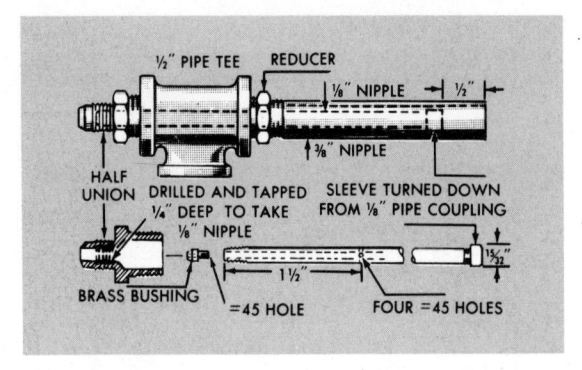

Diagram labels: ½" PIPE TEE — REDUCER — ⅛" NIPPLE — ½" — ⅜" NIPPLE — HALF UNION — DRILLED AND TAPPED ¼" DEEP TO TAKE ⅛" NIPPLE — SLEEVE TURNED DOWN FROM ⅛" PIPE COUPLING — BRASS BUSHING — 1½" — =45 HOLE — FOUR =45 HOLES — 15/32"

Tongs should be designed to grip the crucible firmly when removing it from the furnace. Be especially careful when pouring hot metal into the flask.

⅛-in. pipe tap to take a nipple which should extend ¼ in. inside the end of the burner when it is assembled. The nipple has four No. 45 holes drilled equidistantly through its wall as shown. A steel sleeve fits the burner end of the nipple and a brass bushing, drilled centrally with a No. 45 drill, fits into the other end of the nipple where it screws into the half union.

Pipe and tubing unit: Use ½-in. pipe for the air supply line and ⅜-in. copper tubing for the gas supply line. Compression fittings were used on the tubing in the model shown. For these the ends of the tubing must be flared carefully with a flaring tool to produce tight, nonleaking joints. Each burner has a separate gas valve for individual adjustment of each flame but a single air valve serves both burners. Having the air and gas supplies connected midway between the burners equalizes the resistance of pipe and tubing.

SOME COMMON ALLOYS

Percentages indicate proportions by weight. Metals are given from left to right in the order of their progressively lesser melting points.

ALUMINUM BRONZE	Copper 90%, Aluminum 10%
BABBIT	Copper 3%, Antimony 7%, Tin 90%
BEARING BRONZE	Copper 82%, Zinc 2%, Tin 16%
BELL METAL	Copper 78%, Tin 22%
BRASS (yellow)	Copper 67%, Zinc 33%
BRASS (red)	Copper 90%, Zinc 10%
BRAZING METAL	Copper 55%, Zinc 45%
BRONZE	Copper 90%, Tin 10%
PEWTER	Copper 6.8%, Antimony 1.7%, Bismuth 6.5%, Tin 85%
SOLDER (tinman's)	Lead 33%, Tin 67%
SOLDER (plumber's)	Lead 67%, Tin 33%
TYPE METAL	Antimony 15%, Lead 82%, Tin 3%
WHITE METAL	Copper 1%, Antimony 19%, Lead 75%, Tin 5%

Melting points of above metals in degrees F.

Aluminum	1220	Copper	1980
Antimony	1160	Zinc	787
Lead	624	Bismuth	520
Tin	449		

If the rubber hose for the gas line is too small to fit on ⅜-in. tubing, make an adaptor from short lengths of tubing, one fitting inside the other, then sweat-solder together. Also make an adaptor of close-grained hardwood to fit into the end of the vacuum-cleaner hose. Pipe-joint compound is used only at the tees where the half union and reducer screws into the tees, and where the ⅜-in. burner nipples screw into the reducers. All the joints of the gas line should be tested.

Crucible, tongs: A graphite-clay crucible is best, but for economy you can use one made up from a malleable-iron pipe cap and nipple of suitable size. A 3½-in. pipe cap provided with a 6-in. nipple were used for the model shown. By providing the pipe cap with 4 machine-screw legs turned into tapped blind holes in the bottom to raise the crucible ½ to ¾ in., the flames will meet under it and the heat will be absorbed faster than if the flames contact only the side of the crucible. Curvature of the jaws of the tongs depends on the crucible diameter. The contact should be uniform and the tongs should be tested for holding before being used.

Curing the lining: After the 3-day drying-out period you ignite the gas and allow small flames to burn without any air blast for about an hour to complete the curing of the lining. To ignite the furnace place a lighted match inside near a burner and turn on the gas supply slowly to produce a small flame. Then turn on the other burner to ignite from the first and turn it down for a small flame.

After an hour's time the air blast is used for about 10 minutes. First open the gas valves farther so that the flames will rise above the furnace top. Then, while the air-supply valve is closed completely, turn on the vacuum cleaner, after which you open the air valve slowly until the flames become light blue. Too much air in proportion to gas will extinguish the flames. Avoid this by turning the gas valve almost fully open, then turn the air valve wide open after which you gradually decrease the gas supply to each burner to reach the point of maximum blast without flame flutter. After 10 minutes close the air valve first and then the gas valves.

When the furnace has cooled you inspect the lining for cracks which are almost certain to develop. Fill the cracks with prepared refractory cement or fire clay and allow this to dry out before the next firing. Crack filling is repeated if more cracks develop. When operating at maximum blast, the furnace can be covered almost entirely with a piece of asbestos-cement board to retain heat. To inspect the charge you remove the cover with a pair of tongs and observe the contents of the crucible through colored glasses. Use the skimming ladle to drop some borax into the molten metal. Use technical grade borax available at photo-supply houses. Skim off the resulting dross or scum before removing the crucible for pouring.

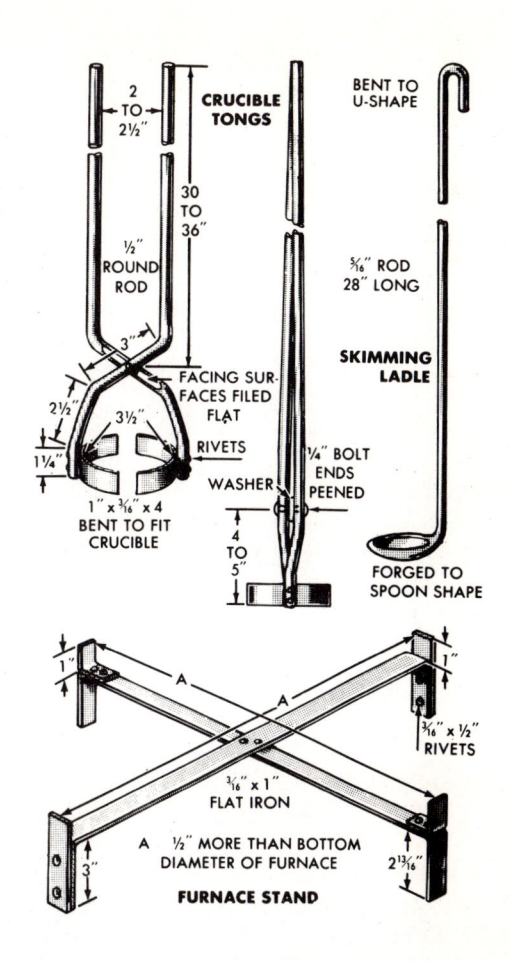

Safety rules: An LP gas tank should be located outside the building, and the gas piped through a ⅜-in. copper tube provided with one gas valve at the tank and another inside the building.

Locate the furnace on an earth or concrete floor that slopes away from walls or combustible material. The latter should be kept a safe distance from the furnace. A sheet-metal box about 6 in. high and about 3 ft. square, two-thirds full of dry sand, should be located next to the furnace. The molding flask is set on the sand. The crucible is held over the sandbox on its way to the molding flask for pouring.

See also: arc-welding; propane torches; vacuum cleaners, shop; welders; welding.

snow fort

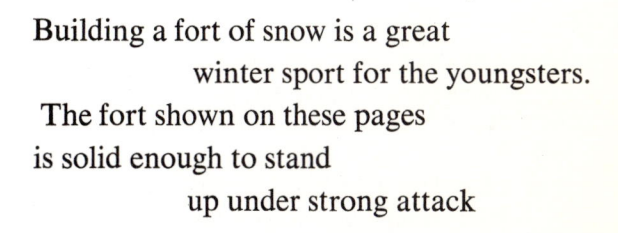

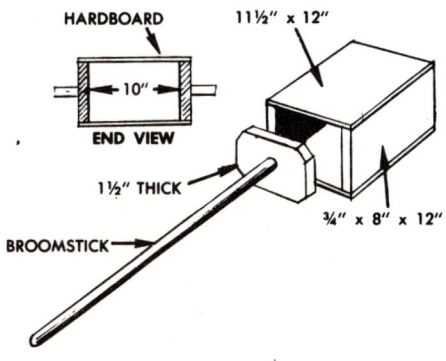

Building a fort of snow is a great winter sport for the youngsters. The fort shown on these pages is solid enough to stand up under strong attack

Snow fort for winter fun

BY HI SIBLEY

■ REDUCING FORT SNOW by storm will call for organized frontal attacks by the enemy from several directions with lots of spirit and drive. Taking it by siege could involve all the near-teens and early-teens for blocks around. Either way, the fort will mean a lot of fun for everybody. It's solid, with ice-encrusted walls and tower built of compacted snow blocks made in a push-out form and laid up masonry-fashion as in the details on the opposite page. The blocks are then sprayed with water, which freezes quickly.

See also: skiing; sleds; toboggan.

---

snow skiing: see skiing
snow sleds: see sleds
snow toboggan: see toboggan

2401

socket checker

Triple check on three-wire outlets

BY RONALD L. IVES

■ THIS SIMPLE AND INEXPENSIVE device checks three-wire outlets for presence of voltage, for correct polarity and for an effective ground connection. In electrical work, assuming you've got a good ground just because you're using a three-wire socket can cost you your life.

When this unit is plugged into 115 or 220 volts, the neon lights tell you if you've got power, if the ground connection is effective, and if polarity is correct (if polarity is reversed, your electrician hasn't been doing his job).

The schematic diagram shows all components which are mounted on the cover of a bakelite instrument case. Triangular arrangement of neons in the schematic is the same as in the rear view shown in the photo below.

See also: electrical wiring; electric power control; testers, electrical.

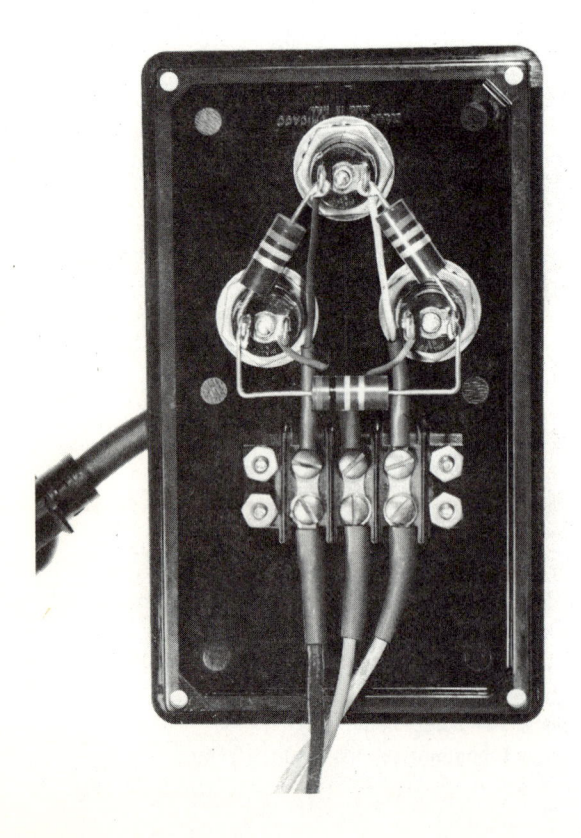

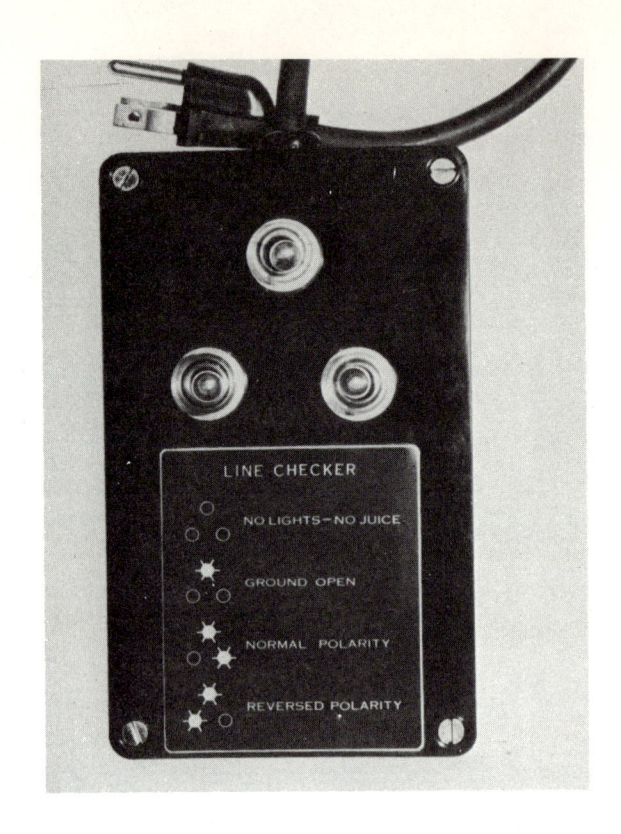

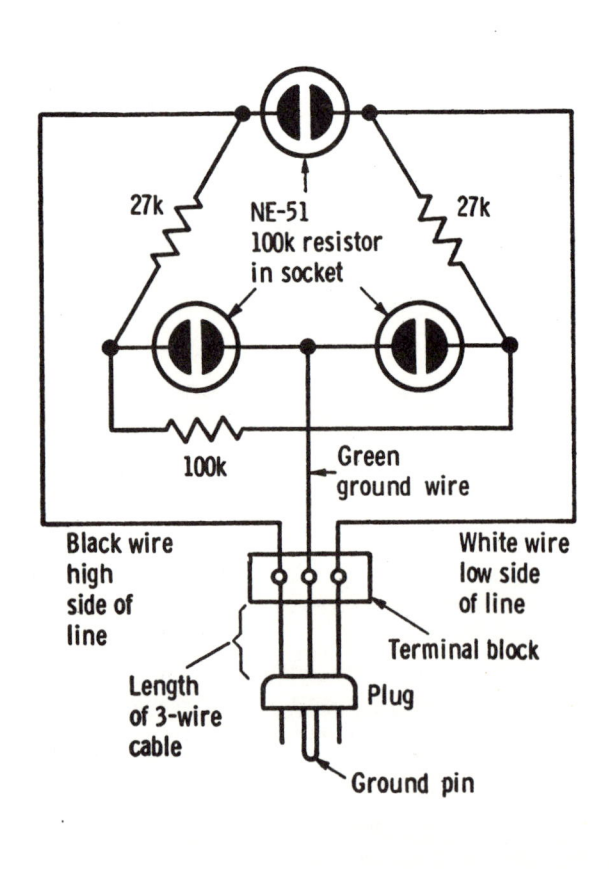

clever ideas

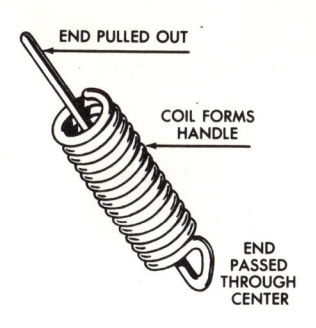

Solder will be easier to handle if you cut a 2-ft. length from the spool and coil this around a pencil so that it resembles a spring. Pass the loose end down through the center and feed more solder through as required.

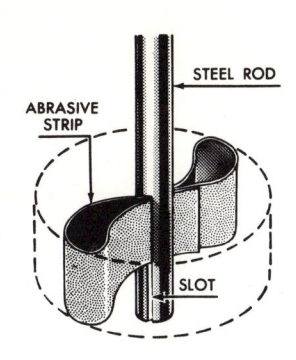

To enlarge a hole slightly, fold a strip of abrasive paper or cloth so that it is a little longer than the diameter of the hole and slip this into a slot cut in the end of a steel rod. Then chuck the rod in your drill.

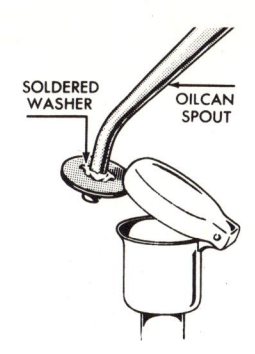

Lifting caps on hard-to-reach oil cups won't be a problem if you solder a small washer around the spout of your oilcan near the tip. Hook the washer under the edge of the cap, lift and slip the tip into the cup.

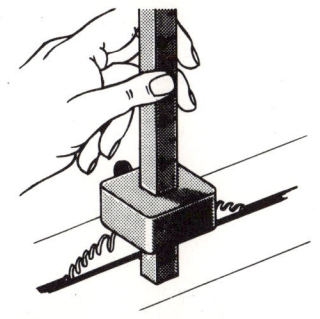

While most circular saws are equipped with a depth scale, a lot of craftsmen will still use a rule to set the depth of cut. Here you may find a marking gauge better than a rule since the adjustable head provides a stop.

To clean hardened cement from the edges of boards used in making forms, try using a length of angle iron. This improvised tool will glide along the edge of the board without slipping off and do the job quickly.

When sharpening a saw, protect the tips of your fingers by slipping a rubber bulb from a medicine dropper over the free end of the three-cornered file. This fingertip grip can easily be removed whenever necessary.

How do you edge-plane short boards on a sawhorse? It's simple as can be if you make the adjustable stop shown here. Bend a length of steel rod to form the stop, then drill holes for the legs in the crossmember of the horse.

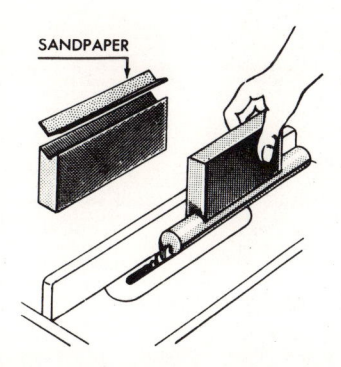

To make a hold-down block for use when grooving dowels on a bench saw, cut a V-shaped notch in one edge of a piece of 1-in. stock and line it with abrasive paper. Adjust the saw fence to center the dowel over the blade.

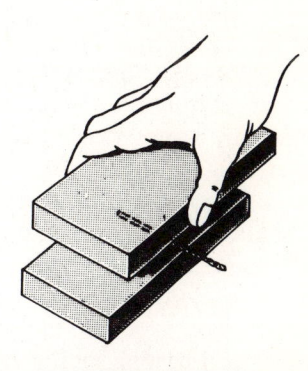

Wire-size twist drills are easily bent if you are not careful. To straighten one don't hammer it like a nail. Instead place the drill between two blocks of wood and roll it back and forth. The drill will be straight again.

2403

solar motors

Light powers this electric motor

BY HAROLD P. STRAND

■ JUST SET THIS TINY MOTOR in direct sunlight or under your reading lamp and away it goes. Powered by two series-connected silicon solar cells as a light battery, the motor drives a propeller attached to its shaft at high speed. The solar battery develops a maximum of about 1 volt around 200 milliamperes. Since the solar cells last indefinitely, there is no power loss from continued use as there is with batteries. The motor is ball-bearing and is equipped with special low-resistance, low-friction brushes.

It can be built easily from scratch and will interest schools, teachers, students and electrical experimenters since it teaches the principles of the direct conversion of light to electricity. When you experiment with this project, you will be working with the same type of solar energy that is used with our satellites to power their transmitters and other vital instruments.

It also makes a most interesting conversation piece on a desk where visitors are sure to marvel at the operating motor powered solely by light.

The base consists of a piece of black 3/16-in. plastic for good appearance, but, of course, a base of hardwood can be substituted if desired. Two aluminum bracket pieces are bent as detailed to form a support for the motor.

The latter consists of two Edmund Scientific silicon cells mounted on a piece of 1/8-in. plastic as a base. The cells are connected in series or the black lead of one cell is connected to the red of the next one, see R and B leads in the detail, the splice soldered, and a small piece of spaghetti tubing slipped over the splice to insulate it. The base is attached to the support with two 2-56 screws. The remaining cell leads are then connected to the motor leads in a similar manner and the insulated splices turned down back of the cells. The notched disk detailed serves as a spacer for the black lead from each cell.

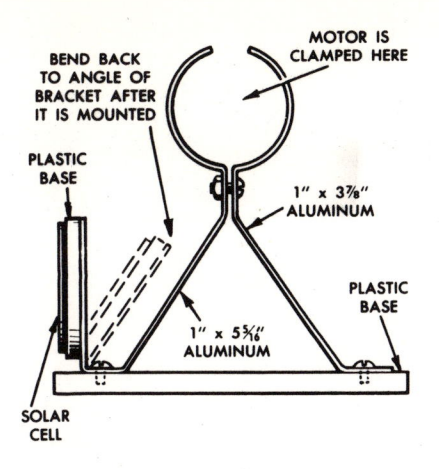

The motor is secured in the cradle-type brackets with two 4-40 screws and nuts to hold it firmly in place, placing the motor in position so that the propeller will clear the cells when turning. The propeller is made from a piece of thin aluminum with a short aluminum rivet and two washers. The rivet is passed through the center hole in the prop and peened over the washers to form a hub. A center hole is drilled in the hub to be a tight press fit on the motor shaft.

See also: engine models.

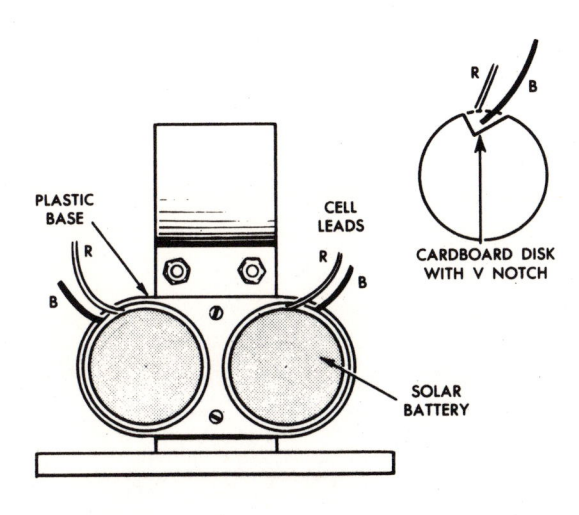

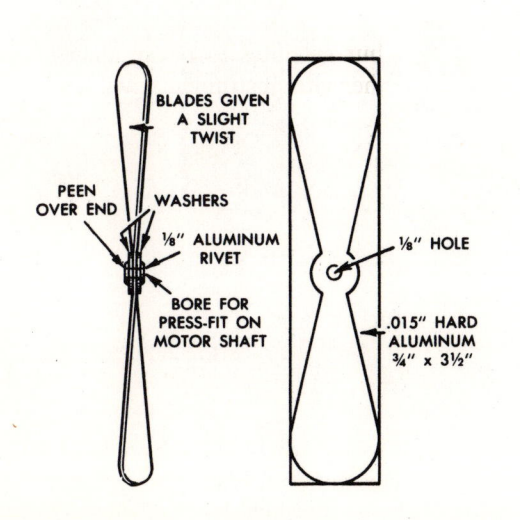

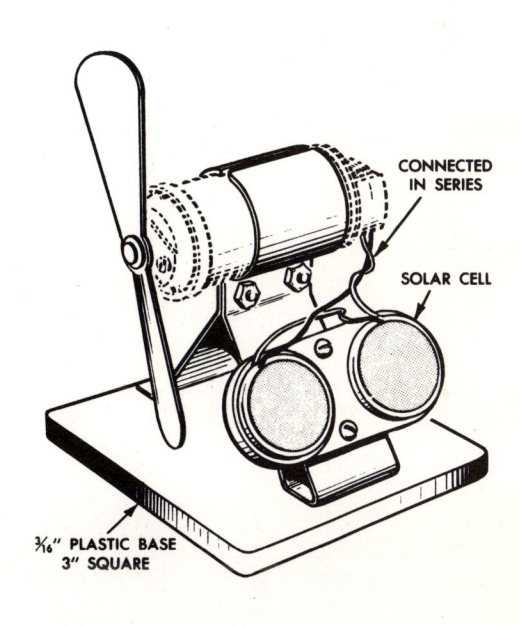

MATERIALS LIST

1 piece black plastic 3/16" x 3" x 3". (base)
1 piece half-hard sheet aluminum about .032"–.033" x 1" x 3⅞" (bracket)
1 piece same stock 5 5/16" long. (bracket)
1 piece half-hard or ¾-hard sheet aluminum about .015"–.016" x ¾" x 3½". (fan)
2 washers about 5/16" O.D., ⅛" hole, about .030"–.032" thick.
2 Edmund Scientific No. 30,538 silicon solar cells with color-coded leads
1 piece clear plastic ⅛" x 1 5/32" x 2 5/16". (cell base)
1 Edmund Scientific No. 40,902 ball bearing motor.
4 4-40 roundhead screws, 3/16" long. 2 4-40 nuts.
2 2-56 roundhead screws 3/16" long.
Order solar cells and motor from Edmund Scientific Co., Barrington, New Jersey 08007

solar motors

■ POWERED BY THE SUN, this simple electric motor is easy to build and fascinating to watch in operation. Cut the base about 4½ in. square from ⅜-in. stock. Grind one end of a 3½-in. length of coat-hanger wire to a tapered point and drive it through the base. Drill a hole to take the wire through the head of a heavy-duty, horseshoe-type alnico magnet; place it on a spike.

Drill a 5/16-in. hole through a large bottle cork to fit an eyedropper tube, then cut a 5/16 x ⅛-in. groove endwise around the cork and insert the tube, pointed end up. Wind 350 turns of 32-ga. enameled wire in the groove and take a few turns around the dropper to hold it in place. Connect the coil ends to the leads from two B2M photocells, as shown. Cement cells to opposite sides of the cork, then place the armature assembly over the spike. Then set the motor in direct sunlight and start it spinning.

Electric motor spins in the sun

BY ROBERT BRAMMS and MAX PARNES

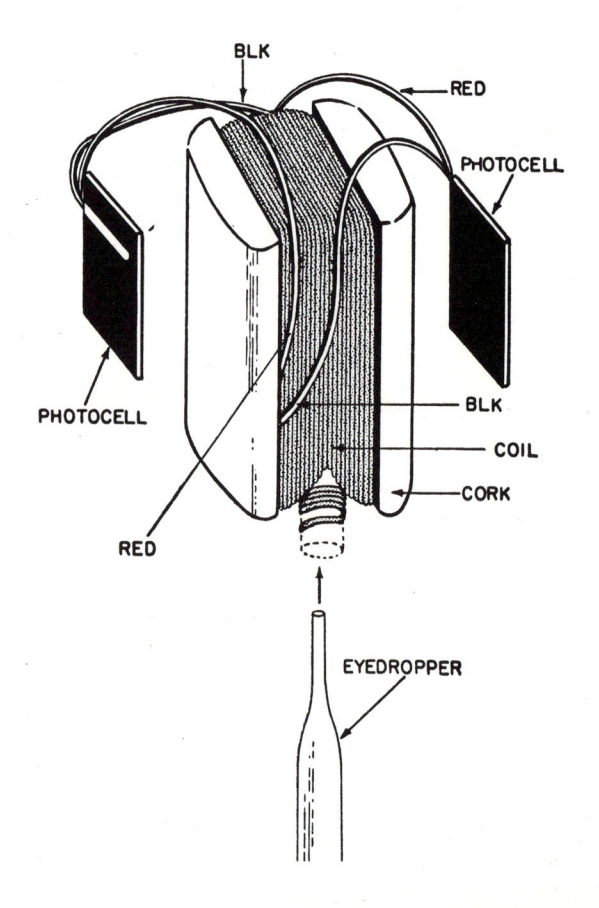

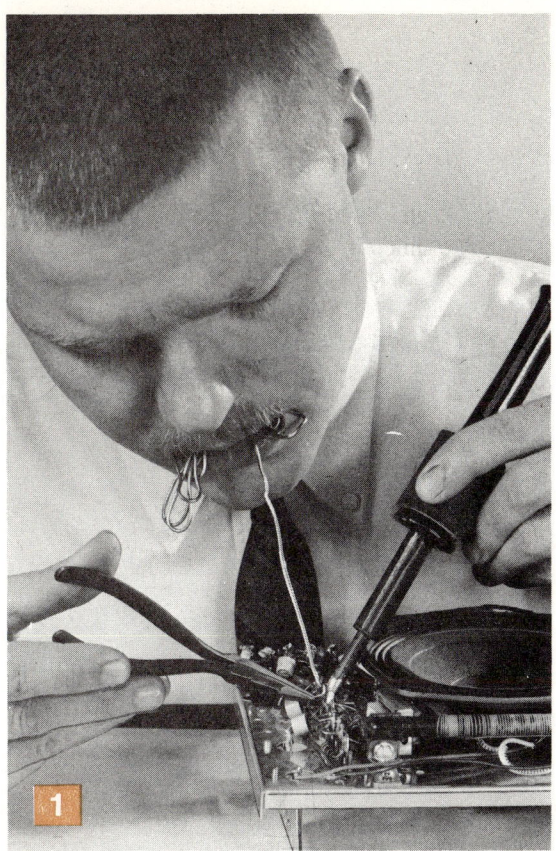

Soldering tricks from the professionals

■ A LARGE MAJORITY of the kits sent to manufacturers for repairs have nothing more wrong with them than such simple wiring faults as a cold-solder joint. This is one in which the solder fails to form one smooth, solid fillet binding wire and lug together.

In some cases, the cure is simple. In all cases, it is easy to avoid the problem if you learn how the experts tackle a soldering job.

Preparing the tools. Soldering guns or irons which range from 60 to 100 watts are good for work on small radios. Too much heat may damage a component, so use only enough heat to make the solder liquefy completely. Too little heat will result in a cold-solder connection where the solder has softened but not melted. You can also make a cold joint by pulling on the wire before the solder has cooled completely.

Curing a cold-solder joint is easy, however;

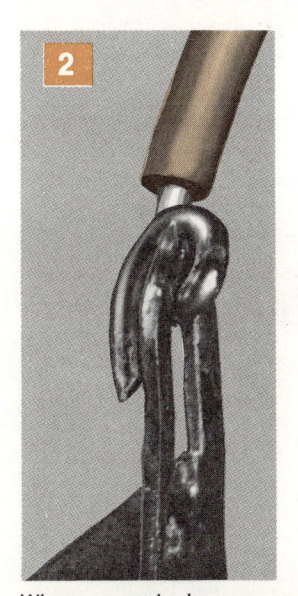

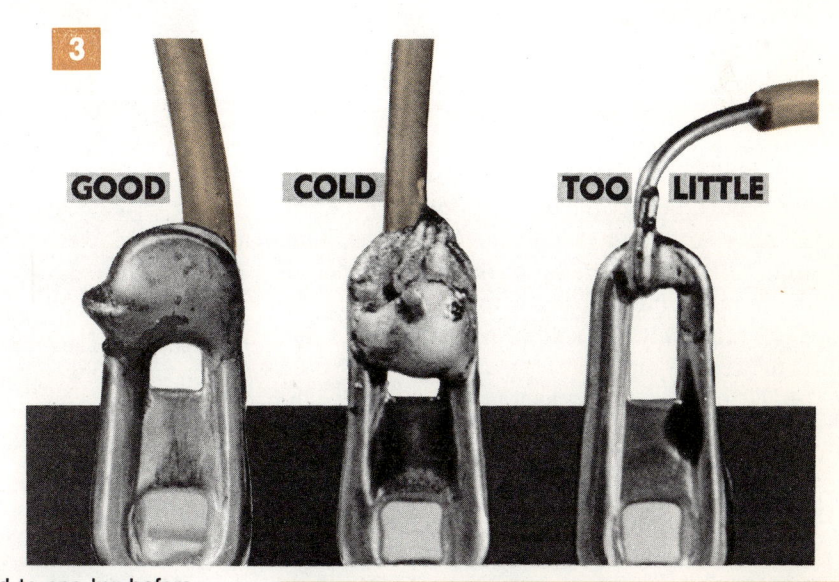

Do you feel like you need a third hand? You can hold solder between your teeth while your hands are busy. Use pliers or clips on component wires to draw away any excess heat which might damage a component

Where several wires are connected to one lug before soldering, it's wise to "lock" the mechanical connection as at the left. Note in Fig. 3 above, from left to right: good connection with smooth solder fillet; a rough, partly dull, cold-solder joint caused by insufficient heat; and at the far right, a joint made with too little solder and insulation

solid anvils: see stake plate
solid wood paneling: see paneling, wood
sorter, clothes: see weekend projects
sound movies: see movies, sound
soundproofing: see acoustics

2407

soldering

simply reheat the joint until the solder flows evenly, withdrawing the excess solder on the tip of the soldering gun.

If your soldering tool has a plain copper tip, file it to dress down all oxide pockets, then apply a little solder to the tip, and wipe with a rag, leaving the tip's surface clean and lightly coated with solder. This process is called "tinning" the iron. Irons with silver- or gold-plated tips should not be filed. Simply apply a little solder and wipe the excess away.

Preparing the wire. To remove insulation without nicking or breaking the inner wire conductor, you can use a wire stripper (Fig. 6). If you don't have one, hold the edge of a sharp knife blade against the insulation at right angles. Then press the wire into the knife with your thumb and pull the wire at right angles to the knife blade.

If the wire is stranded, twist the strands together tightly and lay the wire across your soldering iron. Place a drop of solder over the heated strands and the solder will flow through the wire, bonding it into a single easy-to-work conductor.

Preparing the connection. With about ¼-in. of wire exposed from its insulation, grasp the wire at about the ⅛-in. point with long-nose pliers (Fig. 8), bend the hook through the terminal lug, and crimp the hook against the lug with the pliers. Where you will make several connections before soldering and don't want the wire jostled loose until you solder it, you can lock the wire in place by bending the end of the wire back over the lug once again (Fig. 2). A good mechanical connection must precede any soldering in order to make a sound joint.

Soldering. The trick in good soldering is to use enough heat. Molten solder flows downward, so place your iron somewhat below the joint, with a flat side of the tip contacting as much of the terminal lug and the wire as possible (Fig. 9). Then apply the solder, not to the iron but to the heated joint.

The iron heats the joint, the joint melts the solder. When enough solder has flowed in place to form a smooth, well-shaped solid fillet between the joint and the wire, remove the solder coil from the joint. But keep the iron in place for another moment to be sure the solder has completely liquefied. Then remove the iron, but do not disturb the joint.

Printed circuit boards. In their anxiety to avoid burning foil conductors away from the plastic of a printed circuit board, many people fail to use sufficient heat. The result is poorly soldered connections, cold solder joints, and

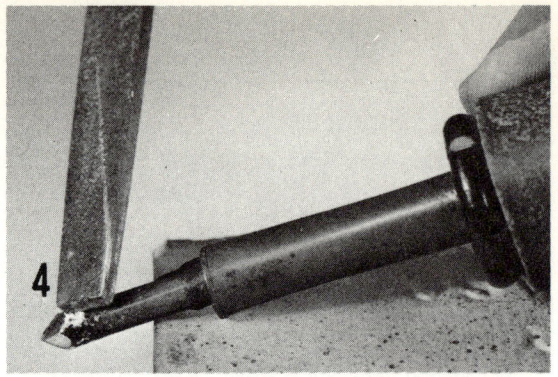

To prepare the iron, rest it on a heatproof surface, dress with a medium-fine file to remove oxide pockets

Stranded wire should be twisted into a single strand, then tinned by flowing solder over the twisted strands

Most kit builders don't apply enough heat to printed circuit-board connections. Make sure solder flows

much unhappiness all around. Use an iron in the 100-watt range, and touch it to both the conductor and the wire. Be sure the solder flows completely before removing the heat! If you use a gun, be sure the tip is hot enough to flow the solder before applying it to the board.

Heat sinks. Very often, you have to solder to components which are sensitive to heat. Some diodes, transistors and thermistors could easily be damaged by excessive heat. To protect these

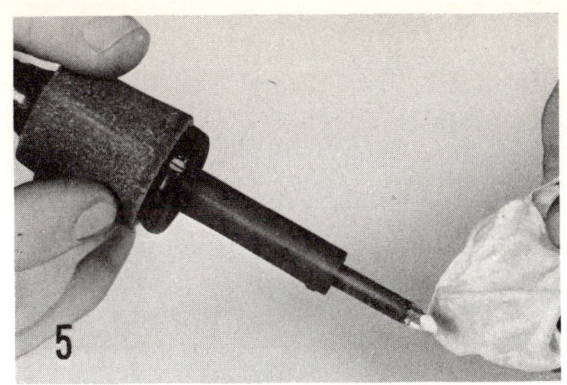

5 Tin the iron by melting solder over the dressed tip, then remove excess with a soft cloth or steel wool

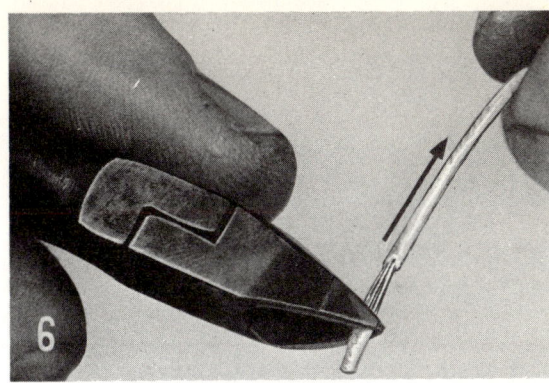

6 An old pro's trick for stripping is to grasp the insulation with cutters and pull quickly. Don't squeeze

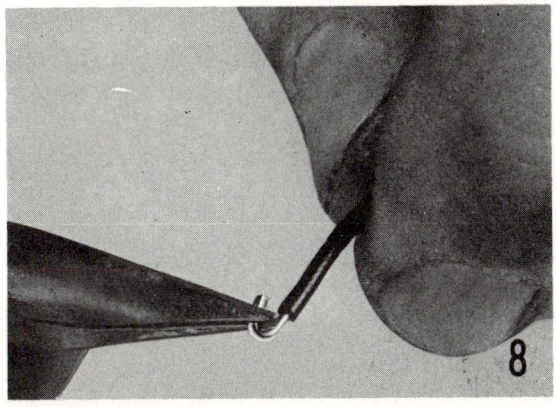

8 Strip the insulation back ¼ in., then form a neat hook for a mechanical connection before soldering

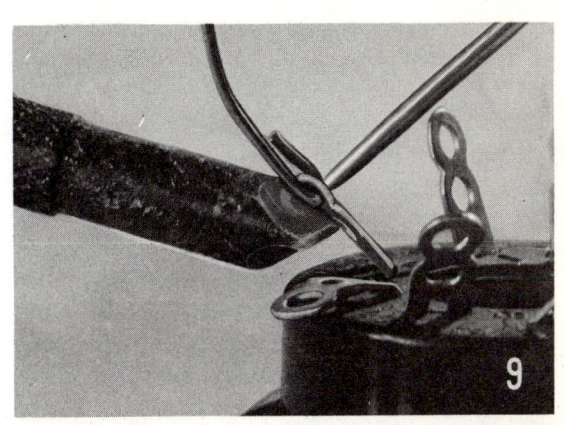

9 Heat the terminal and let solder flow from above over it and the wire. Note position of the iron and solder

11 For multiple connections, organize all mechanical connections first. Solder the whole joint at once

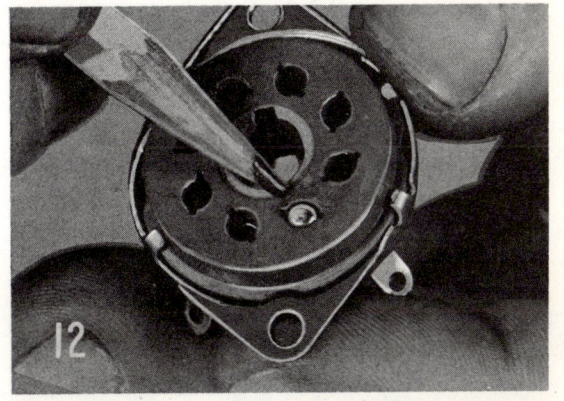

12 Too much solder on a tube-socket terminal will block the socket hole. To correct, reheat from below and shake

units during soldering, temporarily attach pliers, an alligator clip or a forceps between the solder joint and the component. Clamp this heat sink to the wire lead, and the excess heat from the soldering iron will be directed away from the delicate component.

Multiple connections. When connecting more than one wire to a terminal, make all the mechanical connections first before soldering.

Arrange the wires from the terminal so they will lay in the proper direction along the chassis.

If the wires are to run in a bundle (called a cable), then dress them all in the same direction with no tangling (Fig. 11). When soldering a multiple connection, it is important that solder flow completely in and through each wire in the connection. After cooling, check each wire by tugging gently; it should not move on the lug.

See also: arc welding; bandsaws, blades; welders; welding; yard lights.

2409

sparkplugs, auto

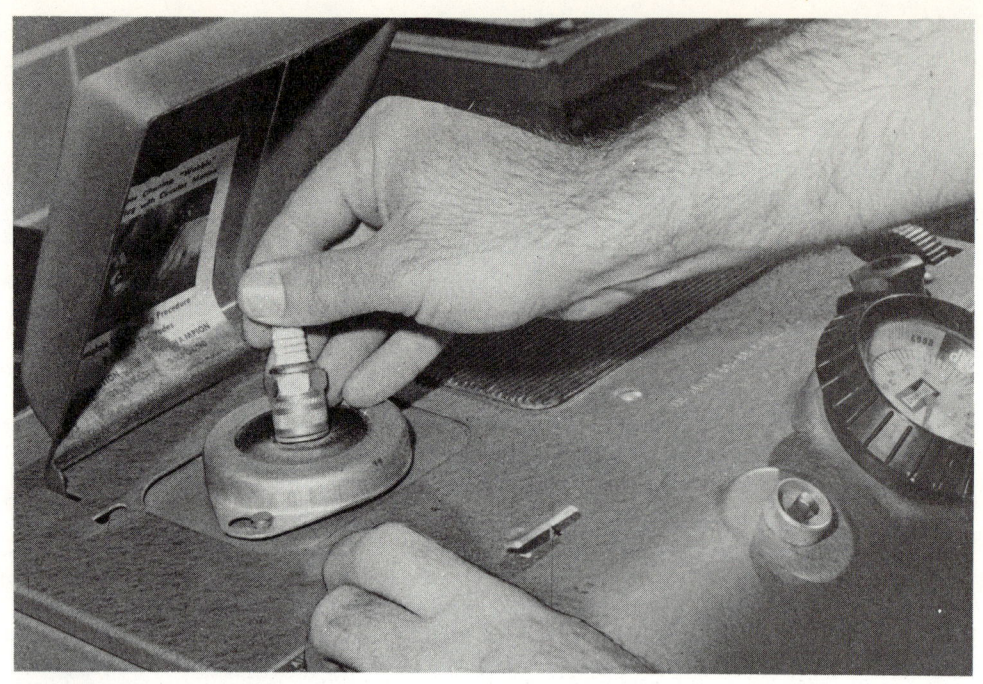

Plug servicing is done with mechanical cleaners and testers. They are available individually or in combination units which do both. Here, a plug is being cleaned by abrasive action similar to sandblasting

Sparkplugs are built-in engine analyzers

BY MORTON J. SCHULTZ

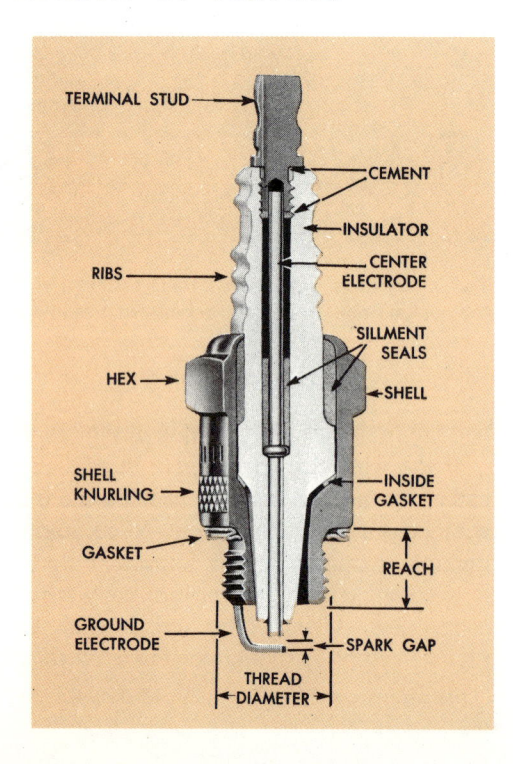

DID YOU KNOW that your car has a set of built-in analyzers that can tell you a great deal about the engine's performance? Well, it does, and they're among the simplest parts in the car's engine—the sparkplugs.

The motorist who services his own plugs, by examining them carefully, has an excellent opportunity to gain valuable insight into the operation of his engine. And, in most cases, once the trouble indicated by examination of the plugs has been corrected, the plugs usually can be restored to service—even though they've already seen a lot of mileage.

Before getting into service and how to analyze the plugs' appearance, you'll first want to bone up on sparkplug nomenclature. The drawing on this page shows a typical plug and the names of its parts.

Secondly, you'll want to know how often to service the plugs. Most manufacturers suggest every 5,000 miles.

How about sophisticated service equipment,

such as an ignition scope and plug cleaner and indicator, like the pros use?

Well, an ignition scope costs about $85. It's nice to have, but not necessary. According to the plug manufacturers, careful visual examination is effective.

On the other hand, a sparkplug *cleaner* is usually needed to blast foreign matter away from the cylinders. But don't go out and buy one. Most gas stations have these, and the station you give your business to will often let you use it gratis. The indicator portion of the cleaner can tell you much, also, as you'll soon see.

Plug service involves four general steps, each having its own tricks of the trade. They are: removal, analysis, cleaning (or replacing with new ones), and installing.

Start by pulling the plug wire from the plug. In doing so be sure to grasp the *terminal boot*—not the wire itself—or you may rip its internal strands apart. Next, use a deep-well socket, an extension (if required), and a ratchet handle to loosen each plug only a turn or two. Then, before turning the plugs out by hand, blow any dirt from around each plug with an air pressure hose. This keeps dirt and foreign matter from getting into the cylinder-head threads. If an air hose isn't available, use a brush to clean the dirt away.

Upon removing each plug, write on the insulator the number of the cylinder from which it came, using a felt marker or grease pencil. This is important since each plug is a barometer of engine condition as it applies to the cylinder from which it came. The marking can be wiped off easily before reinstallation of the plugs.

Examine the tip of each plug carefully. The chart and the accompanying pictures tell you what to look for and what the appearance of the tip indicates about engine performance.

The next phase of sparkplug service involves a series of easily followed steps:

1. If the sparkplug tip is oily, solvent-clean and dry it before using the cleaner. Otherwise the abrasive given off by the cleaner can pack itself around the insulator tip. If the plug is then reinstalled some of these particles can work loose and damage the cylinder wall and piston.

As a matter of fact, you should really clean the entire plug in a sparkplug cleaning solvent to remove dirt and rust from the threads and insulator. If this obliterates your identifying mark, simply rewrite the mark. To dry the plug after washing, especially the firing end, play a blast from an air pressure hose over it.

2. Insert each plug in the cleaner portion of the cleaning machine. Abrasive-blast the plug for

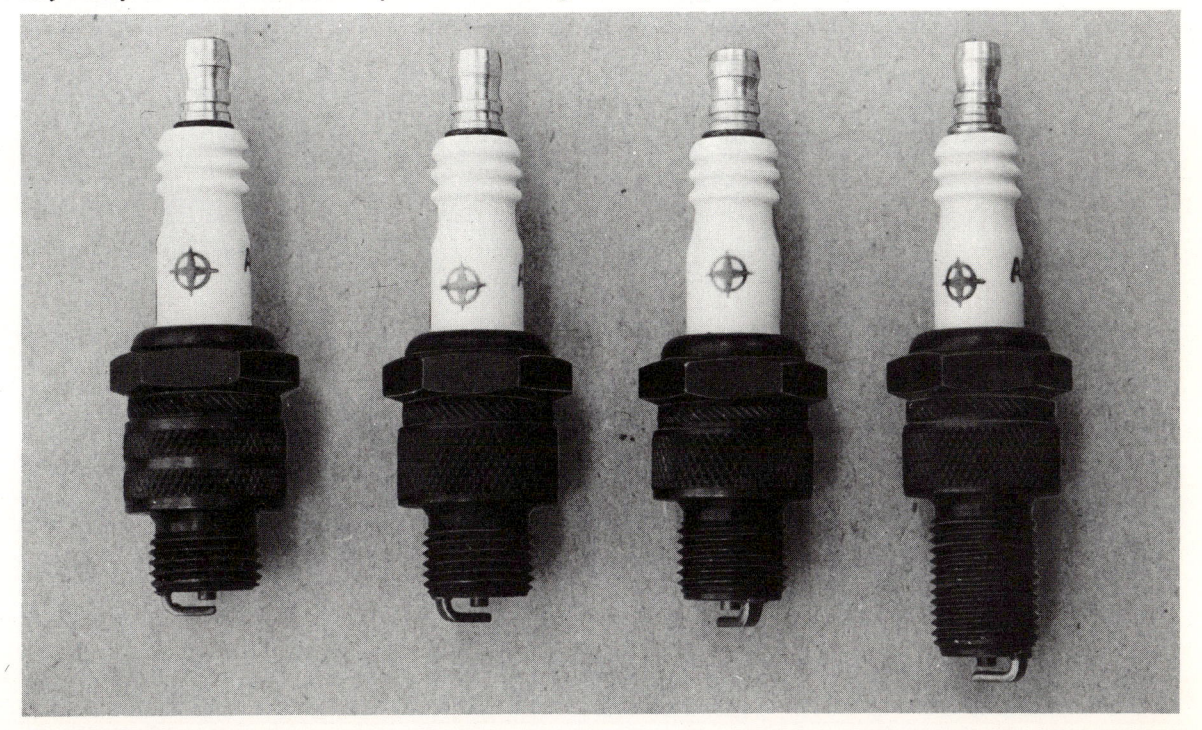

Sparkplugs may have the same thread diameter but their reaches or thread lengths can vary widely. Check manufacturer's specs to find the right thread length for your car

2411

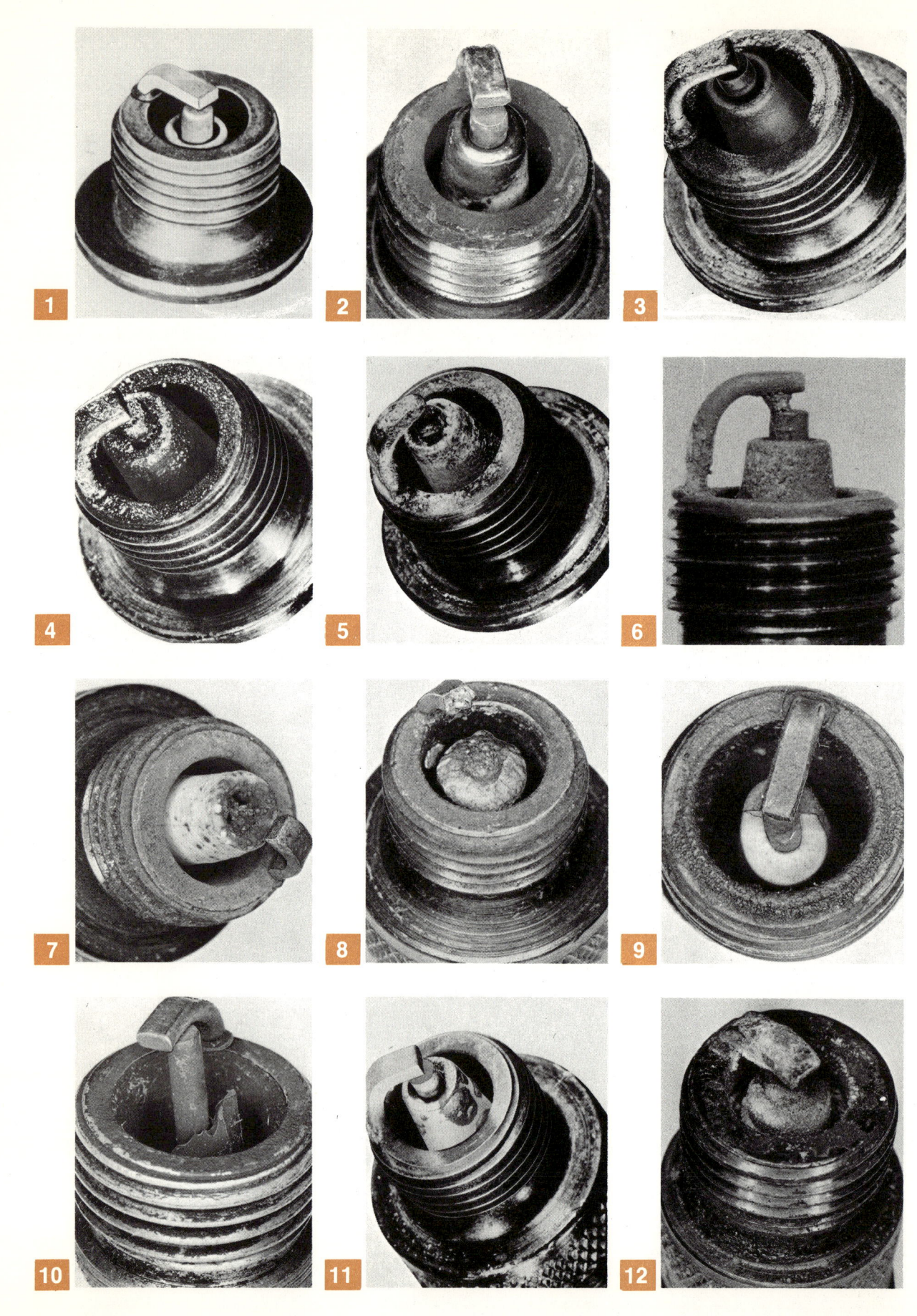

sparkplugs, auto

2412

SPARKPLUG ANALYSIS CHART

CONDITION OF PLUG	APPEARANCE	MALFUNCTION	CORRECTION
Normal (Figure 1)	Light tan or brown deposits. Gap increase of .001" or less for every 1000 miles of operation	None	If electrodes don't show excessive wear, clean and restore plugs to service
Lead fouling (Figure 2)	Dark gray, black, yellow or tan cindery deposits, or a shiny glaze coating of the same colored deposits	Accumulation of byproducts of fuel combustion at high speed and under heavy load conditions	Clean and recondition plugs. If condition continues you may have to change to plugs of colder range
Carbon fouling (Figure 3)	Black, dry, fluffy carbon on tip	If only a couple of plugs are found like this, check for bad high tension lead, burnt or sticky valve, faulty breaker point, weak coil or condenser. If all plugs are in this condition, troubleshoot for too lean a fuel mixture, inoperative automatic choke, dirty or clogged air cleaner, stuck manifold heat control valve, or too much stop-go operation	Correct defect found in troubleshooting. Clean and restore plugs to service. If fouling is caused by excessive idling or stop-go operation, replace plugs with next hottest in the heat range
Oil fouling (Figure 4)	Wet, black, oily deposits	Can occur in a new or rebuilt engine before piston rings have become properly seated. In older cars, it indicates worn rings, cylinders, pistons, valve guides	If it's a new or rebuilt engine, degrease plugs, clean and restore to service. In older engines, correct the cause of oil consumption—otherwise cleaning or replacing plugs will only be a temporary help. Use of hotter plugs in engines with excessive oil fouling usually permits longer periods of service until defect is corrected
Overheating of plug (Figure 5)	White insulator tip, bluish-burnt cast on center and ground electrodes, too much electrode corrosion after short period of operation	Incorrect plug heat range, over-advanced ignition timing, too lean a fuel mixture, or inoperative or partially clogged cooling system	Check heat of plugs against that recommended for your car. Make any repairs indicated, and install new plugs of the heat range demanded. Discard old plugs
Gap bridging (Figure 6)	Deposit lodged between ground and center electrodes	Improper fuel combustion. Or deposits shredded from combustion chamber during rapid acceleration or high speed operation, thrown against hot electrodes and fused on contact to short out plug	Check fuel mixture. Clean and restore the plugs to service
Initial pre-ignition (Figure 7)	Melting of center electrode and, later, of ground electrode. Also blistered insulator, or aluminum or metallic deposits on insulator	Incorrect plug heat range, burned valves, over-advanced timing, inoperative or partially clogged cooling system, lean fuel mixture, or detonation caused by improper octane rating or low grade of fuel	Check heat range of plugs against that recommended for your car. Repair or replace faulty engine components. Replace plugs with those of correct heat range. These old plugs can't be restored to service
Sustained pre-ignition (Figure 8)	Ceramic firing tip melted	All the conditions described above, but allowed to continue for a longer time. By this time, there's a good chance that other engine components have been damaged by pre-ignition	Check engine carefully, and repair or replace damaged parts. Replace plugs with those of the correct heat range
Chipped insulator (Figure 9)	Cracked, split or chipped insulator at firing end	Excessive center electrode temperature or severe engine detonation. However, a defect of this sort is usually caused by use of incorrect gapping procedure—generally, bending the center electrode	Replace the plug. Make sure the correct gapping procedure is used. Check and set the timing. If the condition recurs, switch to a colder plug
Broken insulator (Figure 10)	Broken insulator	Foreign object in the combustion chamber. Since small objects can travel from one cylinder to another because of valve overlap, always check other cylinders as well to prevent recurrence of damage	Purge cylinders of foreign matter and replace the plug. This one can't be reused
Splash fouling (Figure 11)	Splotchy deposits on insulator	Long-delayed tuneup needed	Tuneup car and clean the plugs. Restore plugs to service
Scavenger deposits (Figure 12)	White or yellow accumulation around tip and on ground electrode	Normal with certain brands of fuel	Although deposits appear heavy, they can be easily flaked off. Clean, restore plugs to service
Dishing	Ground electrode is cupped or dished	Reverse polarity	Check primary coil leads and switch, if necessary, to correct polarity. Check gap. If it's not excessive, restore plug to service after routine cleaning and reconditioning
Worn-out	Severely eroded or worn center and ground electrodes. Light brown to tan deposits on insulator	Normal when gap wears at rate of .001" for every 1000 miles of operation	If you can re-gap to specifications, you can keep the plug in service by cleaning and reconditioning. However, if gap growth exceeds .010", replace the plug

sparkplugs, auto

Always regap plugs with a round wire gauge. A flat gauge can "bridge" erosion pits in the electrodes and give you a reading that is smaller than the actual gap. Wire should pass through with slight drag

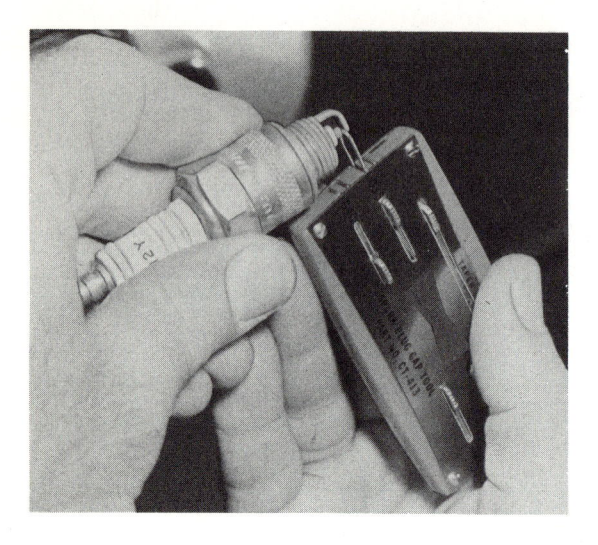

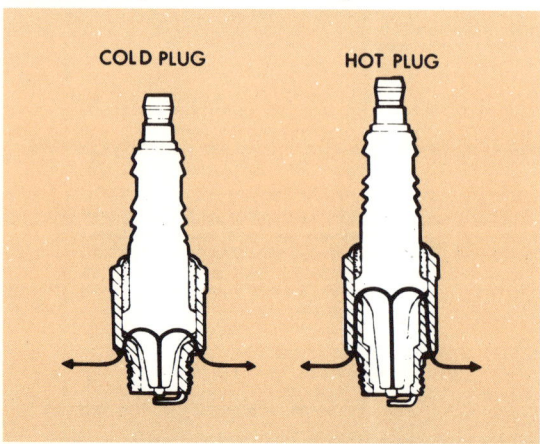

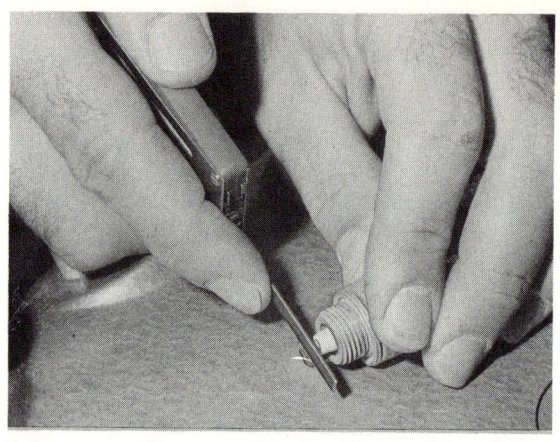

Before regapping, open the ground electrode slightly and file it, plus the center electrode, flat and square. Surfaces of electrodes should be parallel and the tip of ground electrode centered

about 5 sec., rotating it as you do. Remove the plug and examine the tip for cleanliness. If necessary, blast it again until clean. If, when examining the clean tip, you see any hairline cracks, discard the plug without further ado.

Hot and cold plugs differ in how fast they dissipate the heat of combustion (arrows). Hot plugs run hotter merely because the heat has a longer distance to go and does not produce a "hotter" spark

COLD PLUG   HOT PLUG

3. With a bending tool, which is usually part of an approved sparkplug gapping tool, open the ground electrode slightly and file both the ground and center electrodes until they're flat, square and bright with a point file. Adjust the ground electrode until it's parallel to the other. *Don't* use pliers for bending. Also, never bend or apply any pressure to the center electrode or to the insulator. This can split or crack the insulator tip. Bend only the ground electrode.

4. Use a round-wire-type sparkplug gapping tool and gap the plug to your car's specification. The gap is properly adjusted when there's the slightest drag on the gapping tool as you slide it between the two electrodes.

5. At this point, you can test each plug on the testing portion of the cleaning-testing machine. But be aware of this point stressed by plug manufacturers:

Many perfectly good sparkplugs with thousands of miles of service yet to be utilized are scrapped due to misinterpretation of the information obtained from a pressure-type tester.

This misunderstanding comes about because of the differences between conditions in the tester and actual conditions in the engine. The tester, for example, operates on the principle of increasing air pressure in the testing chamber until a spark no longer occurs between the electrodes. The air pressure in the tester is usually at room temperature, while sparkplugs operate in an engine at temperatures ranging from 300 deg. F. at idle speed to 1700 deg. F. with the throttle wide open.

To get a true reading from the tester, use the following procedure, but keep in mind that when all is said and done, the best and final test is how those plugs will operate when in use on the road:

- Make sure the plug electrodes have been filed as mentioned before so they have sharp corners. Round corners could give a "bad" indication, even with a plug that's in good condition.
- Make sure the plug insulator is clean and dry.
- Check the operation of a *new* sparkplug, gapped the same as yours, in the tester first. Note the pressure at which the plug no longer fires.
- Now, check the pressure at which your reconditioned plug no longer fires. If the difference between the two does not exceed 30 percent, the reconditioned plug is suitable for reuse.

expect flashover

There's one other aspect of this testing procedure you should be aware of. Many plugs when checked in a pressure-type tester are condemned because of voltage flashover—that is, sparking from the plug terminal down the insulator, to ground on the shell. Flashover doesn't indicate a faulty plug. As a matter of fact, it proves the plug insulator's in good condition and signifies that the plug has no cracks or pinholes that could cause misfire. The only time flashover means trouble is when it's occurring through a *visible* crack in the insulator. And you probably would have spotted this crack before now and discarded the plug.

Furthermore, don't be concerned by "corona" —a glow that sometimes appears above the shell around the base of the insulator, especially if you operate the tester in a dark corner. It's caused by electrical stress in the air around the insulator, and is not harmful to plug operation.

When replacing discarded plugs, make sure you get ones of the correct heat range. These are not always the ones spelled out in the specifications for your engine, since they vary with driving conditions. However, the plug recommended for your engine is a good place to start. If you experience trouble with these, as pointed out in the chart, then you can switch to a hotter or colder type.

Plug heat range refers to the ability of a plug to transfer its heat from the firing tip to the cooling system. Plugs might have identical electrode configurations and be of the same size, but could be different in that they transfer heat at a slower or faster rate. This rate of transfer is controlled by the distance the heat must travel to reach the cooling agent, as shown in the drawing on page 2414.

"Cold" plugs have relatively short insulator noses and transfer heat rapidly. These are generally recommended if a car's normally driven under heavy duty or continuous high-speed conditions.

"Hot" plugs have longer insulator noses and transfer heat more slowly. By running hotter they burn off combustion deposits that might tend to foul the plugs during prolonged idle and low-speed driving. Keep in mind that a "hot" plug does *not* produce a hotter spark than a cold plug.

installing plugs

There's a definite science to installing sparkplugs in modern automobile engines. Careless installation can cause a plug to overheat, strip the threads of the plug or those in the cylinder head, break the insulator or damage the shell.

Here's the right way to do it:

1. Make sure cylinder-head threads and plug seats are clean and free of dirt and deposits that could interfere with proper seating. Cylinder-head threads should be cleaned with a greased thread-chaser of the correct size. Clean plug threads with a wire hand brush, but be careful not to hit the electrodes or insulator tip.

2. Always check the gap setting, even of new plugs. The same type plug may fit a dozen different cars, so factory gap settings will not be right for all cars.

3. If possible, use a torque wrench to tighten the plugs. Suggested torque values:

Sparkplug Thread	Cast Iron Heads	Aluminum Heads
10 mm	12 lbs. feet	10 lbs. feet
14 mm	25 lbs. feet	22 lbs. feet
18 mm	30 lbs. feet	25 lbs. feet
⅞ mm	35 lbs. feet	30 lbs. feet
18 mm taper	17 lbs. feet	—

seating

4. If a torque wrench isn't available, screw the plug into the cylinder finger-tight. Then tighten an additional ½ to ¾ of a turn with a socket wrench. Don't overtighten by throwing your full weight on the wrench or using a long extension bar. Too much force will twist the shank of the plug, throwing off the point adjustment.

5. Check the condition of sparkplug wires and boots. Dried-out or cracked wires and bad boots could lead to a plug failure. They should be replaced with new ones of the same type.

See also: auto repair; electrical system, auto; sparkplugs, marine; timing, auto engine.

sparkplugs, marine

Match the sparkplug to your outboard

BY HENRY B. NOTROM

For top performance from your outboard, pick the right sparkplug to match *your* motor with *your* boating habits

■ WHY IS IT that any time an outboard so much as burps, the first thing most owners blame is the sparkplugs?

Sure, 60 percent of all problems reported to outboard shops center on plugs, but sparkplug failure is rarely caused by defective plugs. When a plug goes bad, it's usually traceable to one of three things: using the wrong plugs for your type of operation; improper installation of the plugs; or fouling the plugs with a fuel having a high

---

speaker cabinets: see cabinets, speaker
speakers: see high fidelity; transistor radios
speedboats: see runabout boats

Torque wrench is an absolute necessity when you install sparkplugs. Tightening them too much, or leaving them loose, can cause you plenty of trouble. Borrow a wrench or have your dealer install plugs

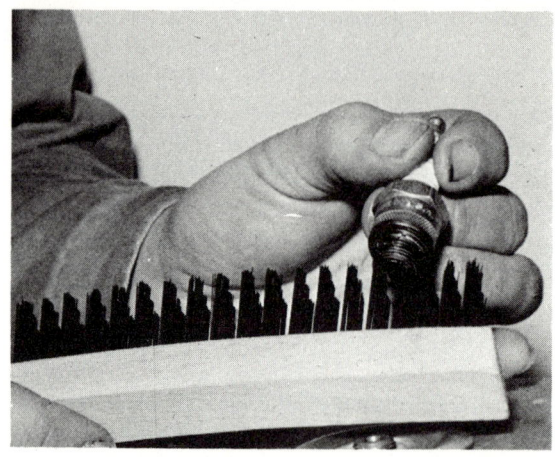

You don't need a sandblaster to clean plugs from outboard engines. A good scrubbing with a wire brush will remove all deposits and save you a trip to the gas station. Use care to avoid damaging insulator

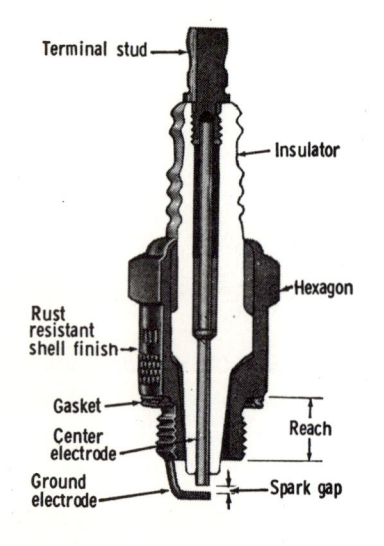

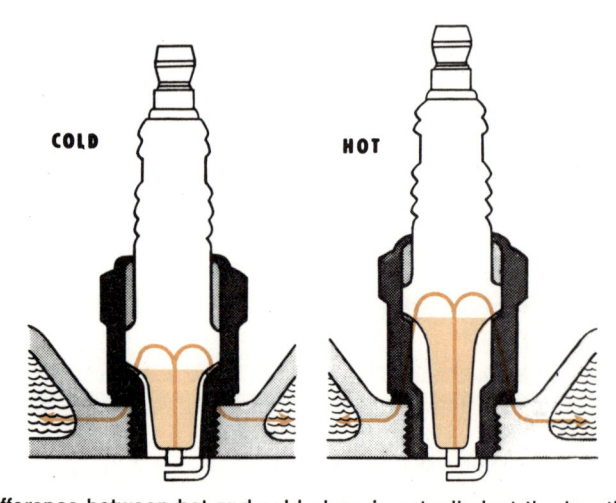

Difference between hot and cold plugs is actually just the length of the insulator nose. A cold plug cools more quickly because heat has a shorter distance to travel to reach the water jacket. Remember that switching to a hotter plug will *not* give you a hotter spark

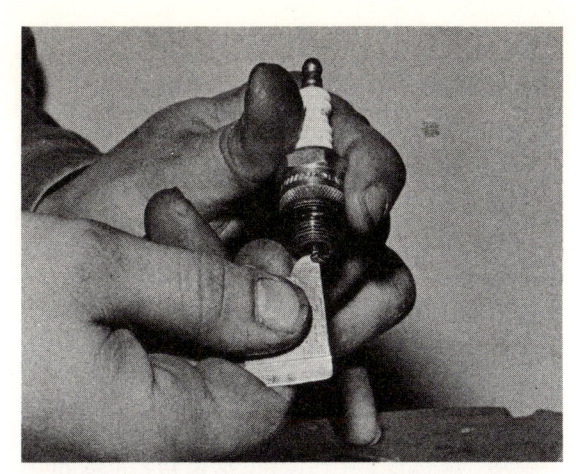

To get at electrodes for filing, bend the ground electrode open slightly. The feeler gauge shown here has a special tang at one end just for this job. Don't ever try to bend or move center electrode

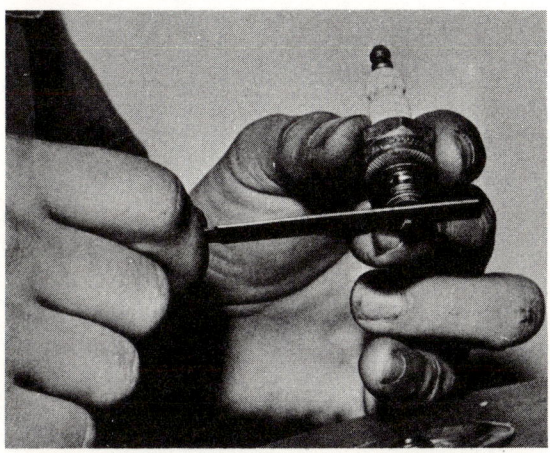

Don't be afraid to use that ignition file. Give both ground and center electrodes a good filing to clean and smooth the surfaces. You can reset the gap later, making sure the surfaces are parallel

tetraethyl-lead content. Simply replacing the plugs, without correcting the condition which caused them to fail, doesn't make sense.

Recognizing that there is a problem certainly isn't difficult. Your engine will practically climb off the transom to tell you about it. Any of the three above conditions will cause it to miss or fail to develop full speed. A fouled or improperly installed plug can prevent it from starting, while your use of the wrong type of plug may cause rough idle or overheating.

Of course, any of these malfunctions can result from a multitude of other conditions inside the engine, so a careful examination is necessary. Servicing and analyzing plugs is a breeze. The only tools needed are a torque wrench, $13/16$-in.-deep socket, wire brush, point file, feeler gauge and your eyes. Remember that sparkplugs have only one job—to transform the voltage provided by the ignition system into a spark of from 300 deg. F. at idle to 1700 deg. F. at full throttle. This spark ignites the fuel mixture which makes your engine go.

begin with the wire

Remove the plug wire by grasping the boot and giving it a twist. Pulling on the wire itself may part strands.

Give the boot a careful examination inside and out. Look particularly at the inside where it was in contact with the plug porcelain. If you discover fine cracks along this surface, replace the boot. It's old and has lost its sealing ability. A long crack in the boot can indicate that the plug itself is cracked, allowing high voltage to leak through. That could well be the reason why your engine is misfiring. If you find such a crack, both plug and boot will have to be replaced.

To replace the boot, just pull it loose from the plug wire. On most engines, you'll notice a little coil spring set crosswise on the end of the wire that keeps the boot in place and making contact with the plug terminal. Incidentally, it will be a lot easier to put the boot back on the wire if you spray the inside with silicone lubricant.

After you have the plug out, how can you tell whether it's been the right one for your type of operation? The best tip-off is the color of the porcelain. If a plug is right for operational conditions, the insulator body turns a dark brown or coffee color. An insulator that is pure white or has flaky white blisters on it indicates the plug is too hot for your type of engine operation. You've probably been doing high-speed running with a plug intended for lighter use. That plug wasn't able to dissipate operational heat fast enough and became too hot, causing the insulator to sear or blister. Switch to a colder plug.

Conversely, if the plug you removed from the engine has an insulator that's black, it signifies the plug is too cold for engine operation. The plug has been transferring heat too quickly to burn off combustion deposits. You've probably done a lot of idling and low-speed running, while the plug is really meant to meet the needs of higher speeds.

Generally, then, a colder plug is needed when most of your operation is going to be at high speed. A hotter plug is needed when most of your operation is at idle, low speed and light-load trolling.

Whether a plug is rated "hot" or "cold" has

sparkplugs, marine

MERCURY'S POLAR GAP

THUNDERBOLT is the name Kiekhaefer has given to the electronic ignition system used on its larger engines since 1965. According to the company, its voltage impact far surpasses that of conventional coil-and-battery systems. The super-cold Polar Gap plugs used with this system are said to operate at temperatures between 800 deg. and 1000 deg. cooler than standard plugs, virtually eliminating preignition, even with leaded fuels. Don't buy them for your motor, though. These plugs will only work with Thunderbolt ignition.

---

sparkplug type for "normal" operation—that is, a fairly equal amount of low-speed and high-speed operation. This is where to start. You'll find the recommended plug for your engine in the operating manual.

Now, if you have to switch to a colder or hotter plug, do it gradually. Don't jump all the way to one end of the heat range scale. Go only one step up or down.

For example, suppose you have a 1963 Mercury 500, which normally takes a Champion J6J plug (or an AC M44C, or an Autolite A3X). After several weeks' use, you find that the insulator remains white, pointing to the probability that the plug is too hot for your type of operation. You want a colder plug, so you say to the supply man:

"I've been using a J6J, but I need a plug that's one step colder."

He'll go to his conversion chart and give you that colder plug, which is a Champion J4J (or AC M42K or Autolite A21X).

It's as easy as that.

While a great many problems can plague the electrode end of automobile sparkplugs, years of testing by outboard manufacturers show that one single factor affects plug life far more than any other—the gasoline used in the engine. Much of that trouble is simply lead fouling from too much tetraethyl lead.

It's a fact that marine white gasoline virtually eliminates lead fouling. It also does away with carbon fouling caused by the way in which some fuels burn to leave a gummy residue. (Carbon fouling can have other causes, however. Check the chart on this page.)

nothing to do with whether it provides a hotter or colder spark. A hot plug doesn't produce any hotter spark than a cold plug.

Where do you begin on the heat range chart? Each outboard manufacturer recommends a

---

HOW TO "READ" A MARINE PLUG

PROBLEM	APPEARANCE	MALFUNCTION
Normal wear	Light tan or gray deposits. Little gap wear. Electrodes not burned.	None. Clean, file, re-gap and reinstall.
Wet (carbon) fouling	Wet or damp black oily deposits.	Gummy fuel residue; prolonged trolling (plug too cold for use); fuel not mixed well; improper fuel-oil mixture. Clean, file, regap and reinstall after correcting problem.
Overheating	Badly eroded electrodes. Blistered white or gray insulator.	Plug too hot for engine use; fuel mixture too lean; timing far advanced; piston rings sticking; bad water pump; engine lugging; clogged water jackets. Replace plug.
Gap bridging	Deposit lodged between ground and center electrode.	Accumulated deposits in combustion chamber probably resulting from too much trolling. Operate at high speed to clean out engine.
Worn out	Badly eroded electrodes. Light brown deposits on insulator.	Plugs kept in use too long. Should be changed every 100 hours of operation.

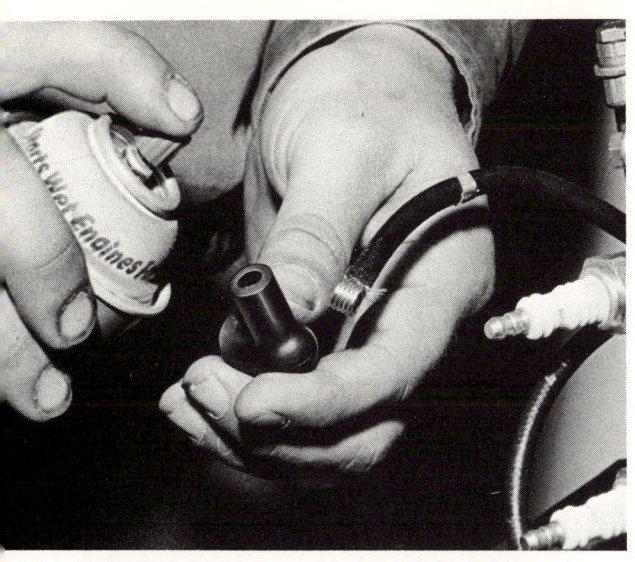

Replacing the boot on the plug wire will be much easier if you take the time to spray the inside with a silicone lubricant first. Note the small spring on the wire, designed to keep the boot in place

Marine gasoline has an octane rating of 75 to 80 and contains no tetraethyl lead—not good enough for your car, but more than adequate for lower compression marine engines.

Even with leaded gasolines, the lead content can sometimes vary greatly from area to area. With one particular brand, for example, it was found that the lead content was 0.58 cc in Wichita, Kans., and 2.95 cc in Dallas, Tex.— that's an increase of over 400 percent in about 1000 miles.

If your plugs are lead-fouling, you'll find yellow or brownish deposits on the electrode end. No need to throw them away, though. They can be cleaned, filed, regapped and put back into service. However, the question remains as to what can be done to eliminate fouling.

In the absence of marine white gas, stick to the lowest octane possible—keep switching from brand to brand until you hit the right one.

To clean plugs, simply scrub the electrodes with a wire brush. It does a good job. When a plug is brushed clean, open the ground electrode slightly. Use a bending tool which is part of most feeler gauge sets. No screwdriver or pliers, please. You can crack the electrode off too easily. By the way, stay away from the center electrode with the bending tool. Once that electrode cracks, splits or chips, the plug is useless.

File both ground and center electrodes flat, square and bright with an ignition-point file. Now gap the plug to specification. Most plugs for outboards are gapped to either 0.025 in. or 0.030 in., although some go up to 0.035 in. Check the manual.

Remember to bend only the *ground* electrode when gapping. Don't touch that center electrode. Proper gapping is obtained when you feel a slight drag on the gapping tool as you slide it between the two electrodes.

It matters little whether you use a round-wire feeler gauge or a flat gauge. If filing was done properly, it will have eliminated any irregularities that would cause a flat gauge to bridge the electrode.

gap new plugs, too

Also, always make sure that *new* sparkplugs are gapped to specification. Don't take it for granted that because they are new, they are properly gapped.

Older model engines may have plugs with separate gaskets. Replace them each time you remove the plugs. On newer models, with gaskets a part of the plug body, you've got to discard the plug if that gasket is flattened or corroded.

Put the plug back into the cylinder hole and run it up until finger tight, then use a proper size deep socket in conjunction with a torque wrench to tighten the plug properly. Make sure you use a socket that fits correctly or you may crack the plug. Most outboard plugs should be tightened (and removed) with a $^{13}/_{16}$-in. 6-point deep socket. Torque to correct specification (check manual), normally 20 ft.-lb.

If you think this information on installation is academic, take a look at what can happen if plugs *aren't* properly installed:

Compression loss and early sparkplug failure. Insufficient torquing, preventing full seating.

Early destruction of plugs because of inability to dissipate heat. Excessive torquing.

Early plug failure due to overheating; high engine temperature; possible compression loss. Use of badly corroded or flattened gaskets.

High engine temperature and early plug failure because of overheating. Corroded threads in sparkplug hole (not too common, but if found, brush the threads clean before installing plugs).

When should you check plugs? If a problem suggests a plug breakdown, right away isn't too fast. Otherwise, every 50 hours of operation is sufficient.

See also: carburetor, outboard; magnetos, outboard; outboard motors, overhauling; outboard motors, repair; sparkplugs, auto.

speedometers

Is your speedometer telling the truth?

BY G. C. EDMONDSON

If you never really
      know how fast you're
    driving, you're like
  almost every other driver
    on the road—for almost
every speedometer lies

THE CAREFUL MOTORIST not only keeps his car in good repair, but also knows how fast he is going at all times. Or does he? On any car that's been driven 10,000 miles or so the speedometer is likely off.

One reason is that an initially accurate reading on a car will be wrong after 1/16-in. of tire-tread wear. Accuracy at one speed doesn't mean true readings at all speeds, only fairly accurate readings over the normal driving range.

To find true car speed (as well as odometer error), with the average load carried, head for the nearest tollway or any other road with mile posts.

Hold the needle on 60 mph and time the trip between mile posts. If the speedometer checks out right on the nose, a mile in 60 seconds, that's fine—for that speed.

This doesn't necessarily mean accuracy at other speeds, however. At 80 mph, for example, a speedometer could be off as much as 15 mph.

Here's how to figure your actual speed at *any* indicated speed: There are 3600 seconds in an hour. Divide the number of seconds it takes you to go a measured mile into 3600, and you'll have your answer in mph.—

$$3600 \div 75 \text{ secs.} = 48 \text{ mph.}$$

(With a slide rule, you can set the 6 on CI-scale over the 6 on D-scale, read off your speed in seconds-per-mile on CI-scale, and directly below on D-scale will be your speed in mph.)

If you don't want to figure while driving, use the table. Above 60 secs., the table reverses itself. If you go a mile in less than 60 secs., read the time in the right-hand column; your speed will appear on the left.

To correct the speedometer, it is easier to recalibrate the dial than the needle, which entails a minute adjustment of a very delicate spring; even this is usually unsatisfactory for all speeds. You can calibrate the speedometer and make up a new dial to paste over the old one, or determine actual speed in increments of 5 mph through the useful daily range and attach a chart with these figures to the instrument panel. Tire wear or load change necessitates recalibration.

To check odometer, drive over a measured 10 miles, noting the reading before and at the end of the stretch. The difference should be 10 miles; if it isn't, the ratio of error can be determined and applied to an odometer reading for any length trip.

See also: auto repair; fuel consumption, auto; headlights, auto; tires; wheel alignment, auto.

SPEEDOMETER

Seconds per mile	Miles per hour	Seconds per mile	Miles per hour
180	20	76	47.4
170	21.2	74	48.6
160	22.5	72	50
150	24	70	51.4
140	25.7	68	52.9
130	27.7	66	54.5
120	30	65	55.4
115	31.3	64	56.3
110	32.7	63	57.1
105	34.3	62	58.1
100	36	61	59
98	36.7	60	60
96	37.5	59	61
94	38.3	58	62.1
92	39.1	57	63.2
90	40	56	64.3
88	40.9	55	65.4
86	41.9	54	66.7
84	42.8	53	68
82	43.9	52	69.2
80	45	51	70.6
78	46.1	50	72

speed reducers

The drive pulley on the jackshaft can be left belted to the bandsaw even when the geared drive is not in use. The pulley is engaged and disengaged by a removable pin inserted through the pulley hub. A safety cover of sheet metal can be made to enclose worm gears

Speed reducer for your bandsaw

BY HAROLD P. STRAND

A dual-motor drive, plus a worm-gear attachment, lets you switch quickly from high to low speed without changing a belt

■ YOU JUST CAN'T SWITCH to a metal-cutting blade and expect to saw steel with a wood-cutting bandsaw—the machine simply runs too fast. The high speed will ruin the blade and friction will heat up the work. But with a speed reducer to slow down the machine, your bandsaw will cut metals smoothly.

You can rig the 30-to-1 reduction drive shown by attaching a worm-gear jackshaft to a second motor. The original motor still drives the saw for wood cutting, whereas the second one takes over for metal cutting. Each motor is controlled by its own switch, and aside from having to switch blades, the changeover from one speed to

speed reducers

the other involves nothing more than the insertion or removal of a steel pin in an idler pulley on the worm-gear jackshaft.

Whether you can mount both motors exactly as shown depends upon the saw's stand. If the saw is now driven by a motor mounted below, there's no reason why the motor cannot be left there. In any event, a second pulley for the second motor must be added to the drive pulley on the saw. However, since the saw's arbor usually does not project far enough to permit adding an extra pulley on the arbor, the extra pulley has to be attached to the face of the saw's pulley with bolts and pipe spacers as detailed on page 2423. With a 5-in. pulley on the saw, a 4-in. pulley on the jackshaft produced the proper speed for cutting metal.

As you see from the photos on page 2421, the

MATERIALS LIST

1 pc.—1/8" x 1" x 1" steel angle 5" long
2 pcs.—1/4" x 1" x 2 7/8" mild steel—or length required for worm gear to clear motor end cap
1 pc—1/2" cold-rolled shaft 7 1/2" long
1 pc—3/16" steel pin 1 3/4" long
2 pcs.—Steel pipe spacers about 5/8" O.D., 1/4" I.D., 1/4" long
1—4" dia. cast-iron V-pulley, 1/2" hole
2—10-32 x 3/16" hollow-head setscrews
1—5/16"-18 x 3/8" hollow-head setscrew
1—5" dia. V-pulley, 1/2" hole
*—Bronze or cast-iron worm gear 30 teeth, 2 1/2" pitch dia., 1/2" hole (Bronze Cat. No. GR1051, cast iron G1051)—Iron Cat. No.
*—Worm gear to match, steel, 1/2" hole (Cat. No. GH1056)
*2—Bronze shoulder bushings, 1/2" I.D. 5/8" O.D. (Cat No. FB-810-8)
*4—Shaft collars, 1/2" I.D. (Cat. No. SC50)
2—Hardened thrust washers, 1/2" hole, 3/4" O.D.
*1—Plain bronze bearing, 1/2" I.D., 5/8" O.O., 1/2" long (Cat. No. B-810-12)
*These parts available from Boston Gear Co., Boston, Mass.

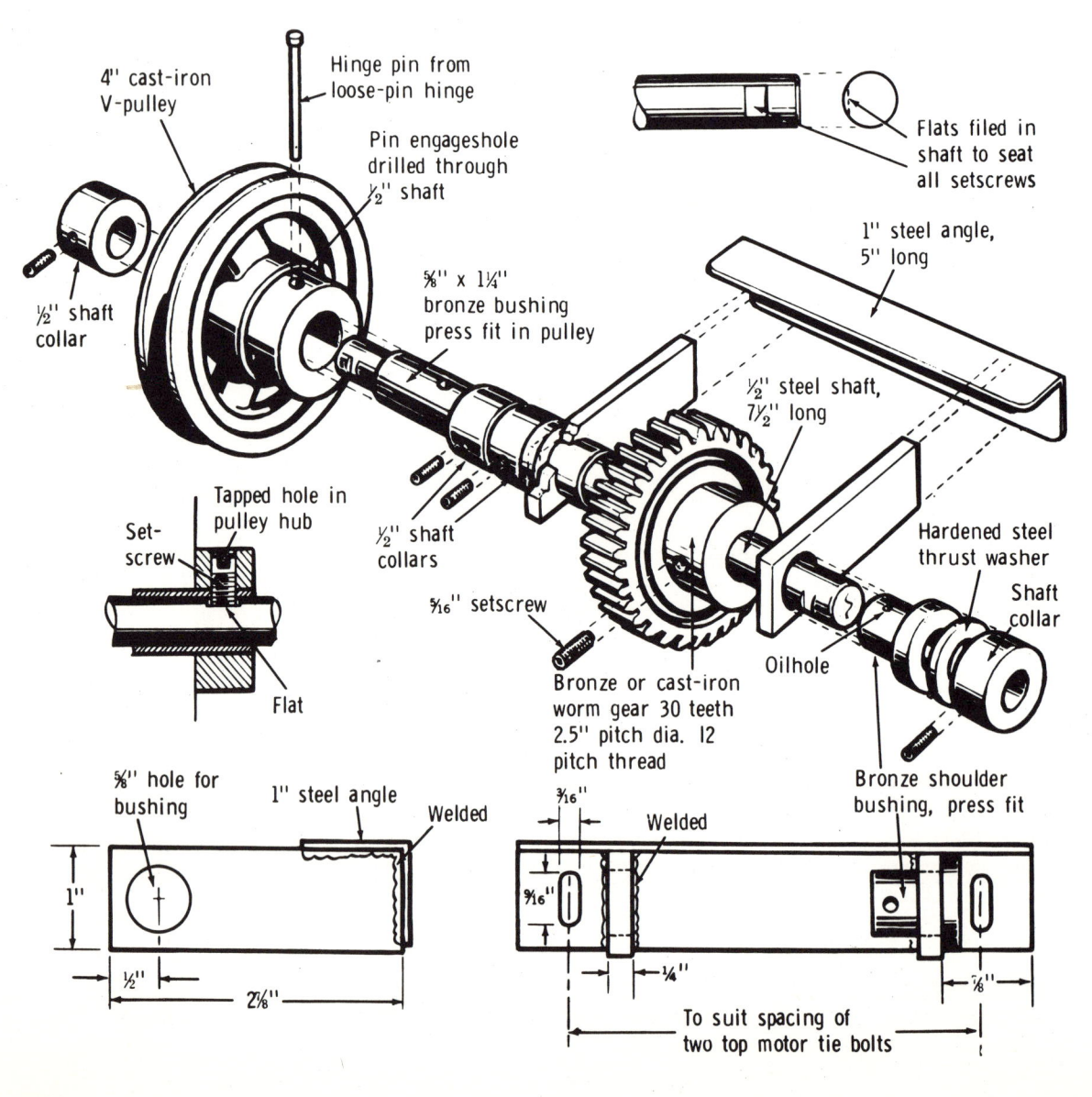

2422

motor supports the jackshaft in that its bracket is bolted to the motor's tie bolts. The details show how the supporting bracket is welded up of flat steel and angle after its three parts are drilled for shouldered bronze bushings and slotted to suit the spacing of the motor tie bolts. The shaft must turn freely in the bushings.

The hub of the large worm gear is drilled, tapped and locked to the shaft with a 5/16 in. x 18 hollowhead setscrew and is held centered over its matching gear on the motor shaft by shaft collars placed on each side of the bracket's arms. Collars likewise are used to retain the free spinning V-pulley after the setscrew hole in its hub is aligned with a locking-pin hole drilled through the shaft. The locking pin should fit just tight enough to stay in place. The motor tie bolts are drawn up tight after the mating gears are in proper mesh and work smoothly.

See also: bandsaw; bandsaws, blades.

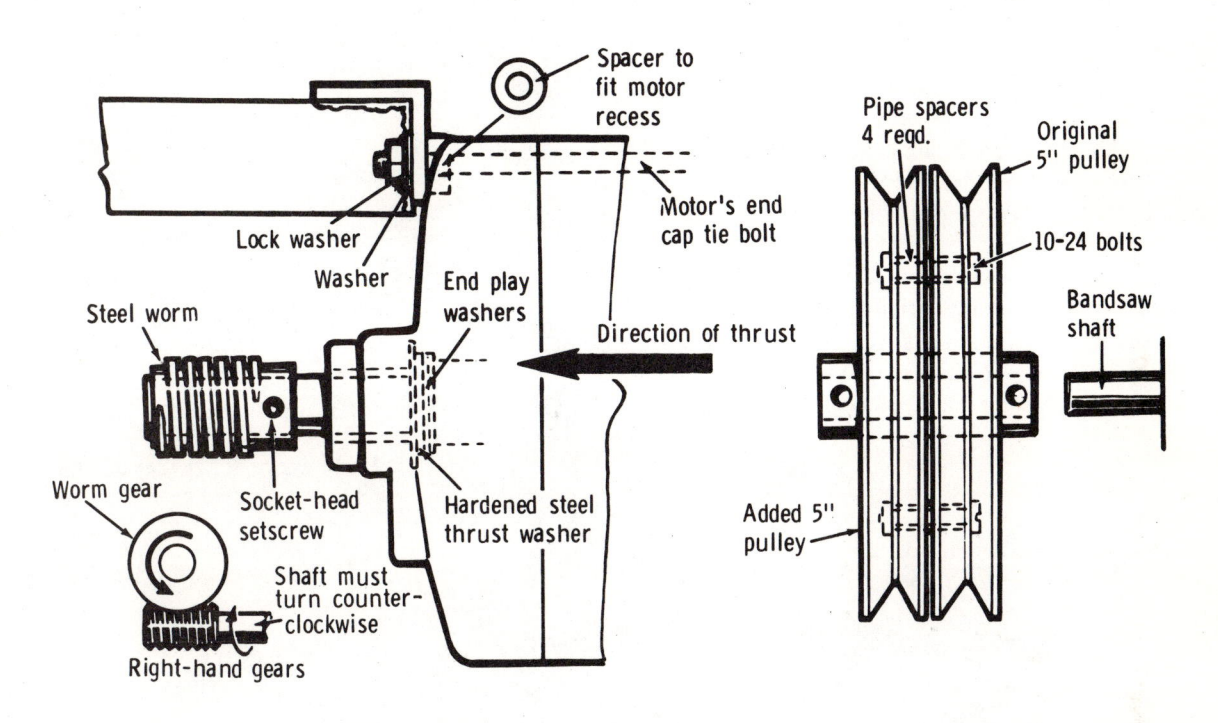

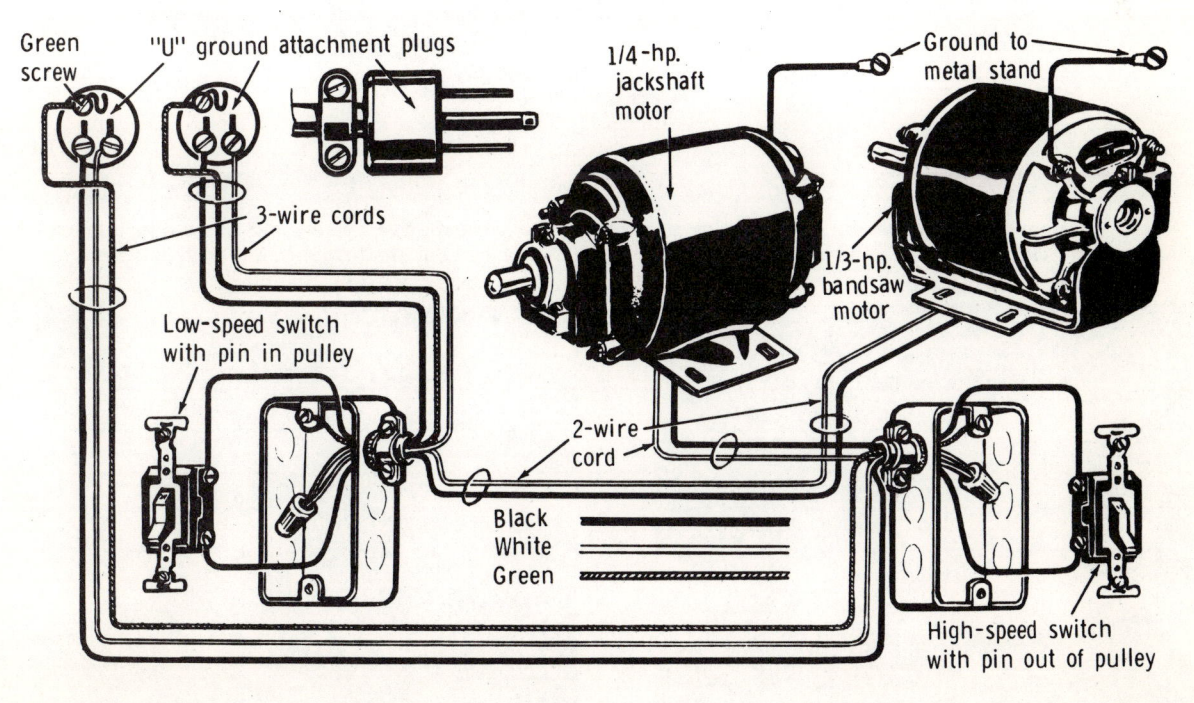

spice chest

Great-grandmother's spice chest

BY JACKSON HAND

■ WALL-HUNG SPICE CABINETS probably were favorite do-it-yourself projects of early American craftsmen. They not only served a useful purpose but were easy to make. The cabinet here is a copy of an authentic antique and it is reproduced in complete detail for easy construction. Although it can be made with hand tools, a table saw and jigsaw speed the job.

White pine in ½ in. solid stock is used for all parts, except the ¼-in. plywood drawer bottoms and sides which in the original were of ¼-in. solid stock. All joints are glued and nailed. The exterior surfaces are stained a medium brown color, using a wiping stain especially developed

1 After outlining the back, the drawer dividers and rails on pine stock, the back is cut to shape with a jigsaw

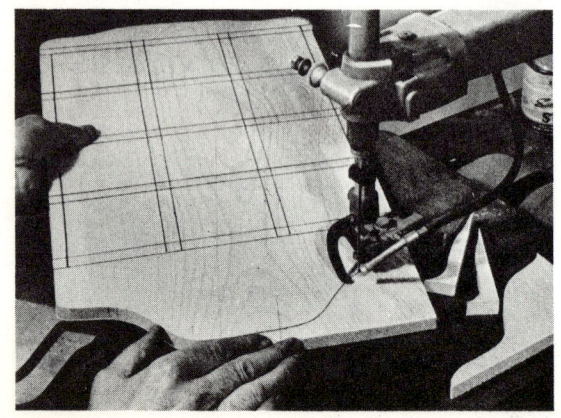

2 The drawer dividers and also the rails are cut to a uniform length with the aid of a stop block clamped to the rip fence

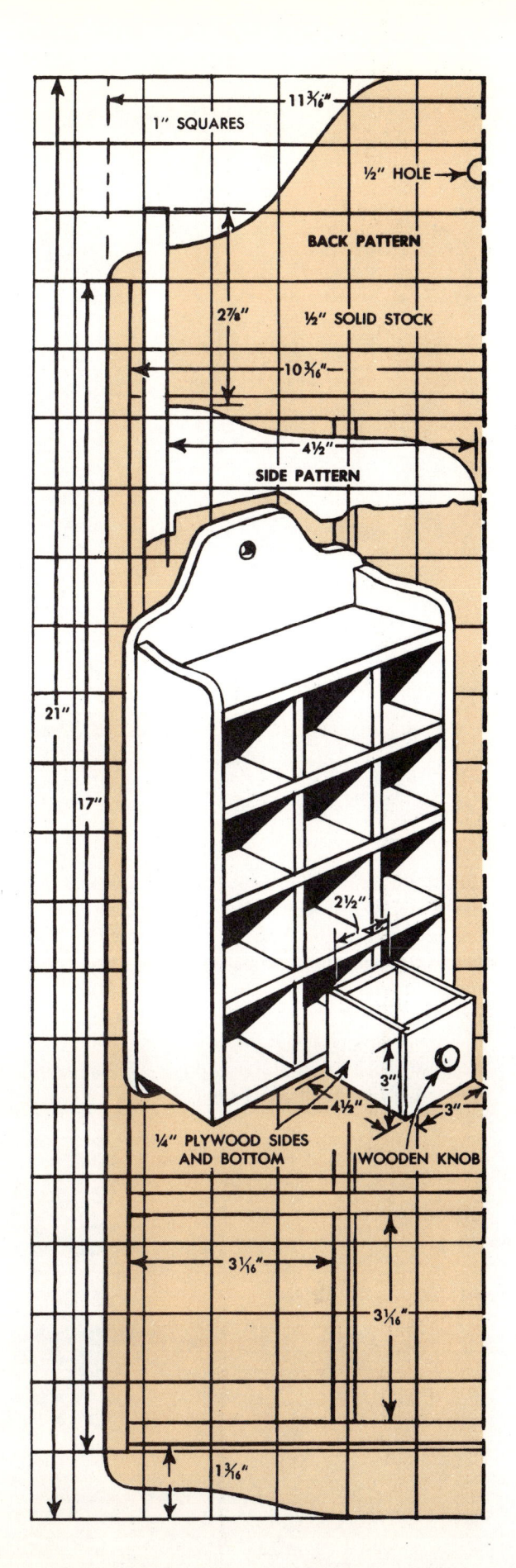

3 The back is first nailed and glued to one side and bottom. The dividers go on next, then the rail and other parts

for use on pine. All inside surfaces, except insides of drawers, are enameled in turquoise.

The main steps in the assembly sequence are shown in Figs. 1, 2, 3, and 4. Holes for the pulls should be drilled before putting the drawers together. The squared drawing at the left gives the patterns for the back and sides. Locations of the drawer dividers and rails are laid out directly on the cabinet back. All exposed edges of the completed cabinet are rounded off with sandpaper, unevenly in some places to simulate wear.

See also: home improvement; kitchens; spice racks.

4 The cabinet back is clamped securely in a bench vise for easy nailing of the rails. Then the left side is nailed on last

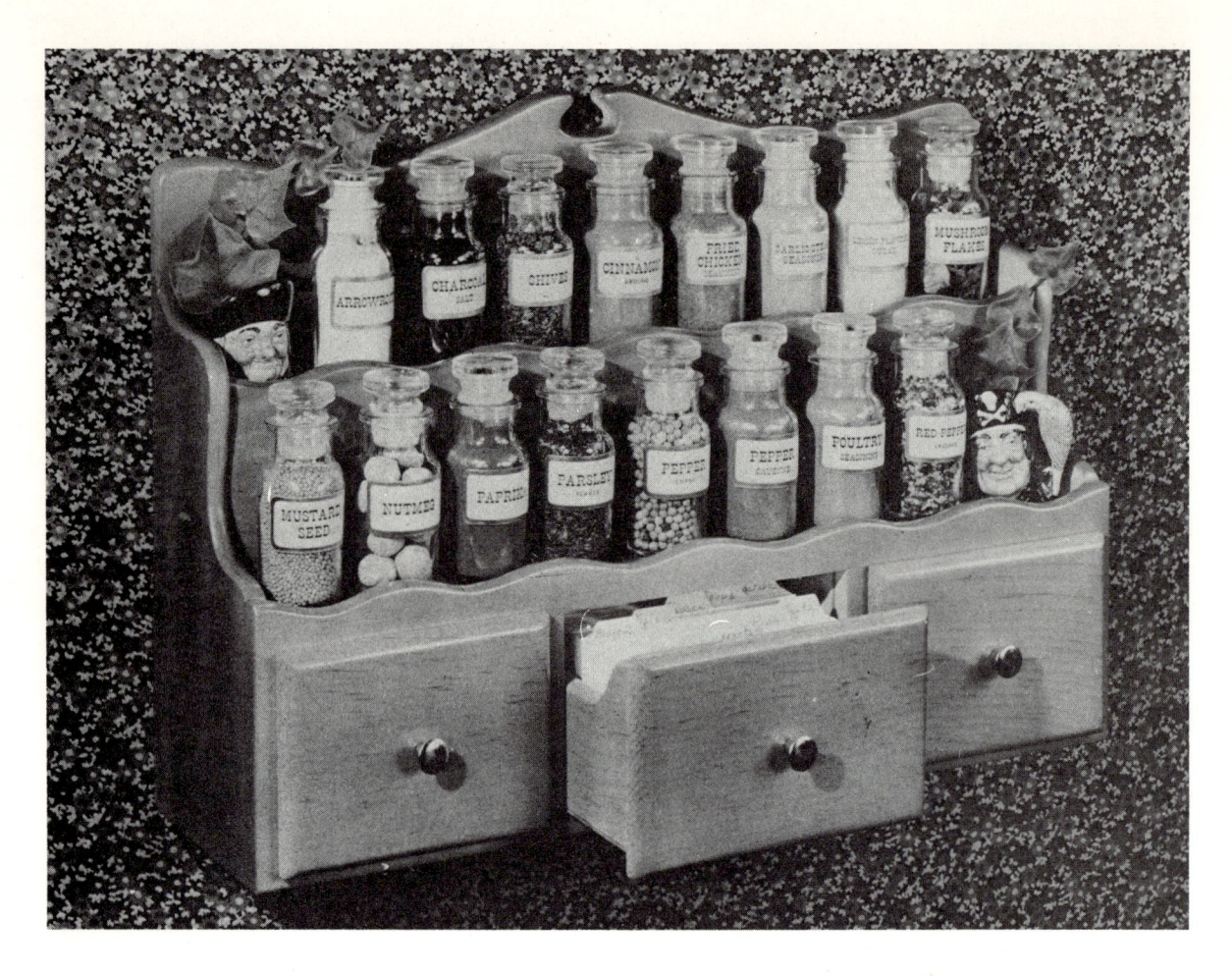

spice racks

Two ways to add spice to your kitchen

■ THREE ESSENTIAL INGREDIENTS for a good meal are the proper spices, good recipes and correct timing. But how many times have you been in the midst of preparing a meal and been unable to find that can of pepper or discover that you've lost the recipe for a certain dish?

Or perhaps you've burnt your family's dessert because the kitchen clock is on a faraway wall and you forgot about the timing.

The front-drawer facing goes on last as you make the colonial rack. Use glue to assemble all parts

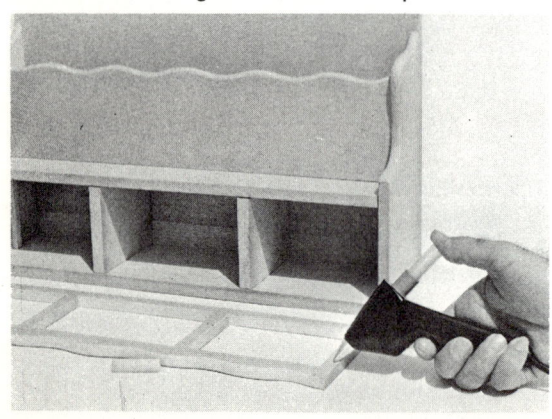

Fast-setting stick glue eliminates clamps in drawer assembly. Lay bead along edges, hold 20 sec.

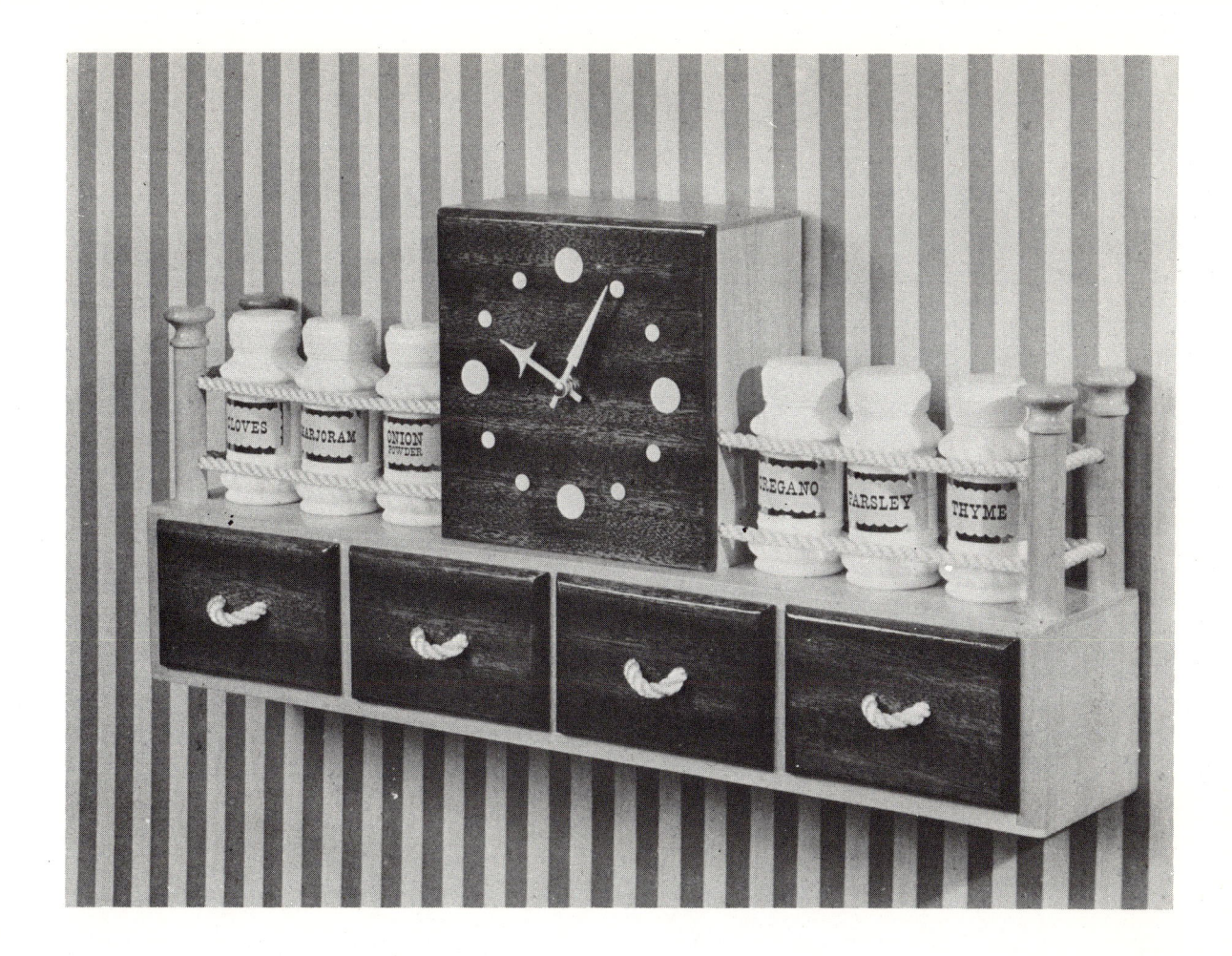

You can eliminate these problems with these two attractive spice racks that you'll surely want to build for your kitchen wall or counter. Both serve a dual function. The rack with the Early American design features a tip-out recipe file to make finding that needed recipe in a hurry an easy task. And the nautical-looking rack contains a clock so you'll always have a timepiece nearby while cooking.

These are quickie projects that can be made in a weekend, possibly from scrap material in your woodbox. Gum wood and dark mahogany were combined in the nautical rack above, whereas pine, finished with a warm colonial stain, was used to make the Early American design. Assembly is made even easier if you have an electric glue gun.

Your jigsaw will come in handy for cutting the

A dab of melted glue in holes secures dowel corner posts. Make sure rope holes are in line

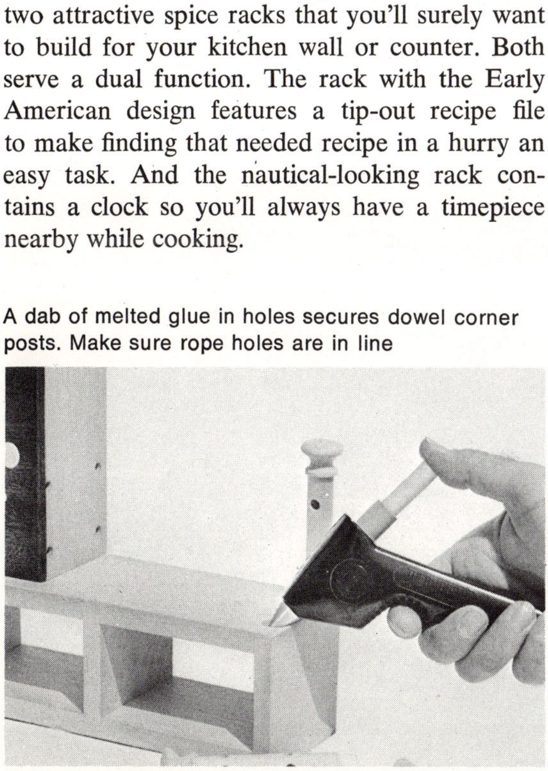

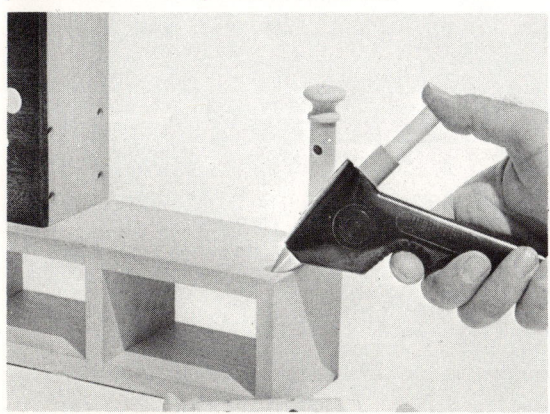

Thermosetting glue is ideal for anchoring ends of nylon rope in holes in clock case and drawer fronts

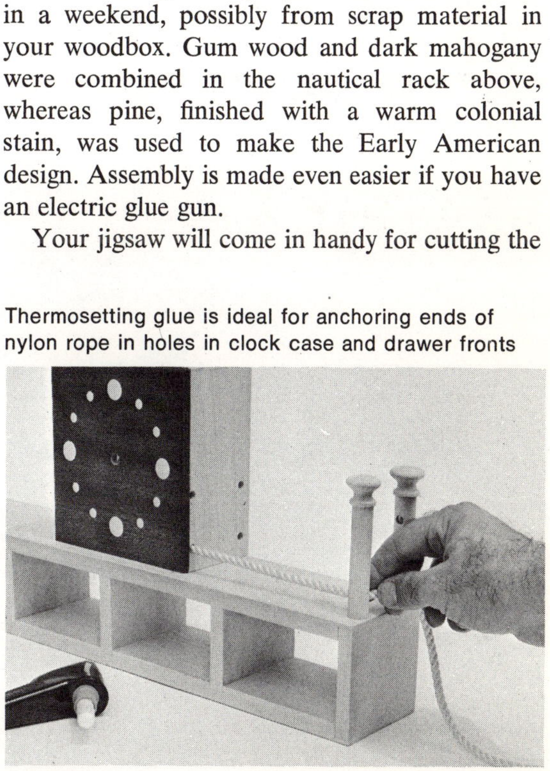

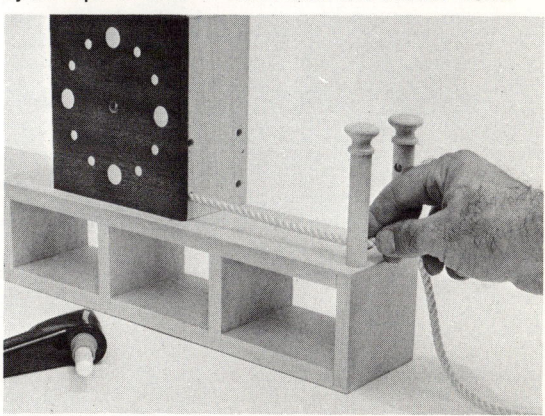

spice racks

PATTERNS FOR CONTOURS

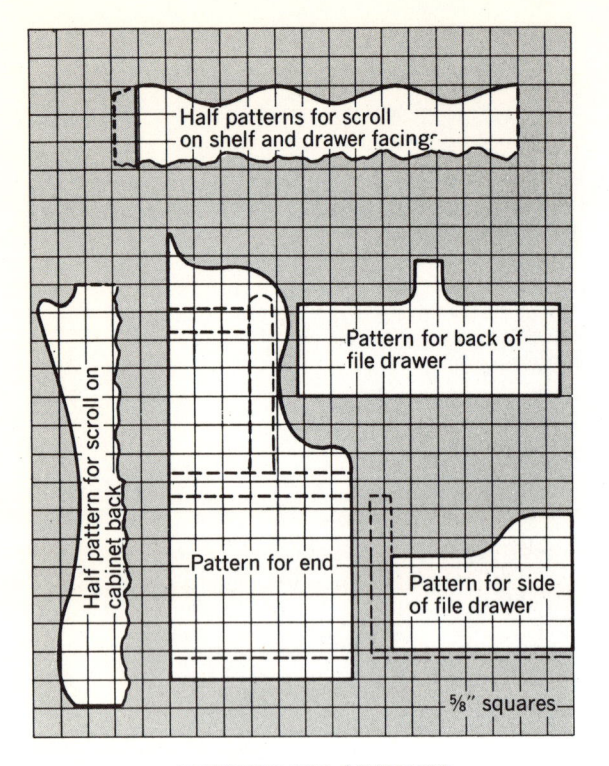

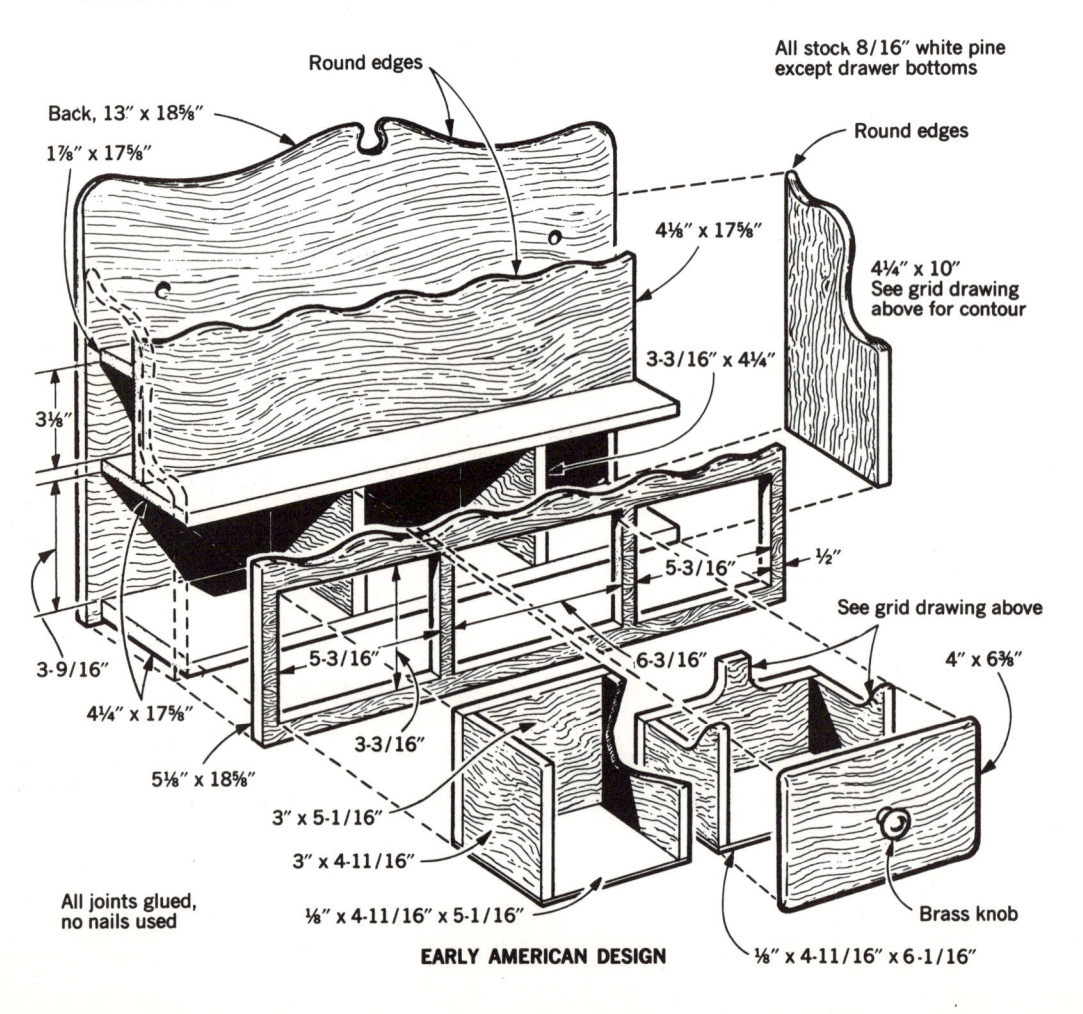

curved edges of the fronts, ends and back members of the colonial rack. You'll notice that the drawer openings in the front facing are actually cut in a single piece—although, if you wish, you can assemble the facing from separate strips, butting and gluing vertical ones to horizontal ones. You'll notice, too, that the front facing is made to lap the ends. This is also true of the back.

All shelf members should be cut to exactly the same length by using the stop rod on your saw's miter gauge. Then they'll fit perfectly between the ends.

Of course, you can give the rack a real professional look if you can round the curved edges with a shaper cutter. Patterns for the scroll-cut edges will have to be enlarged from the grid drawing at the left. Note how the sides and back of the center file drawer are shaped to let you tilt it when installing. The tab at the back serves as a stop so you can't pull the drawer all the way out.

EARLY AMERICAN DESIGN

The clock spice rack is equally as simple to make, as you can see in studying the drawing. No facing is required for the drawer openings; the lipped drawers simply lap the edges of the compartments. The clock case is made separately and later centered and glued in place on top of the drawer unit.

The dial for the face of the clock is made by pressing slices of maple dowel in holes drilled equidistantly around a 3-5/8-in. circle drawn on a piece of 1/4-in. mahogany. The hands come with the clock works. The completed face laps the edges of the clock case. The rope fence and drawer pulls, as well as the wood drawer pulls glued to the tops of the corner posts to simulate capstans, impart a nautical flavor.

The nylon rope ends are anchored with melted glue in the sides of the clock case after passing them through right-angle holes in the corner posts. A rounded lip on all drawer fronts laps the edges of the openings.

See also: home improvement; kitchens; spice chest.

If you want to use the same clock, you can get one from Armor Co., Box 290, Deer Park, N.Y.

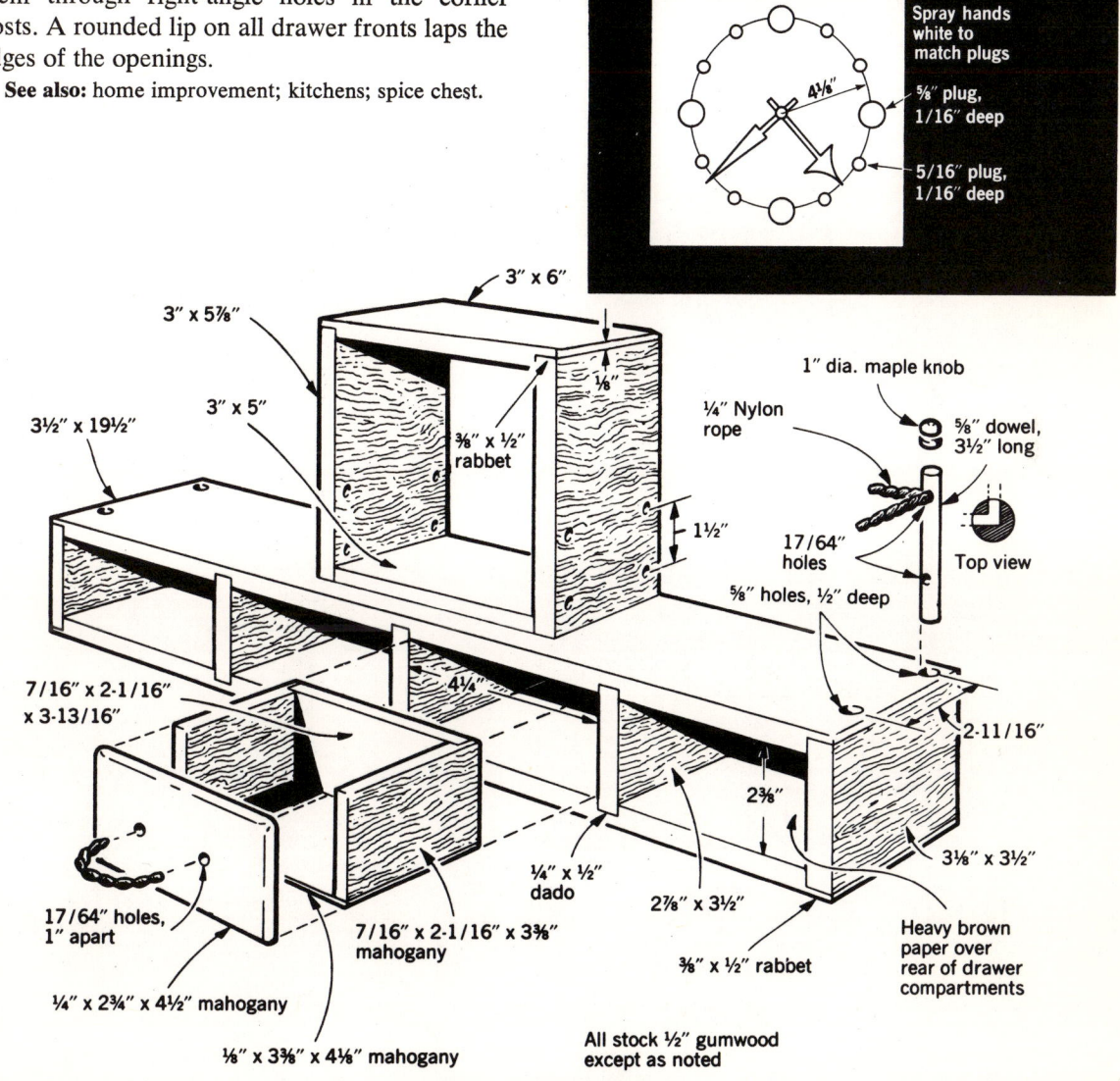

NAUTICAL MODERN DESIGN

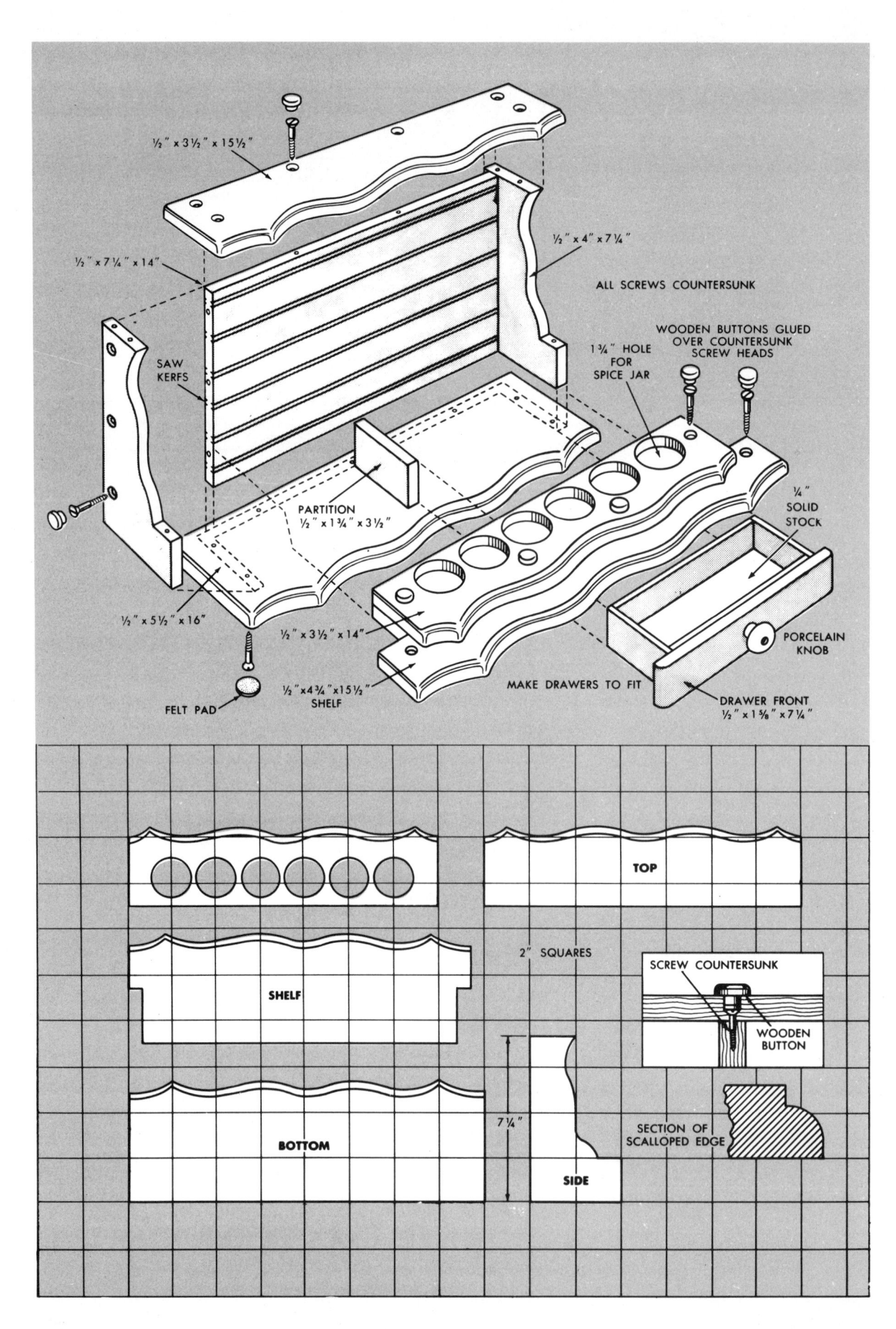

spice racks

2430

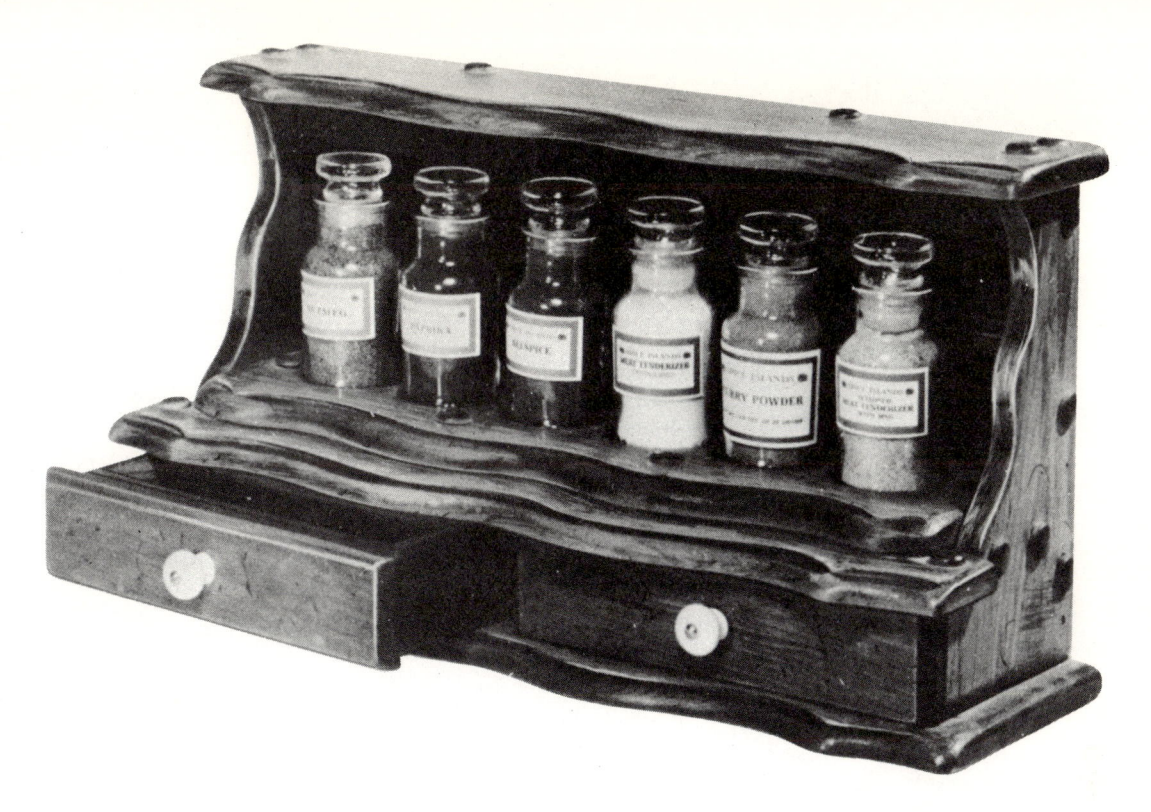

Early American spice rack

BY A. J. CANADA

■ IN MOST CASES, making a piece of Early American furniture is just a matter of copying an original piece. However, this isn't the case with a Colonial spice rack. Our forefathers didn't use this kitchen accessory; they generally kept spices in little drawers built into other kitchen furnishings.

The project, however, can be simple if you follow the details closely. Start by cutting the framing pieces from ½-in. pine, after first enlarging the patterns shown on the opposite page. You can use a jigsaw on the scalloped edges, but a saber saw, bandsaw or hand coping saw can do the job quite easily. Next, shape the scalloped edges with a router, then cut the jar holes with a hole saw in an electric drill.

Cut the back piece out of ¼-in. solid pine (if you can't find any, use plywood), and decorate it with six horizontal saw kerfs as shown.

Assembly is simple and straightforward, using white glue and ¾-in. No. 6 flathead screws. Countersink the screws halfway into the wood and cover them with wood buttons to simulate pegs.

Assemble the drawers with brads and glue.

An important step in making "antique" furniture is to simulate a hundred years or so of use. You can solve this problem by sanding all edges —rubbing a little harder at the corners. As an optional treatment, you can distress the surfaces by nicking them with a chisel, gouge or ice pick.

The final step is finishing. Applying a good Colonial pine stain gives a perfectly satisfactory appearance, and this method is best if you want convenience and speed. However, you can achieve a somewhat more realistic effect with a mixture of charcoal and boiled linseed oil, rubbing in vigorously with a soft cloth. The advantage of this technique is that the charcoal tends to accumulate in corners and surface nicks, thus enhancing the desired antique effect.

spindle sander

Here's factory-fast sanding of curved work, a piece very difficult to sand by hand. Table can be raised or lowered to equalize wear on the drum or swung aside for free-hand work

Make a spindle sander in one evening

BY JOHN BURROUGHS

For sanding irregular
   work, you can't beat a
      spindle sander for speed.
And it's quick to assemble

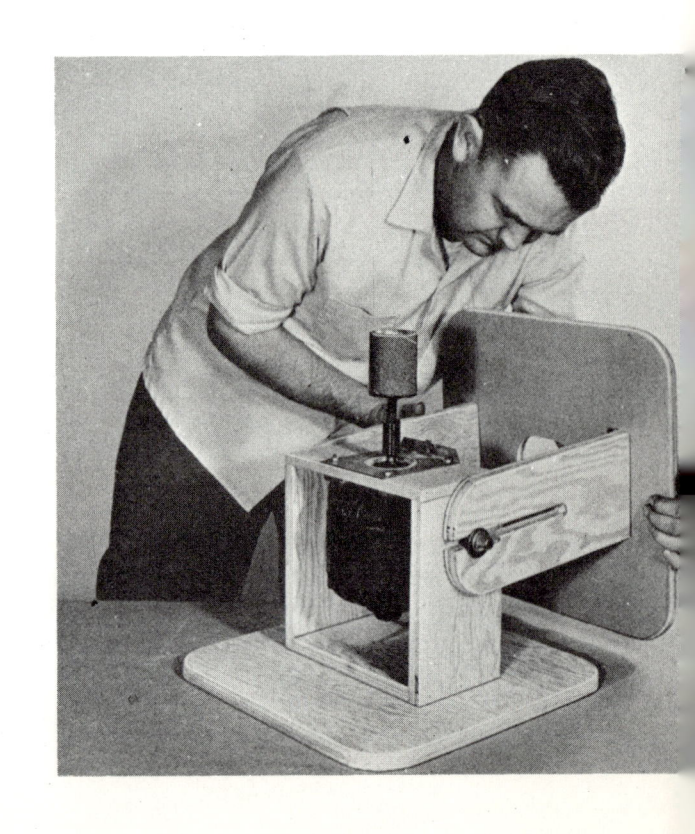

■ NEED A SANDER for your shop? This one beats hand sanding all hollow when it comes to smoothing the curved edges of scroll work and other irregular workpieces. It can be made for a song if you should happen to have a ¼-hp. motor.

A glance at the details on this page shows you how it's made. The motor is mounted vertically by substituting steel rods threaded at each end for the long bolts that normally hold the motor end shields in place. The threaded upper ends of the rods (upper when motor is in vertical position) pass through holes drilled in the horizontal plywood member, and also through holes drilled in a steel plate. Note how the nuts are run on the upper ends of the rods to space the motor from its support and to adjust it for height. Note also that the rods serve as bolts holding the motor end shields.

The sanding drum can be any desired diameter and should be of the type having a tapped hub which will screw onto a threaded motor arbor.

The motor support is simply an open box of plywood which is screwed to a base of the same material. The motor support carries two slotted members which are held in any desired position by carriage bolts and wingnuts. The table is attached to these members by corner irons and screws. This permits adjusting the table for height, allowing use of all the abrasive area of the sanding drum.

See also: abrasives; band sander; belt-disk sander; drill presses; pad sander; sanding jig.

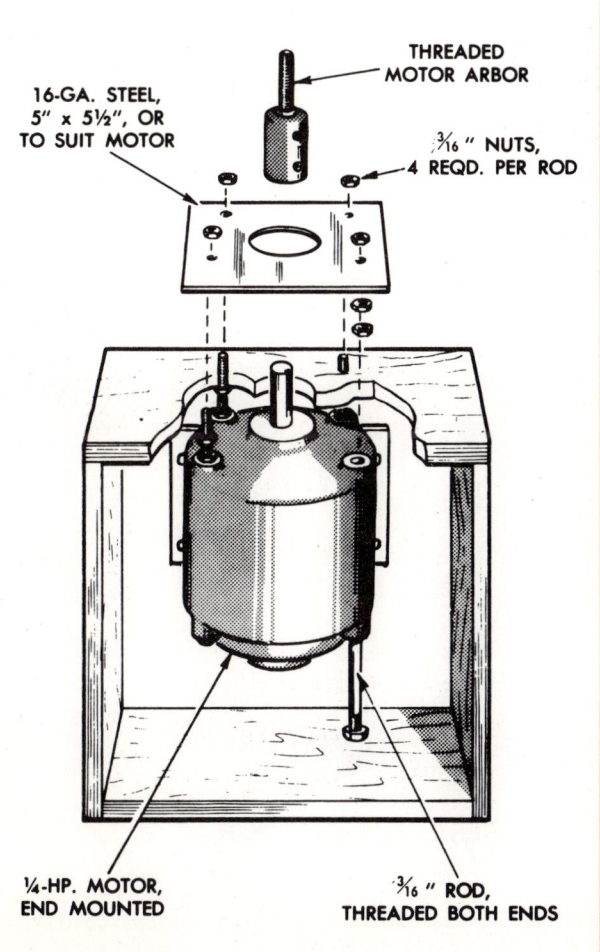

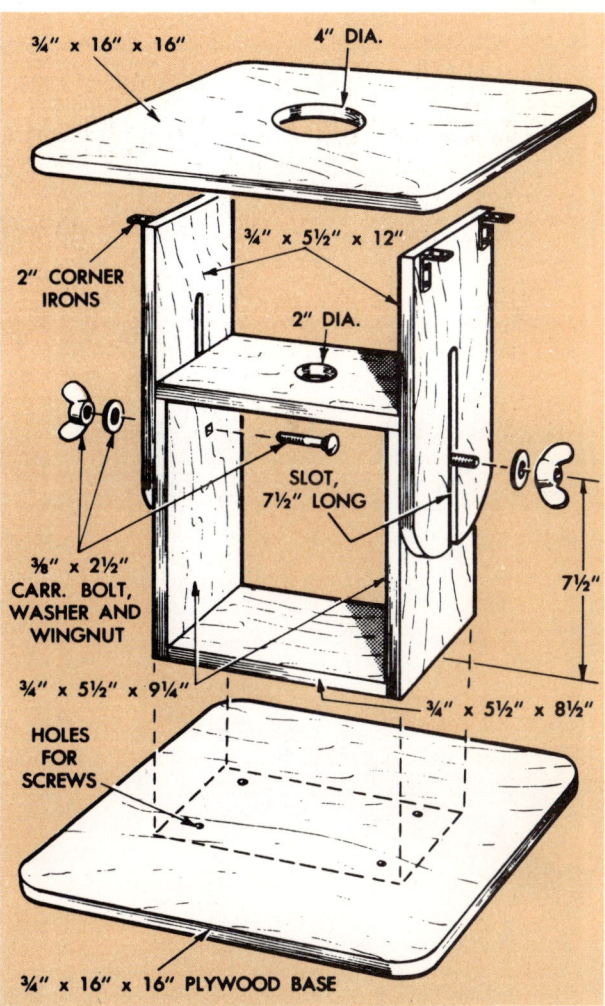

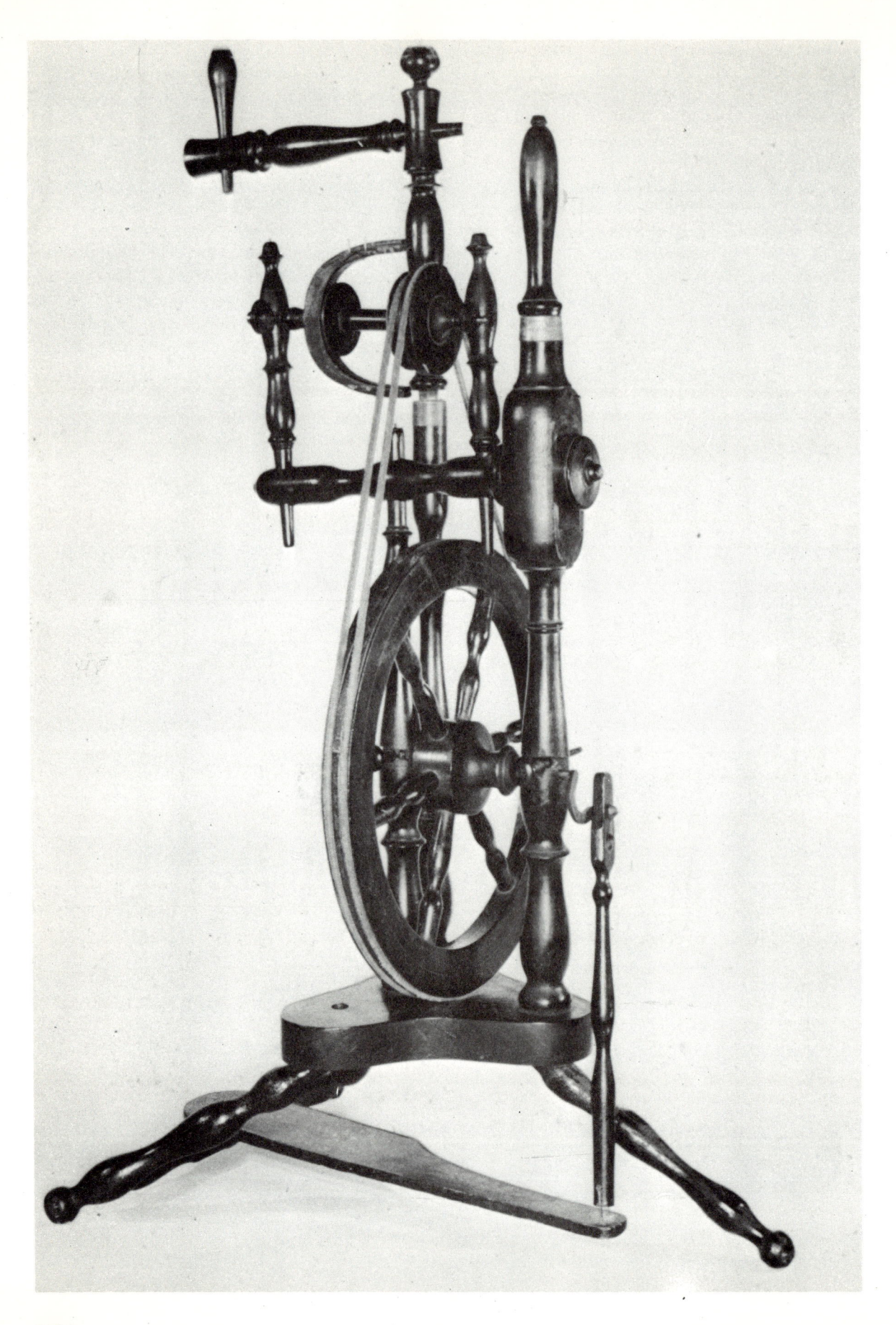

spinning wheels

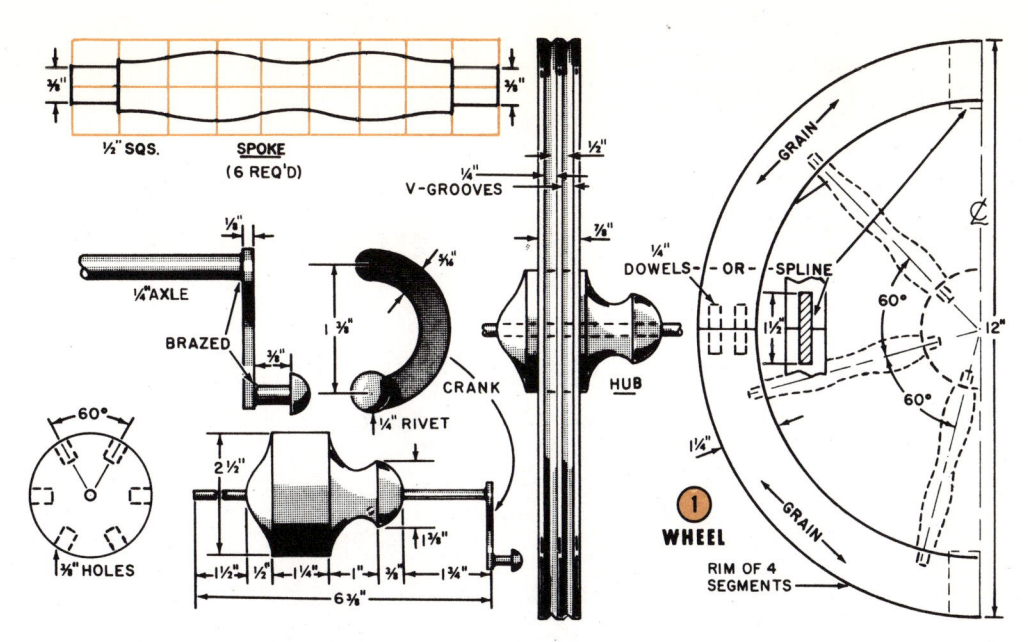

Make this spinning wheel on your lathe

BY E. R. HAAN

■ AN OLD SPINNING WHEEL in the parlor is a nostalgic touch missing from most modern homes. Today's smaller rooms just can't spare the space for a large treadle wheel. But a small vertical wheel can be both a decoration and a conversation piece.

Shown here are working plans for the ideal model for modern living rooms or dens. Reproducing this valuable antique can be one of the most rewarding lathe projects you've ever assembled. As a decoration it will deserve the small amount of space it *does* take up. Even if your wife doesn't warm to the idea of knitting sweaters from the fur of a pet angora, she'll enjoy being the center of attention as she demonstrates a forgotten skill to fascinated friends.

The original detailed is the vertical type with the flyer and bobbin *above* the wheel. It might be called the Spinning Wheel that Won the West, since it's the one that was favored by our prairie-crossing ancestors. It was probably born when some square-jawed pioneer balked at loading his wife's regular machine in an already crowded covered wagon, and she declared: "If *it* stays, *I* stay!" What could the poor man do but design a "portable" that would tuck right into a corner of a prairie schooner?

Worth noting is that it's possible for your wife to learn how to spin. If she does, by writing to a place such as Old Sturbridge Village, Mass., for

You can't buy one just anywhere
    but you can turn an exact copy
of this old spinning wheel
    that was so popular
      with American pioneers

instructions, you might end up with some of the handsomest sweaters you've ever owned.

Your job should start with a study of the keyed drawing on page 2439 to familiarize yourself with what individual parts are called. Great-great-grandma got pretty cute, sometimes, when putting *names* to items encountered in everyday chores. Thus the horizontal bar (Key No. 7) that positions the spinning mechanism (11) is a "mother-of-all." Sprouting from this are two posts called "maidens" (2); bridging these is the

---

spinning-wing autogiro: see gyroplane model
spiral candlestick: see candlestick
spiral staircase: see vacation homes
splicing, rope: see rope

2435

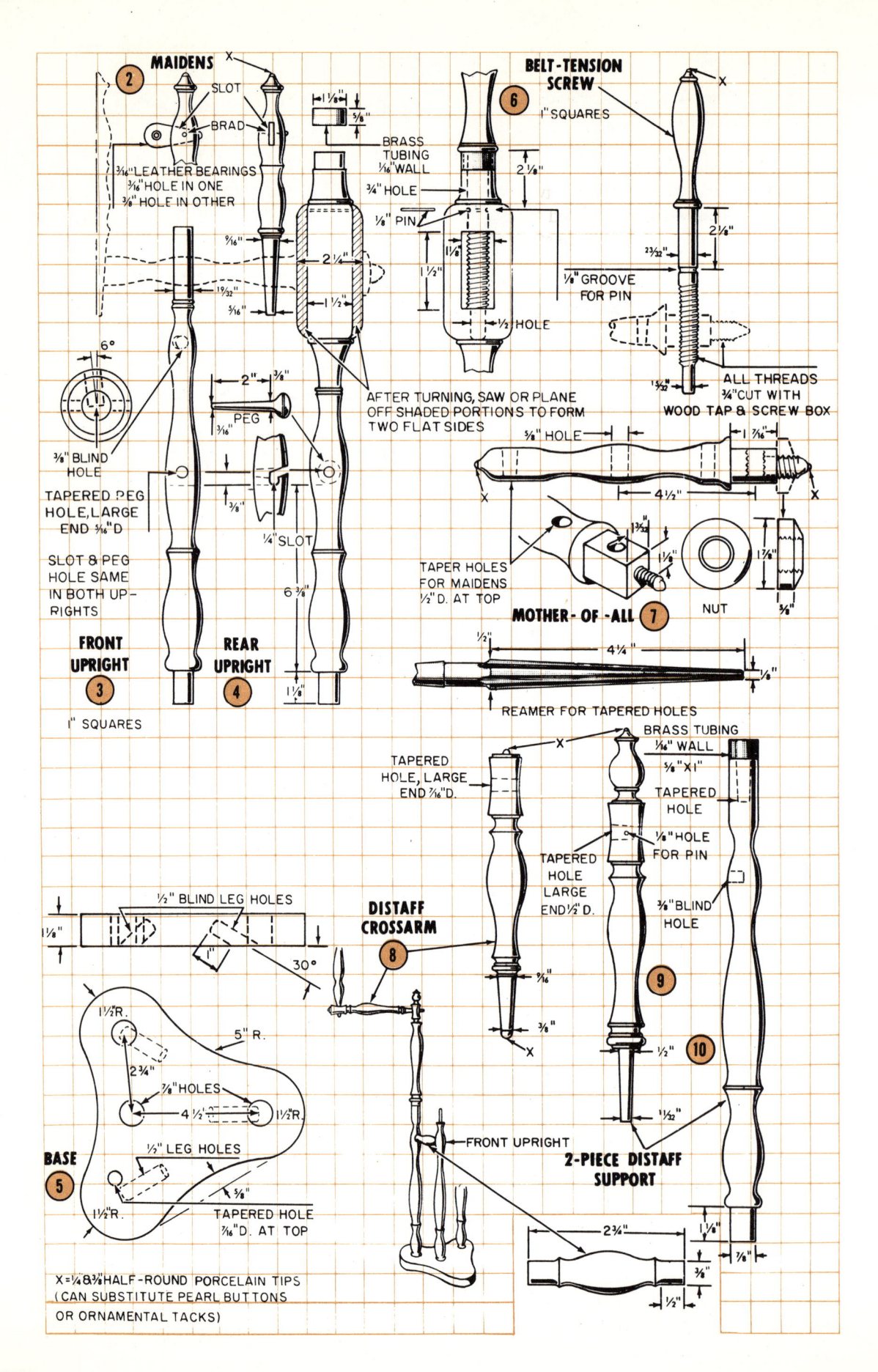

spinning wheels

2436

spindle—a solid-steel axle, hollowed at one end to form an eye through which the raw fibers pass. The fibers emerge at a side hole and are twisted by the horseshoe-shaped "flyer," which then guides the string onto the bobbin. The flyer is pinned to the spindle, so its rate of revolution is controlled by the larger of the two whorls, which is actually a V-pulley fastened to the spindle with a setscrew. A smaller-diameter whorl is turned onto an end of the one-piece bobbin. The difference in diameter is important: Since both whorls are spun by means of cords (called driving bands) that pass around the rim of the wheel, the bobbin spins slightly faster than the flyer, keeping the thread taut for winding. Tension is kept on the bands by means of an adjustment screw (6) that lets you inch the mother-of-all farther from the wheel as the bands stretch.

The speed of the wheel is, of course, controlled by the treadle (15). The up-and-down action of the treadle is converted to the rotary spin of the wheel by means of yet another quaintly-named member—the footman. This is simply a stick (13) that connects the treadle to a crank on the end of the axle.

the start of construction

Now that we know how the main parts relate to one another, let's start construction. All wooden members should be made of a close-grain hardwood such as maple. The wheel rim consists of four band-sawed segments splined—or doweled—together. Splining is easiest, since the splines can be driven in position after the spokes have been assembled to the rim segments and hub. Use a relatively slow-setting glue so you can complete the entire assembly before it hardens. A rope around the rim, applied like a tourniquet, keeps the segments butted tightly while you clamp the wheel between two sheets of ¾-in. plywood. When set, mount the hub in your lathe to true the rim and cut the two grooves for the driving band. Then drive in the axle so it fits tightly, extending the right distance on each side.

Now, begin work on the frame itself, starting with the base and working up, but attaching the legs and treadle last. Make a full-size paper pattern of the base (5) for tracing its shape and the hole locations. Bore the holes for the uprights and the tapered socket for the distaff when it's not in use. (No distaff is used when spinning wool.) After gluing the uprights in place, prepare for boring the sloping blind leg sockets by cutting a small notch with a chisel, to form a seat for the bit. This is done with the uprights installed because the leg sockets notch into the ends of the rear upright and distaff support.

The front and rear uprights support both the wheel and the mother-of-all. They have L-shaped notches cut in them that let you slip the wheel axle in place. The bearing seat for the axle is a bit to one side of the center line to conserve more of the uprights' cross section, for strength. The axle is anchored with tapered pegs. Drill and ream the peg holes before you drill the bearing seat and cut the notches.

A blind hole near the top of the front upright takes a short brace that adds rigidity to the distaff support. The upper end of this upright passes through the mother-of-all and lets it move up and down. The nearly square end of the mother-of-all must be a sliding fit in the slot of the rear upright. To cut this slot, you must first turn the 2¼-in. section of the upright on the lathe, then saw or plane two parallel flats to reduce the thickness to 1½-in. After forming the slot, equip the top end of the upright with a brass reinforcing ring, then bore a centered ¾-in. hole down from the top and into the slot. Now, improvise a sleeve with a ⅛-in. wall to fit this hole and serve as a guide for the auger while you drill a ½-in. hole at the opposite end of the slot. This hole forms a seat for the tension screw. The screw itself does not travel—it rotates and is locked in place with a ⅛-in. steel pin that fits a groove above the threaded portion of the screw.

To cut the threads, you should have a screw-box and wood tap, but you can use a metal-turning lathe equipped for thread cutting.

There are three holes through the mother-of-all—a straight center one that's a sliding fit on the front upright and two tapered sockets for the

2437

spinning wheels

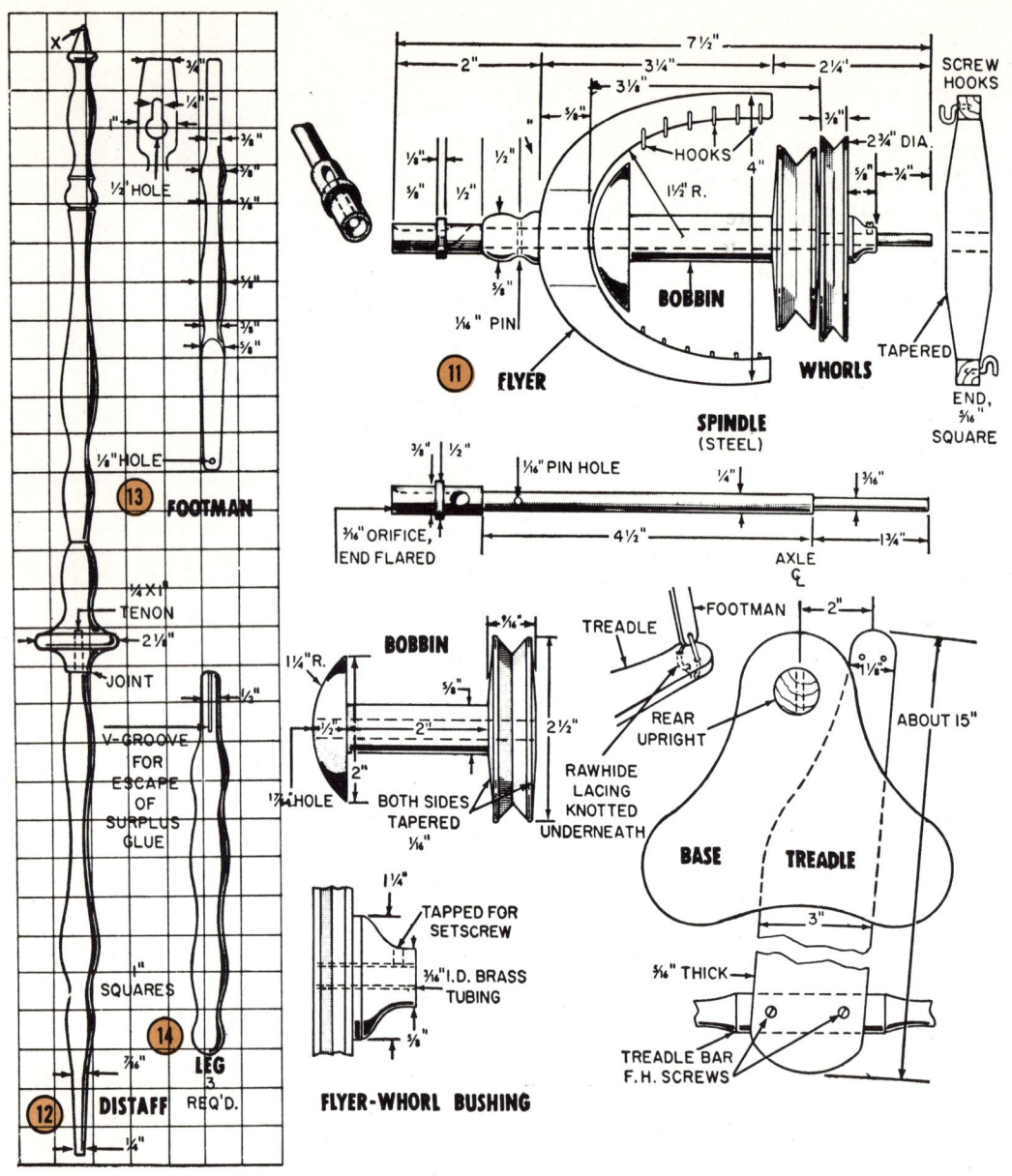

The legs cant only 30 deg. on the original, but this may be increased to 40 deg. to simplify drilling the holes for the legs and to lessen strain

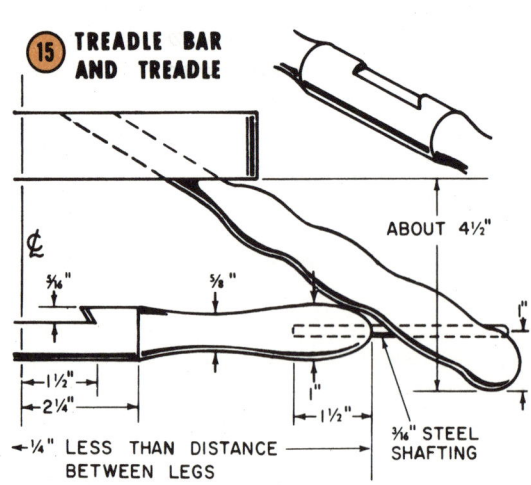

2438

maidens. The threaded extension on the square section can be a dowel, threaded part way. Glue the unthreaded end into a centered hole; then bore and tap the hole through which the belt-tension screw turns. A round, wooden nut snugs the mother-of-all to the rear upright.

The maidens are identical, and are fitted with leather bearings in tapered slots, to take the spindle. Secure each bearing with a brad, but leave the head projecting enough to permit removal if the leather must be replaced.

The lower part of the distaff support (10) is glued in its base socket. A tapered hole in the top end takes the upper part (9). This not only permits removal, but lets the operator turn the distaff for best positioning while spinning flax. A brass ring reinforces the wood around this socket. Both the crossarm (8) and top section (12) also fit into tapered sockets.

the thread-guiding hooks

The thread-guiding hooks on the flyer arms are screwhooks bent to the shape indicated and turned into pilot holes to prevent splitting.

Note the step-down from ¼ in. to ³⁄₁₆ in. on the spindle. This comes at the end of the bobbin whorl and bears against the end of the brass bushing inside the flyer whorl, thus preventing friction between the two. The feeding hole at the spindle's opposite end is drilled and reamed to a funnel shape. A second hole of the same size meets it at an angle through the side of the spindle. This entire path must have perfectly smooth walls; you can achieve this by pulling a narrow twist of emery cloth through it.

With the wheel and spindle assembly complete, you're ready to add the three identical legs to the base. Shallow V-grooves cut along the leg tenons will let surplus glue ooze out when the legs are driven in place. After turning the treadle bar, carefully drill the front legs and the ends of the bar to take lengths of ³⁄₁₆-in. steel rod. These pivots must be a sliding fit in the leg holes but a drive fit in the ends of the bar.

When tying the footman to the end of the treadle with a rawhide thong, adjust it so the end of the treadle won't strike the floor at the bottom of the stroke, or the base at the top of the stroke. You may have to shorten the footman for proper clearance. Dimensions of the footman, treadle and treadle bar depend on the slope of the legs.

It's easier to apply a finish to the individual turnings while they're still in the lathe. The original wheel is stained very dark, then waxed.

See also: rocking chair; settle; woodworking.

PARTS
1. Wheel
2. Maidens (two)
3. Front upright
4. Rear upright
5. Base
6. Belt-tension screw
7. Mother-of-all
8. Distaff crossarm
9. Upper section of distaff support
10. Lower section of distaff support
11. Flyer, bobbin & whorls
12. Distaff
13. Footman
14. Legs (three)
15. Treadle and bar
16. Driving band

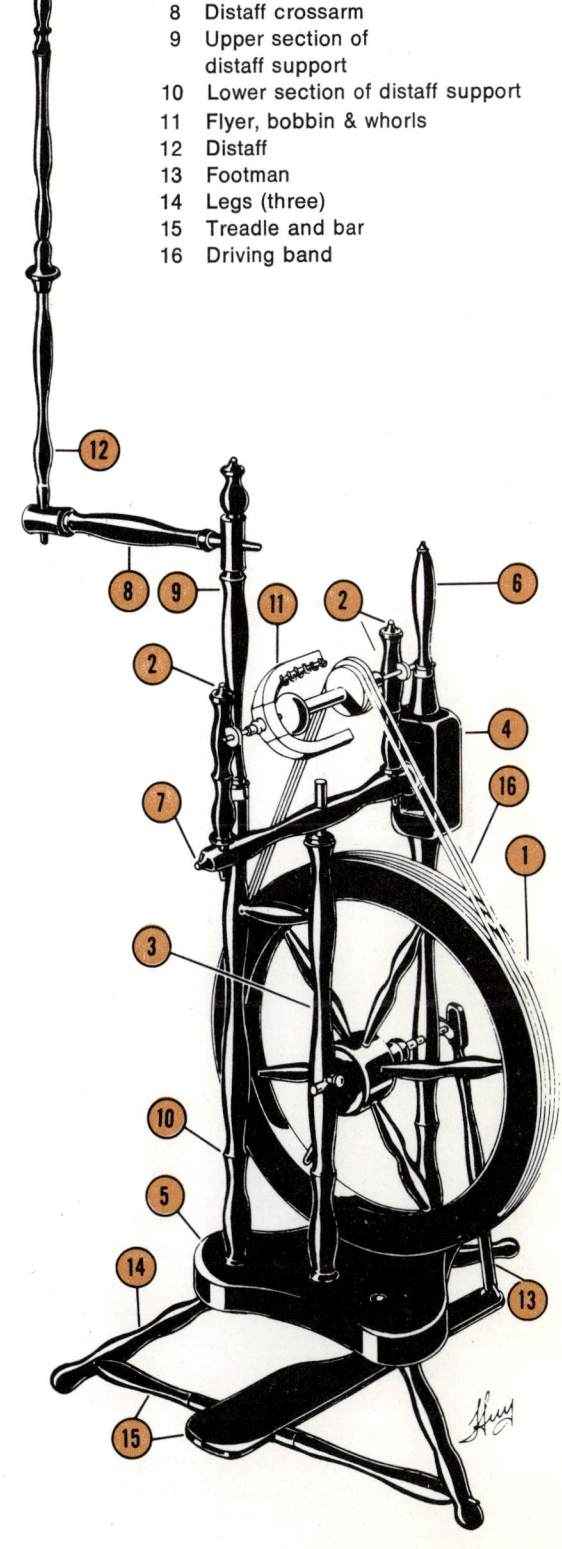

2439

sports boat

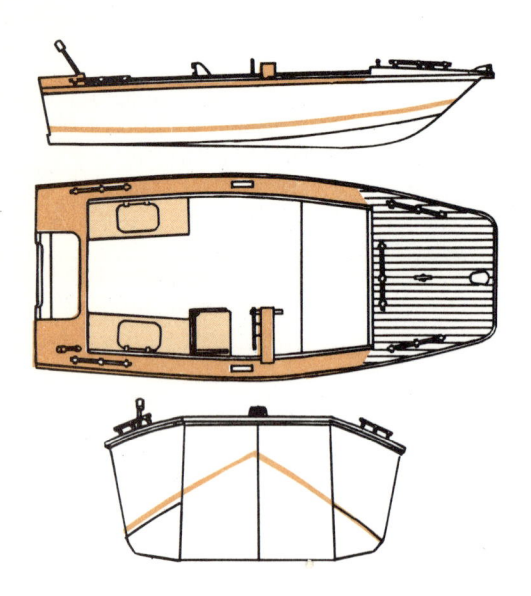

Build a sleek sports boat

BY ARTHUR MIKESELL

Designed by William D. Jackson, this sports sled has 50 sq. ft. of open cockpit and a rugged inverted-V hull. It'll seat six for fishing, yet is great for water skiing

sports cart: see carts
sportsman's cabinet: see hobby workspace
sportsmen's scooter: see scooter
spotlight lamp: see lamps

■ DON'T BE FOOLED by the sleek, racy lines. In spite of its high-style appearance, this soft-riding inverted-V is a rugged, do-anything sports boat that's fine for fishing, sensational for skiing and roomy enough to hold all your scuba gear with plenty of space to spare. And it can take anything you're likely to dish out.

To build it, follow these general rules:
• Frame with the best stock lumber locally available. Douglas fir, Philippine mahogany, yellow pine or even the better grades of hemlock will suffice, so long as the wood is reasonably free of knots. Lumber dimensions denote stock sizes, i.e., a 1 x 4 actually measures $13/16$ x $3 5/8$ in.
• Use annular-ring boat nails (Stronghold Anchorfast or similar) and waterproof glue to secure the 3/8-in. plywood planking to the frame. Galvanized nails and screws are suitable if you

2441

sports boat

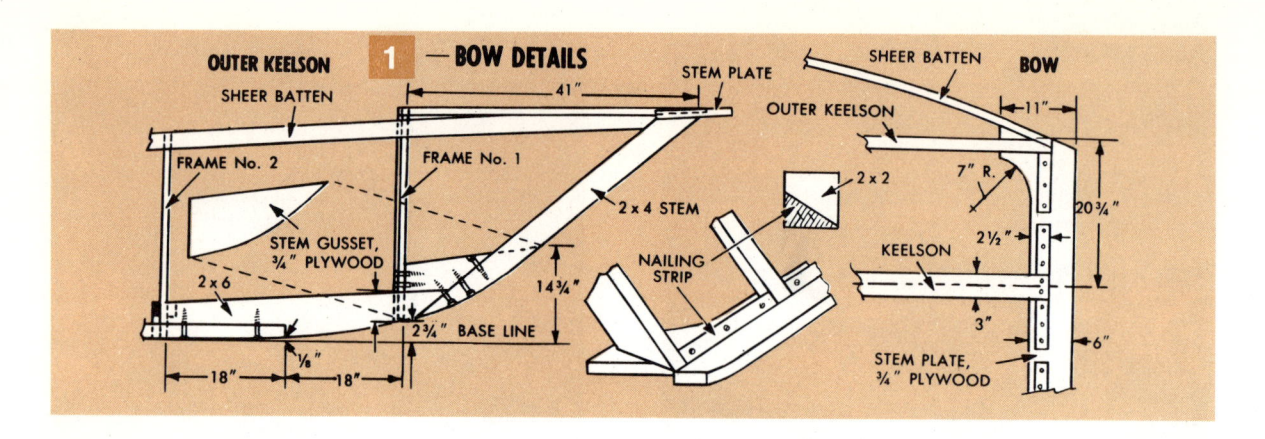

1 — BOW DETAILS

sleek sports boat, continued

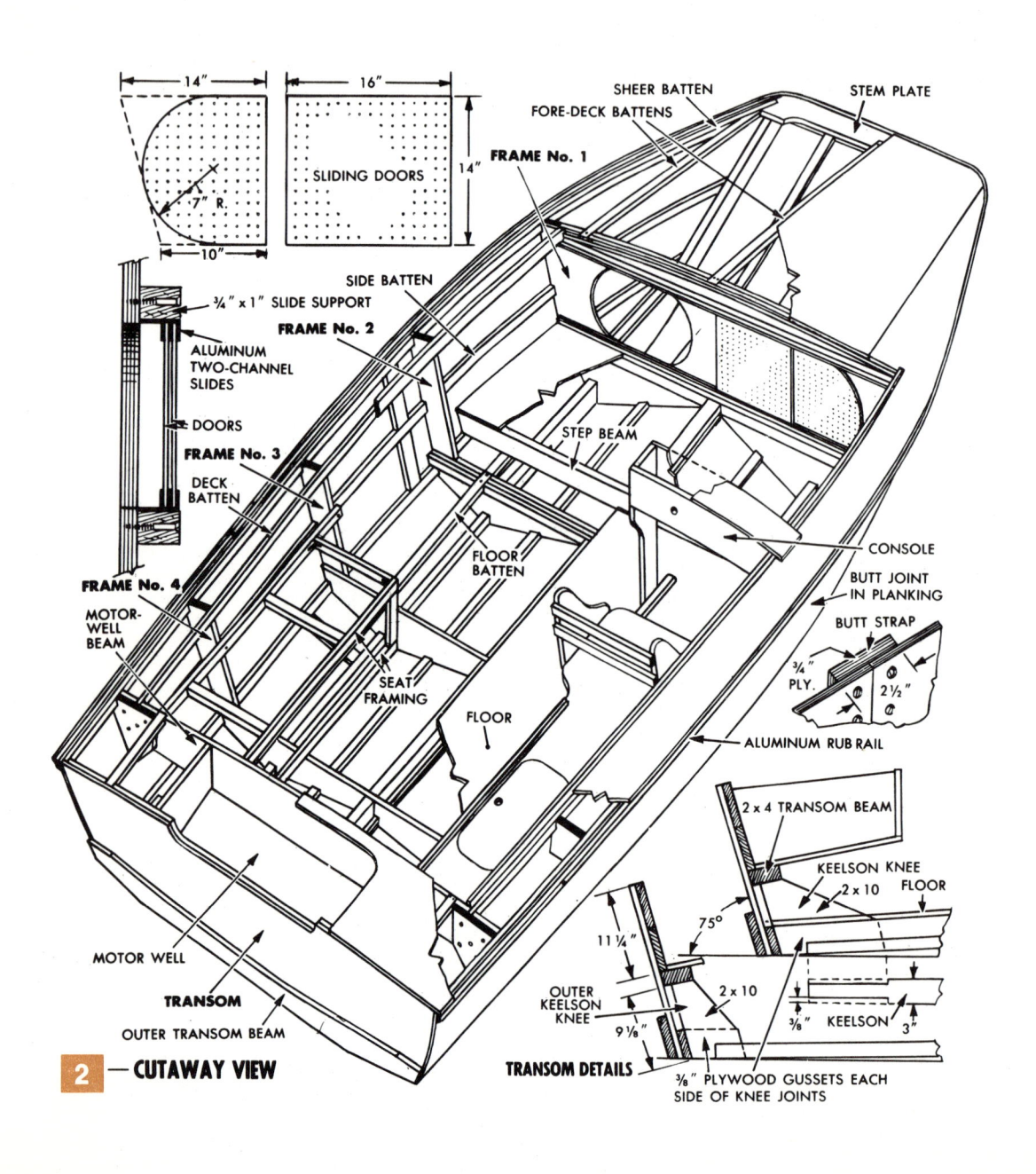

2 — CUTAWAY VIEW

Filler pieces mounted on the keelson are decreasing-angle wedges which give an inverted-V configuration to this member. The trial-and-error shaping of these pieces to receive planking is part of fairing

Start planking at the transom and work forward. The two ½-in. plywood butt straps at the planking joints must be cut to fit between the framing members. Seal all of these joints with fiberglass tape

plan to use the boat only in fresh water, but substitute silicon bronze if it will receive saltwater exposure.

- Where necessary, make full-size paper patterns by using the grid system to enlarge the plan drawings. Transfer these patterns to the lumber or plywood with a dressmaker's toothed wheel. (You can make a suitable substitute by salvaging a gear from a discarded alarm clock and mounting it on a nail between the legs of a wooden clothespin.) Cut slightly oversize to allow for the final fitting.
- Countersink all exterior fastenings slightly and plug holes with wood putty.
- Fiberglassing is a matter of personal taste, but on this particular hull it is strongly recommended that you seal the below-waterline seams with fiberglass tape.

The first step is to cut and assemble all frames, Fig. 7. Fasten the side members to the bottom crosspieces with glue and 1½-in. No. 8 flathead screws, 3 per joint. Use the same size screws to mount the inner transom framing on the ¾-in. plywood transom, spacing them about 3 in. apart. (The outer transom beam isn't installed until after the frame is planked.) Secure the 2 x 4 transom beam by driving 2-in. No. 10 screws from outside the plywood. And remember to coat all contacting surfaces with glue.

When you have finished frames 2, 3 and 4, brace them with 1 x 1 tie bars as shown to prevent distortion during the rest of the building process. Note that frame 2 is braced with 1 x 2 doubling pieces on each side of the bottom crosspiece. Mount these with glue and 1½-in.

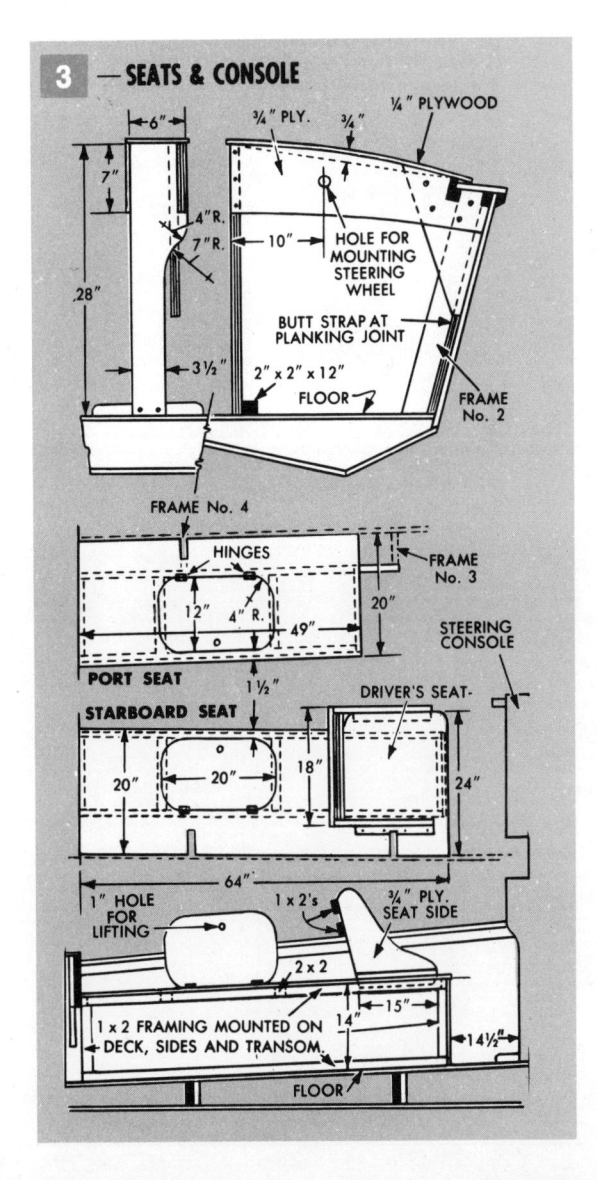

3 — SEATS & CONSOLE

2443

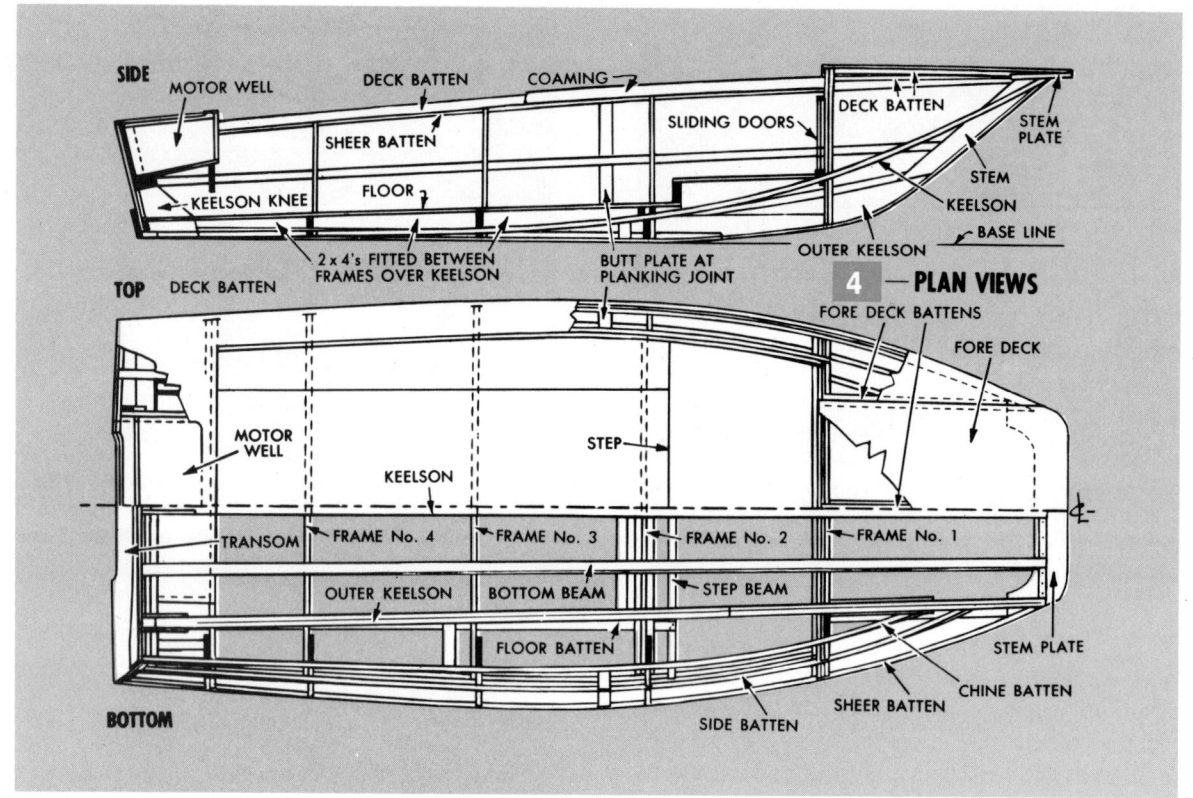

sports boat

4 — PLAN VIEWS

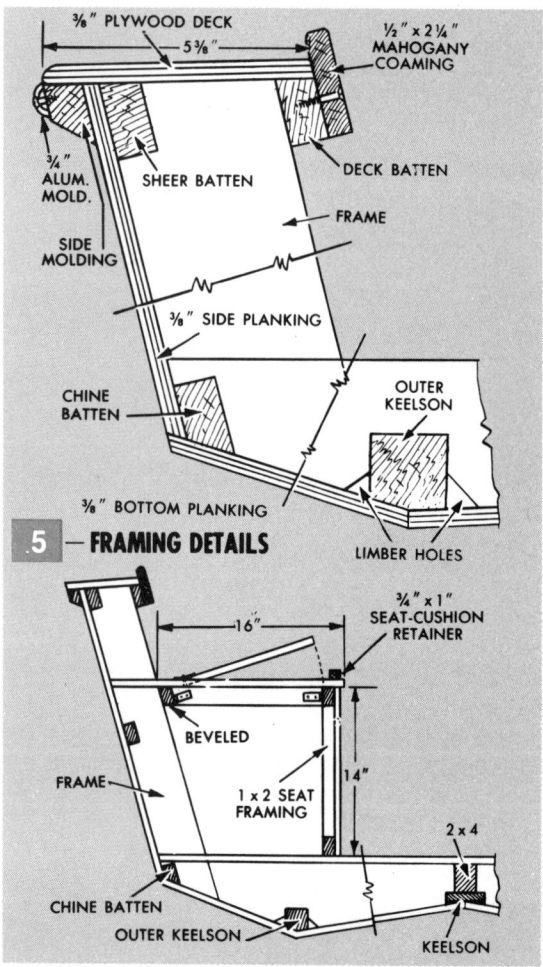

Labels (SIDE view): MOTOR WELL, DECK BATTEN, COAMING, SLIDING DOORS, DECK BATTEN, STEM PLATE, STEM, KEELSON, BASE LINE, OUTER KEELSON, BUTT PLATE AT PLANKING JOINT, 2 x 4's FITTED BETWEEN FRAMES OVER KEELSON, FLOOR, KEELSON KNEE, SHEER BATTEN

Labels (TOP/BOTTOM view): DECK BATTEN, FORE DECK BATTENS, FORE DECK, MOTOR WELL, STEP, KEELSON, TRANSOM, FRAME No. 4, FRAME No. 3, FRAME No. 2, FRAME No. 1, OUTER KEELSON, BOTTOM BEAM, STEP BEAM, FLOOR BATTEN, SIDE BATTEN, SHEER BATTEN, CHINE BATTEN, STEM PLATE

5 — FRAMING DETAILS

Labels: 3/8" PLYWOOD DECK, 5 3/8", 1/2" x 2 1/4" MAHOGANY COAMING, 3/4" ALUM. MOLD., SHEER BATTEN, DECK BATTEN, FRAME, SIDE MOLDING, 3/8" SIDE PLANKING, CHINE BATTEN, OUTER KEELSON, 3/8" BOTTOM PLANKING, LIMBER HOLES

Labels: 3/4" x 1" SEAT-CUSHION RETAINER, 16", BEVELED, 1 x 2 SEAT FRAMING, 14", FRAME, CHINE BATTEN, OUTER KEELSON, KEELSON, 2 x 4

No. 8 screws. Don't forget to notch the upper beam in frame 1 to hold the foredeck battens.

While the glue in the frames is hardening, turn your attention to the longitudinal framing pieces, Fig. 7. Saw all the keelsons, battens and molds first, then set the blade at 30 deg. and rip the chines, Fig. 5.

Because this boat actually has three stems—one on each side of the vee, plus a third running down the center of the tunnel—the framing may look somewhat complicated when you first go over the plans. Once you get into it, however, you'll find that it's actually quite simple.

Begin with the stem assembly, which includes frames 1 and 2. These frames and the two outer keelson-stem members should be assembled right side up, clamping short legs to the stems to elevate them the proper distance above the base line, Fig. 6. First, cut the stem plate from 3/4-in. plywood.

The next step is to cut and assemble the two outer stem-keelson members, Fig. 1. After coating all mating surfaces with glue, secure the two 3/8-in. plywood gussets (per stem) with 1 1/4-in. No. 8 nails, then drive three 3-in. No. 12 screws

6 — LINES

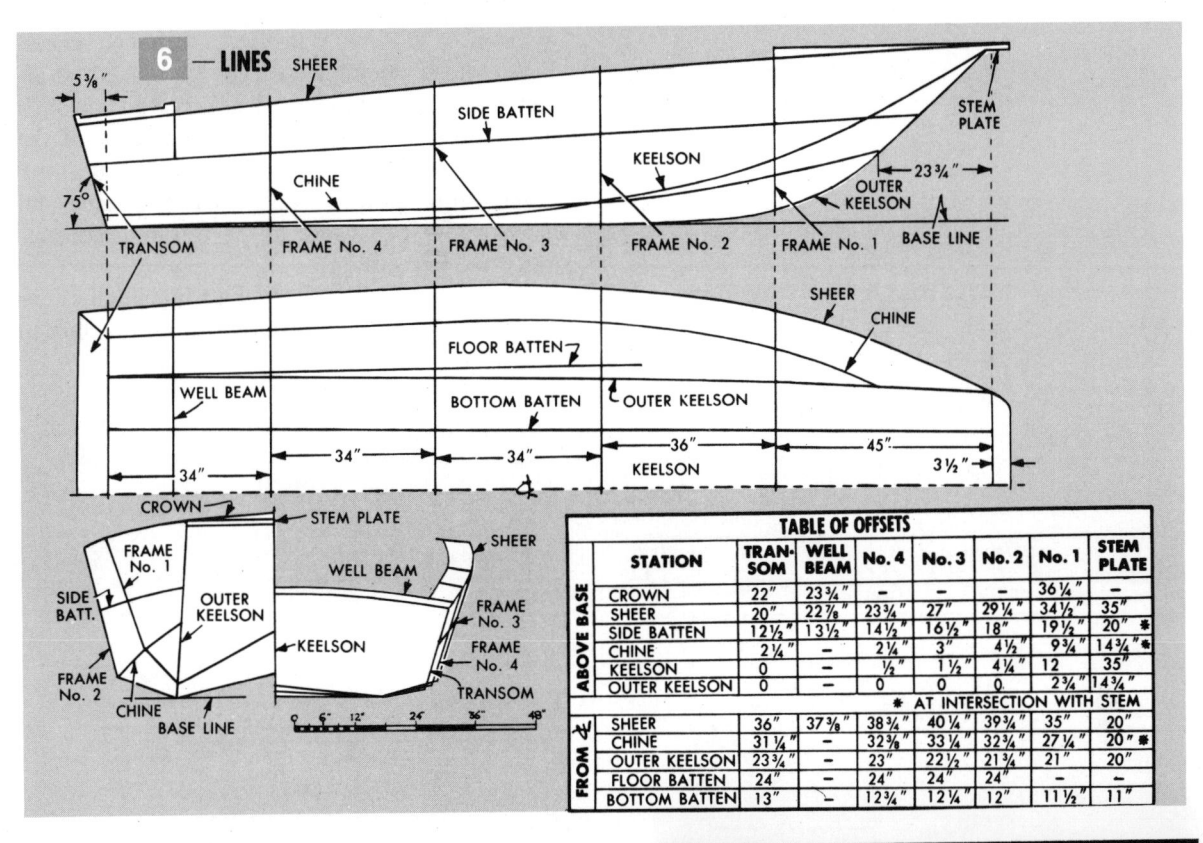

TABLE OF OFFSETS

STATION		TRANSOM	WELL BEAM	No. 4	No. 3	No. 2	No. 1	STEM PLATE
ABOVE BASE	CROWN	22"	23¾"	–	–	–	36¼"	–
	SHEER	20"	22⅞"	23¾"	27"	29¼"	34½"	35"
	SIDE BATTEN	12½"	13½"	14½"	16½"	18"	19½"	20" *
	CHINE	2¼"	–	2¼"	3"	4½"	9¾"	14¾" *
	KEELSON	0	–	½"	1½"	4¼"	12	35"
	OUTER KEELSON	0	0	0	0	0	2¾"	14¾"
						* AT INTERSECTION WITH STEM		
FROM ₵	SHEER	36"	37⅜"	38¾"	40¼"	39¾"	35"	20"
	CHINE	31¼"	–	32⅜"	33¼"	32¾"	27¼"	20" *
	OUTER KEELSON	23¾"	23"	22½"	21¾"	21"	20"	
	FLOOR BATTEN	24"	–	24"	24"	24"	–	–
	BOTTOM BATTEN	13"	–	12¾"	12¼"	12"	11½"	11"

into the fore end as shown, one from above and two from below. These should be countersunk slightly to allow for fairing.

When the glue has hardened, join the 2 x 2 outer keelson to the stem assembly with glue and two 3-in. No. 12 screws. Now notch frame 1 to fit the bottom stem member, and with legs clamped to the two outer stems, slip frame 1 over them and check the fit. Next, position the stem plate on these two stems and mark their location on it. Then, if everything fits to your satisfaction, remove frame 1 and the stem plate, coat all adjoining surfaces with glue and return these parts to position, fastening frame 1 to the outer stems with two 2-in. No. 10 screws per joint, Fig. 1, and the stem plate to the ends of the outer stems with two of the same size screws per joint.

Before securing frame 2 to the outer keelsons, turn the assembly upside down. Coat all mating surfaces with glue and drive one 2-in. No. 10 screw through the frame into the after end of each stem assembly.

Next, add frames 3 and 4 using glue and one 3-in. No. 12 screw per joint. Finally, secure the

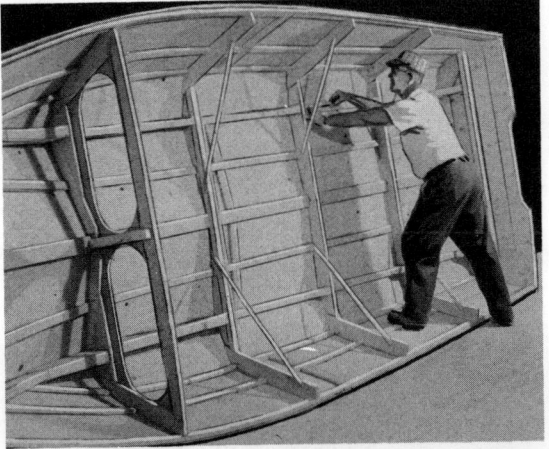

2445

sports boat

sleek sports boat, continued

transom to the outer keelsons with two knees, Fig. 2. Coat adjoining surfaces with glue and attach with three 3-in. No. 12 screws—one through the transom beam, one through the rear of the transom and one through the outer keelson. Then secure the plywood gussets with glue and nails, clamp 1 x 2 legs to the transom and toenail these to the floor.

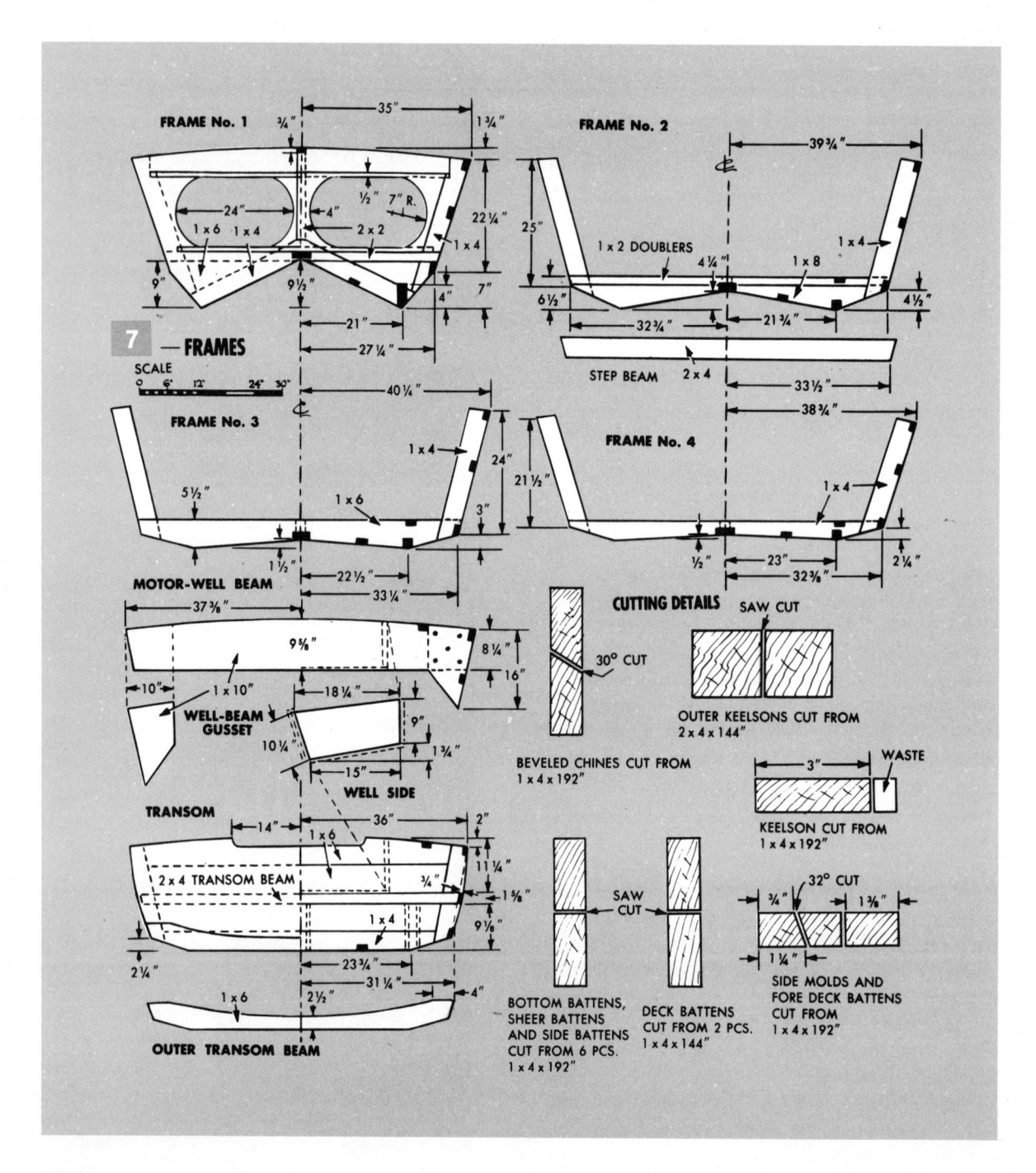

The next framing member to be added is the center keelson. At the transom, this is attached in the same way as the outer keelsons, Fig. 2. Secure it to each frame with glue and one 2-in. No. 10 screw. Bevel the end to fit flush against the stem plate, then coat mating surfaces with glue and fasten with two 1½-in. No. 8 screws.

The precut chines go on next. Cut a 1-in. piece off the end to use as a pattern for the chine notches in the frames and saw these square to each frame; then, with chines in position, run a hand saw between chine and frame notch to insure perfect seating of the chine in the notch. Attach with glue and one 2-in. No. 10 screw per joint. Don't secure the chines to the stems yet, however, because the stems must be beveled first. After completing this part of the fairing operation, bevel the ends to fit against the stems and fasten with glue and one 2-in. No. 10 screw.

Like the chines, the bottom battens are notched all the way through the transom and fastened with one 2-in. No. 10 screw per joint. Position them midway between the center keelson and outer keelsons. To simplify bending, slit about 6 ft. of the forward end by running it through a table saw on edge. Then, after beveling this split end to fit against the stem plate, apply glue to the slit portion and fasten with one 2-in. No. 10 screw.

Follow the same general procedure for mounting the sheer and side battens, but remember that the sheer battens, like the chine battens, shouldn't be secured to the stem until this member is beveled.

Fairing the frame is undoubtedly one of the most difficult steps in the construction of this boat, but if you exercise reasonable care and don't attempt to hurry through this operation, you shouldn't run into any real difficulty. Properly shaping the frame surfaces to insure perfect contact between the plywood planking and the frame members will require the use of a coarse wood rasp and a jack plane.

If one is available, a Stanley Surform wood file will speed up the job.

fair the hull

For those who aren't familiar with this operation, fairing involves laying a 1 x 1 batten across the framing surfaces and removing enough wood from each member so that the batten contacts each one fully. Basically, it's a trial-and-error process—put the batten in place, shave away a little wood from the surface and check the fit.

It may be necessary to remove screws from some members to make possible adequate fairing. In such cases, simply redrill and refasten after fairing. Filler pieces must be attached along the center keelson and on the stem plate between the ends of the bottom framing members. Mount these with glue and 1-in. wire nails when you are satisfied with the fairing; however, during the actual fairing operation they will be easier to shape if you simply clamp them in place.

Planking the hull is simplicity itself. The butt joints shown in the photos and in Fig. 2 should be backed with ¾ x 2½-in. plywood butt straps; fasten these to the planking with glue and 1¼-in. No. 8 screws spaced 1½ in. apart. Use glue and 1¼-in. No. 13 ring nails to secure the planking to the frame, spacing them 2½ in. apart along the transom.

To avoid error, make a corrugated cardboard pattern of the planking sheets on either side of the center keelson in the forward tunnel portion. Then transfer the outline to the plywood.

Once the bottom and side planking has been installed, you can mount the outer transom beam. Then, before turning the hull right side up, seal all seams (including planking butt joints) with 3-in. fiberglass tape and resin. When the resin has cured, you may sand and paint the bottom. However, for an extra-rugged hull which will be easier to maintain, it's recommended that you fiberglass the entire hull.

On the pilot model, we stretched a cotton mason's cord down the center of the tunnel over the glass cloth and impregnated it heavily with resin to protect this joint. As you have probably guessed, the tunnel joint takes the most stress on this type of hull.

turn hull right side up

With the hull turned right side up, you are ready to install the interior framing.

Note that the center keelson is braced with short lengths of 2 x 4 cut to fit snugly between the frames, Fig. 4. After installing these, coat the contacting surface of the side molding and hull with glue, clamp these in place and secure them with 1½-in. No. 8 screws spaced 6 in. apart.

The motor well is next, Figs. 2 and 4. After notching the well beam for the deck battens, attach the gussets with glue and five 1½-in. No. 8 screws per gusset, then secure this assembly inside the hull by driving three of the same size screws from the outside of the hull into the gussets on each side. Cut the two well sides from a 4-ft. length of 1 x 12 and mount these between the beam and the transom with 2-in. No. 10 screws. To complete the well, cut out the ⅜-in. plywood bottom and fasten it to the transom

sleek sports boat, continued

beam, sides and well beam with 1¼-in. nails and glue. Avoid leaks by sealing all well seams with fiberglass tape and resin.

The deck battens extend from the well beam to frame 1 and outline the cockpit. Attach them with one 2-in. No. 10 screw per joint. The foredeck battens are notched into the upper beam of frame 1 and beveled to fit against the stem plate and sheer battens. Use 1½-in. No. 8 screws to secure them.

Fair the deck framing as you did the bottom, and follow the same procedure for applying the planking. The plywood floor panels, notched to fit around the side frames so as to reach all the way out to the inner surface of the side planking, must be supported by two floor battens mounted over the two outer keelsons. These run between the transom and frame 2.

Since the center keelson rises above the level of the main floor between frames 1 and 2, this part of the floor is elevated slightly to form a step, Figs. 2 and 4. To secure the 2 x 4 step beam, drive two 3-in. No. 12 screws through the side planking and into the end grain of this beam. The fore end of the step flooring rests on the 1 x 2 doubler mounted on frame 2.

While it wasn't absolutely necessary, we added 12 cu. ft. of foam-in-place urethane foam flotation under the floor and ahead of frame 1 to provide additional structural strength. This increases the rigidity of the hull and its ability to withstand the tremendous pounding experienced in extremely rough water.

now finish the hull

Once you have put down the cockpit floor, the basic hull is complete and ready for finishing. The box-construction seats and console may be installed and finished later. We used a red-and-white color scheme and covered the foredeck with a white marine vinyl (Nautolev, Du Pont or similar). For safety, we used a nonskid paint on the cockpit floor.

The "trim" aspects of the boat are best left to the taste of each builder. While you may wish to duplicate the original and add mahogany coaming, ⅛-in. mahogany plywood cockpit lining, etc., you can also substitute less expensive coaming and line the cockpit with perforated hardboard, or even skip the cockpit lining. However, if you do line the cockpit, first install the seats and console, then make paper patterns of the lining to fit around these.

The seats and console, Figs. 2 and 3, are simply boxes mounted inside the cockpit. Use corner irons to assemble the 1 x 2 seat framing. The 14½-in. space between console and seat is an average measurement. Test this before securing the console in place, and if more leg room is required, move it forward.

When you have completed the cockpit, install the motor-well drains, hardware, motor and controls and you're ready for a season of water sports like you've never enjoyed before.

See also: aquaplane; hydroplanes; jet runabout; runabout boats.

MATERIALS LIST

LUMBER
Frame 1—1 x 4 x 5'; 1 x 4 x 6'; 1 x 4 x 5'; 1 x 6 x 2'; 2 x 2 x 8'
Frame 2—1 x 4 x 5'; 1 x 8 x 6'
Frame 3—1 x 4 x 5'; 1 x 6 x 6'
Frame 4—1 x 4 x 4'; 1 x 6 x 6'
Transom—1 x 4 x 6'; 2 x 4 x 6'; 1 x 6 x 6' (2); 1 x 4 x 3'
Chines—1 x 4 x 16'
Keelson—1 x 4 x 16'
Outer Keelsons—2 x 4 x 10'
Bottom Battens—1 x 4 x 16'
Sheer Battens—1 x 4 x 16'
Deck Battens—1 x 4 x 12'
Side Battens—1 x 4 x 16'
Side Moldings—1 x 4 x 16'
Stems—2 x 6 x 8'; 2 x 4 x 8'
Keelson Fillers—2 x 4 x 8'
Transom Knees—2 x 10 x 4'
Step Beam—2 x 4 x 6'
Well Sides—1 x 12 x 4'
Well Beam & Gussets—1 x 10 x 8'
Seat Framing—1 x 4 x 8' (4 cut lengthwise to make 8 pcs.)
Floor Battens—1 x 4 x 8' (cut lengthwise to make 2 pcs.)
Coaming—½" x 2¼" x 12' mahogany (2)

PLYWOOD
10 Panels—⅜" x 4' x 8'
1 Panel—⅜" x 32" x 6'
1 Panel—¾" x 4' x 8'

FASTENINGS
3 Lbs.—1¼" No. 13 ga. annular ringed nails, silicon bronze or galvanized steel
1 Gross—1¼" x No. 8 flat-headed screws
2 Gross—1½" x No. 8 flat-headed screws
1 Gross—2" No. 10 flat-headed screws
3 Dozen—3" No. 12 flat-headed screws

MISCELLANEOUS
Paint—White and high-visibility scarlet
    (Baltimore Copper Paint Co. Baltimore, Md.)
Foam, Fiberglas & Resin—Glass Plastics Corp., Linden, N.J.
Deck Vinyl—General Tire & Rubber Co.
    Textileather Div., Toledo 1, O.
Deck Fittings—Nautalloy Products, Inc.
    Auburn, N.Y.
Well Drains (2)—Aqua Mate
    Sterrett Industries
    Montpelier, O.
Seat Cushions—Atlantic-Pacific Mfg. Corp.
    124 Atlantic Ave.
    Brooklyn 1, N.Y.

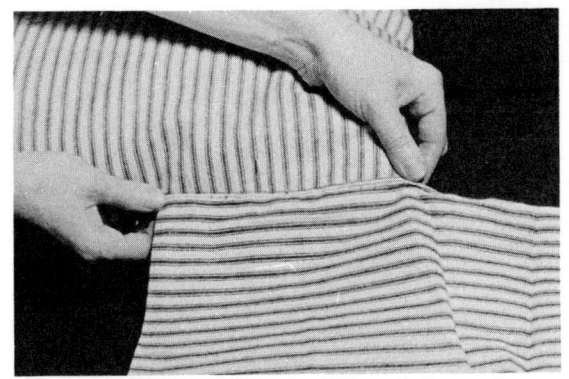

clever ideas

To transfer feathers from one pillow ticking to another, cut a 6-in. slit in the corner of the old ticking. Then baste the openings of the two tickings together and shake the feathers from the old to the new.

Need an extra mirror in the bathroom? Try mounting one on the lower sash of your bathroom window. Such a mirror can be adjusted to the proper height by sliding the sash. Sunlight provides the illumination.

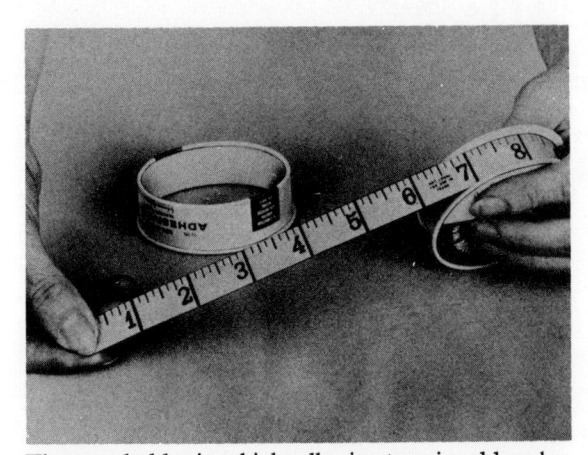

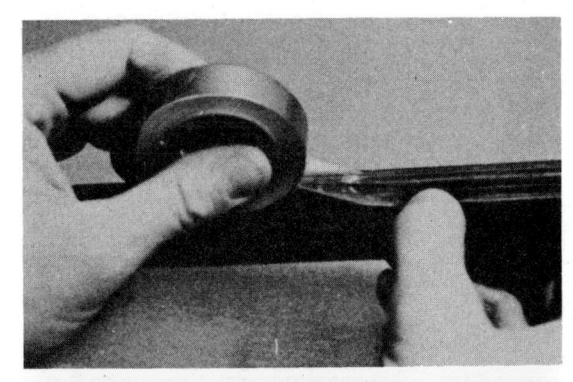

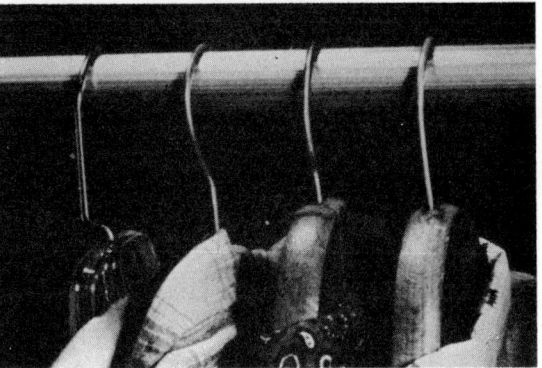

A plastic sleeve for a closet pole allows hangers to slide noiselessly along a metal pole, and protects the finish on a wood pole. Cut it from ribbed polyethylene plastic, allowing a ½-in. overlap, and fasten it to the pole with tape.

The tape holder in which adhesive tape is sold makes a handy spool for a cloth measuring tape. The snap-on metal cover for the spool will prevent the tape from unwinding, keep it clean and make it easier to keep in a tool case or purse.

This quickie toy desk for preschoolers can be made by screwing a heavy cardboard carton to a piece of plywood. For extra strength and durability, add wood supports inside the carton. Be sure to sand the edges to avoid splinters.

2449

spotlight, photo

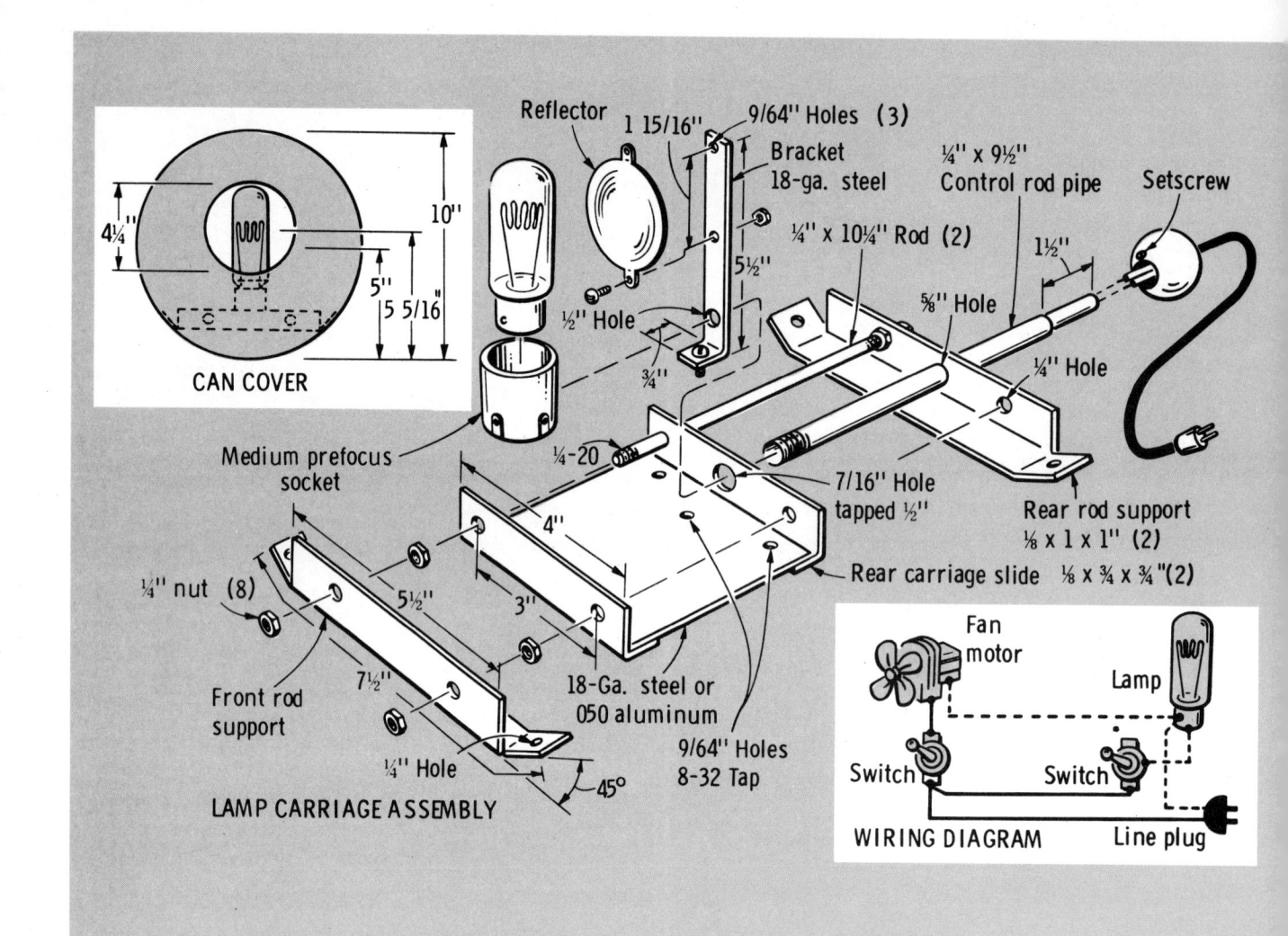

Make glamour pictures with a homemade spot

BY PARRY C. YOB

If your in-the-home portraits suffer from poor lighting, you can solve the problem with this fan-cooled spotlight

---

spot welder: see welders

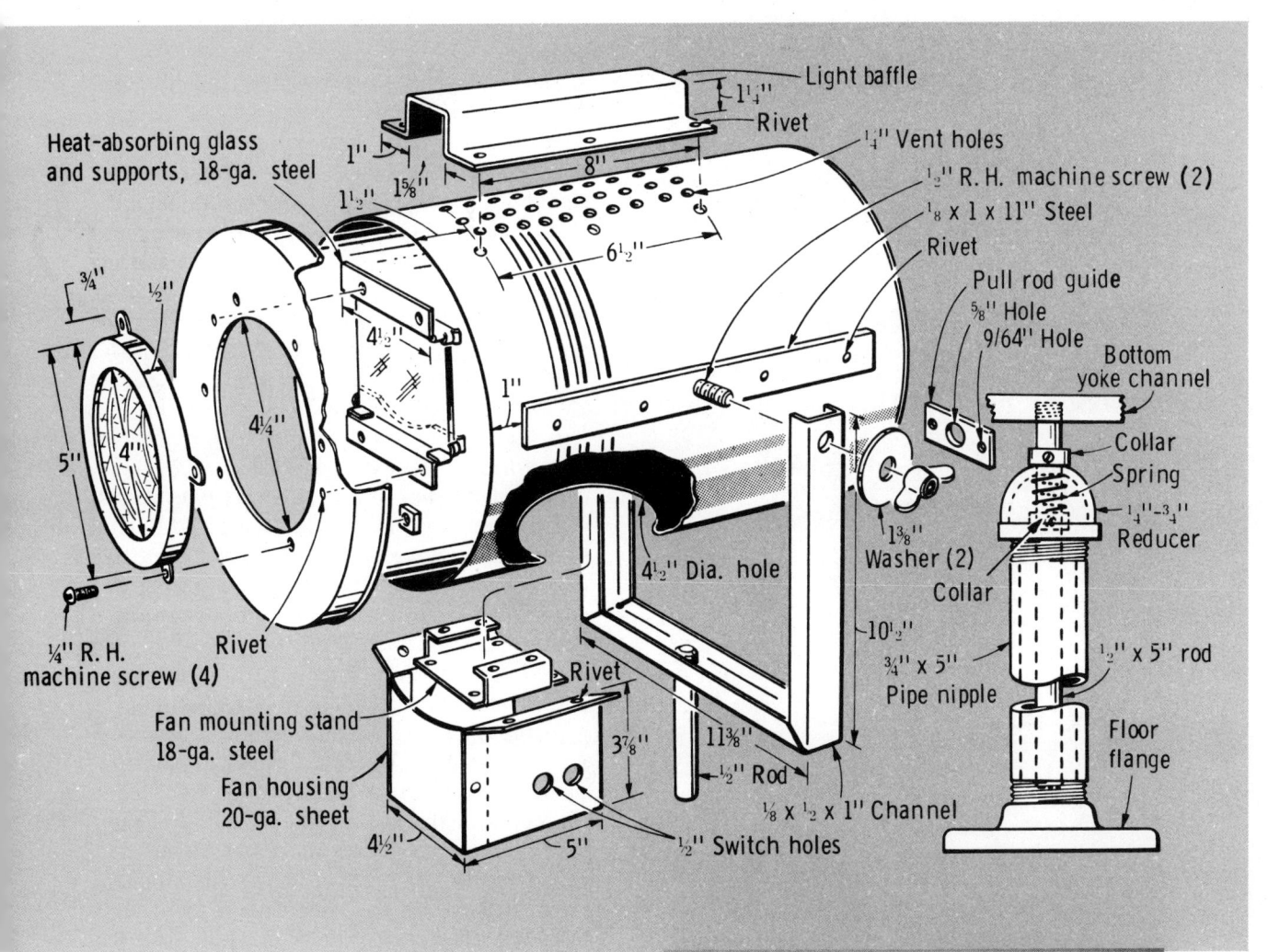

Photo portraits of your family and friends will take on a more flattering, glamorous quality when you pose your model under this professional-looking, fan-cooled focusing spotlight.

Start construction with the lamp carriage. Cut the angle-iron rod supports, clamp them face to face and drill the two outer ¼-in. holes the same distance from the edges. In the center of the rear support only, drill a ⅝-in. hole. This is designed to pass the control rod.

After cutting the carriage-slide angle irons, drill one of the outer ¼-in. holes in the rear slide. Run a ¼-in. bolt through it and the rear rod support, nesting the two, and drill the other outer hole. Then put a 7/16-in. hole through the center and tap it for a standard pipe thread with a ½-in. pipe tap. Repeat this operation for the front carriage slide, omitting the center hole. Align the two slides first.

Drill the mounting holes in the rod-support flanges with a ¼-in. bit and bend the ends up, as

2451

spotlight, photo

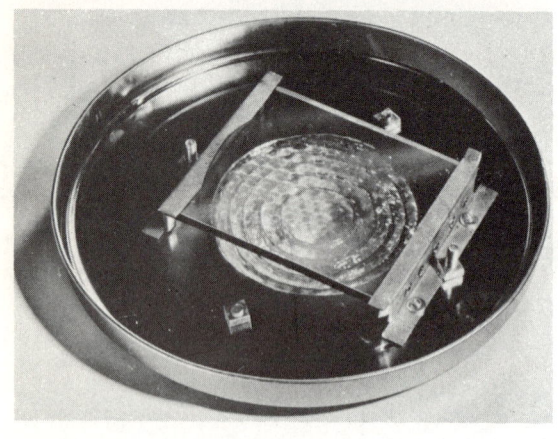

focusing spotlight, continued

The "works" of the spotlight include the carriage assembly, shown at top of page, the can cover with Fresnel lens and heat-absorbing glass in place on the can lid (center). The completed unit is shown above and on page 2451

shown, so as to fit the curvature of the tin-can housing.

Next, cut the carriage plate and cut and thread the two carriage rods for nuts. If you use tank float rod, you can salvage one already ¼-20 threaded end for each rod. Assemble the carriage on the rods, which, in turn, are run through the front and rear supports with nuts turned on at both sides of the holes. Clamp the carriage plate in position and drill through it and the slides in four spots with a 9/64-in. bit. Enlarge the plate holes to 11/64 in. Then tap the carriage-slide holes 8-32. Check the carriage assembly for sliding without binding before tightening the screws.

Dress one end of a ¼-in. pipe to ½ in. o.d., as shown for the control rod. Ream out the inner edges of both ends to prevent damage to the line cord's insulation. Now you can pass the rod through the rear support and screw it into the rear carriage slide. Cut off the projecting end flush. Then remove the reducing bushing from a custom gearshift knob fitted with a setscrew and extend the ½-in. hole all the way through. Mount it after the carriage is mounted in the housing.

Before mounting the medium prefocus socket as shown, insert a T-10P bulb so as to place the filament parallel to the carriage angle iron. Mark for mounting the socket and remove the bulb. Drill 9/64-in. holes for 6-32 screws. Bend and drill the reflector stand as illustrated. Mount a 1⅜-in. reflector on the same side as the stand's base. The reflector face should be 1¼ in. from the center of the bulb. Run an asbestos appliance cord through the control rod and reflector stand and wire it to the socket.

for fitting, remove the rod

For fitting, remove the control rod, but not the cord, and place the assembly in a 30-lb. egg-white can (obtained from a bakery), centered over, and parallel to, the can's seam and 1 in. back from the open end.

Then scribe a 2¼-in.-radius circle centered 4½ in. from the lip of the can and cut on the scribed line. In the opposite side, drill the vent holes. Then drill the lens hole in the can cover.

To admit the control rod, drill a ¾-in. hole in the can's bottom, 1½ in. up from the seam. Make a guide of ⅛ x 1 x 3-in. steel and add a ⅝-in. hole. Drill 9/64 in. mounting holes. Place the assembly in the can once more, while threading the cord through the control rod and the control rod through the guide, the hole in the can and the carriage holes. Before drilling the can for attaching the guide, make sure the guide permits freedom of travel for the control rod. Attach the guide with Pop rivets.

Turning next to the optical system, you'll have to provide a 4 x 5-in. heat-absorbing glass, because the 4½-in. Fresnel lens is not heat-resistant. These items, as well as the socket, reflector, bulb and fan, were obtained from Edmund Scientific Co., Barrington, N.J. The supports for the heat-absorbing glass are bent from 20-ga. galvanized sheet. The hook-shaped ears hold the glass away from the lens, and its bent tabs hold the glass in place.

Before attaching these supports, cut the lens retaining ring with its tabs from the bottom of a 5-in. diameter can. Cut the lens hole indicated in the ring. Drill mounting holes through the tabs and the cover. Place the lower heat-glass support so it will be horizontal when the lid is in place and so it just clears the hole in the lid. Drill through the support and lid and attach it with Pop rivets. Using the heat glass as a guide measure 5 in. and attach the upper support.

Next, place the lens in the retaining ring, centering it with rolled-up pieces of asbestos paper wedged at the edge of the lens at the bolting tabs. Bolt the ring to the lid; insert heat glass, and bend heat-glass-support tabs to retain the glass.

make baffle

To finish up the can, make a baffle to fit over the vent-hole section as shown in the drawing on page 2451. The fan housing is one piece of 20-ga. sheet. Its 1 x 3⅞-in. front tabs are folded inside and riveted. Then drill the ½-in. switch holes. Center the housing over the hole in the bottom of the can, its front 2⅛ in. from the front lip of the can. Drill and rivet the housing to the can with the top 1 x 5-in. tabs bent to follow the curvature of the can.

The fan motor stand will have to be built to suit the motor used. The 3-in. fan blades should be centered in the 4½-in. hole. Check it for clearance by hand turning and then mount in the housing.

Finally, do the yoke and stand. Cut the yoke channel to 32⅜ in. and cut the right-angle V-notches in the sides as indicated to permit folding it at right angles. The two upright arms must be in perfect alignment. Drill ½-in. holes 9½ in. on center from the bottom of the horizontal member. Slip a ½ x 12-in. rod through the holes to check for a free pivoting action. In the center of the horizontal channel, drill a 7/16-in. hole and tap ½-20.

Scribe a line connecting the horizontal diameters of the front and rear of the can along the sides. Prepare the two side plates and mark the can to position them 1 in. back from the lip of the can. Drill into the can where the 7/16-in. center holes are on the side plates. Tap the side plates for ½ x 1½-in. round-head machine screws. Turn the screws in from the inside of the can and rivet the first side plate along the scribed line. Insert the projecting studs through the holes in the upright channels, slide on ½-in. washers with 1⅜-in. diameters and clamp with lock washers and wingnuts. Before fully riveting the second side plate, check for freedom in pivoting. Solder the screwheads to prevent loosening.

toggle switches

Mount two 3-amp, 250-v. toggle switches on the fan housing, and wire according to the circuit diagram.

To mount the spotlight for use, first thread a 5-in. length of ½-in. cold-rolled steel rod ½-20 and attach it to the bottom of the yoke. A photographer's light stand with the sliding rod removed makes an ideal floor stand, but for this you'll need a longer piece of cold-rolled rod.

For your own table stand, first bore out a ¼-¾-in. reducer to ½ in. Shorten the setscrew in a line-shaft collar, mount the collar on a piece of rod and grind it until it will slip into a ¾ x 5-in. pipe nipple. Obtain a 1-in. compression spring made from 18-ga. wire that has an inside diameter of 9/16 in.

Now, assemble these elements. Slip an unaltered shaft collar on the rod attached to the yoke, followed by the reducer and followed by the spring and smaller shaft collar.

Compress the spring to the point where you can tighten the setscrew on the lower shaft collar just outside the reducer. This can best be accomplished by placing the lower collar against a stop and pressing against the yoke. Now clamp the reducer in a vise and pull on the yoke to compress the spring still farther. Slide the upper collar down to the reducer and tighten the setscrew. This setup will make the spotlight stay where you turn it.

Screw the pipe nipple into the reducer and attach a floor flange for bolting down, or attach the nipple to a weighted base.

The spotlight is now ready for family-pleasing photos. Make sure you always turn on the fan first and let the fan run for a few minutes after turning off the light.

See also: floodlamp; light stand; photography; portrait photography; timer, photo.

spray painting

1 The diaphragm sprayer, above, has a direct-connected motor and a separate gun. The sprayer at the right has a turret nozzle, and gives three different spray patterns

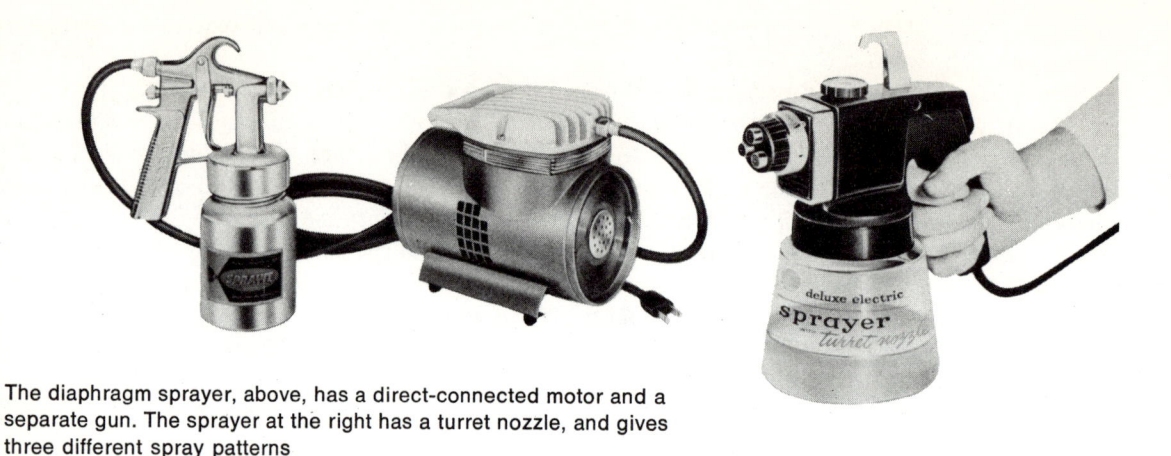

Paint with air

BY E. R. HAAN

You can get a perfect finish every time you paint—no brush marks, no laps, no sags—if you know how to paint with air. You've probably spray-painted already, but here are a few tricks that will give you that professional touch

SPRAY APPLICATION of paints, enamels, lacquers, stains and clear finishing materials gives you the perfect finish on almost any paintable surface and in a fraction of the time necessary to brush-finish the same area. There are no brush marks in spray finishing, no laps, no sags or runs. You simply point the gun or the nozzle of the pressurized spray can, pull the trigger or press the button. It's almost, but not quite, as simple as that. There are a few tricks in handling a spray gun you should know before you begin.

For jobs such as picture frames, small pieces of furniture or touch-up work on your car, the simplest paint-spraying device is the pressurized can. There's no gun to clean, no thinning or straining of finishing materials. But for more

2 This wheelabout sprayer features a belt-driven compressor and a separate gun. The unit is of the diaphragm type and is relatively low in cost

3 This larger wheelabout sprayer has an engine-driven piston-type compressor. It is used where electricity is not available

squeaks, auto: see chassis, auto
squeaks, floor: see floors
stacking bookcases: see book storage

4 This is a compact unit with a direct-connected motor and compressor. The gun, with an attached cup, is the bleeder type

extensive work you'll find a regular spray gun practically indispensable around the house and home workshop. You can use it for interior and exterior painting, lacquering linoleum, applying floor sealer, finishing furniture and other miscellaneous jobs such as mothproofing, and applying weed killers and insecticides, Fig. 5.

Small spray units: There are several types of paint-spray units available at modest cost. Good

6 Did you ever try to brush paint on a picket fence? If so, then you know why a spray unit makes the job easy

5 Nearly all types of sprayers can be used for spraying insecticides effectively. The gun is adjusted to give a fine-mist spray pattern for uniform coverage

7 This gun attaches to your vacuum cleaner and also to the one-quart can the paint comes in. Just hook up the two and you're in business. It is simple to use and simple to adjust

2455

spray painting

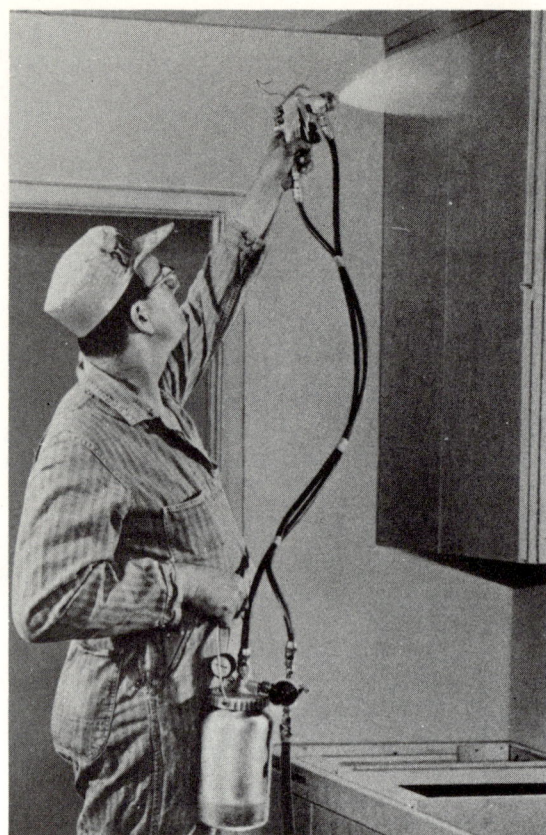

8 This spray unit has a portable paint cup, or container. Unit is operated on an air line from a compressor. Gun and container are small and readily carried from room to room or job to job as needed

paint with air, continued

9 Below is an internal-mix gun of the type used by pros, which is of the type used with a cup, usually of 1-quart capacity. The gun has a range of adjustment for varying patterns

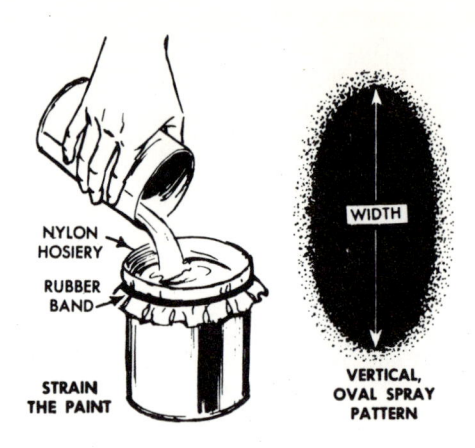

10 Always strain paint before spraying it—especially paint in a can which has been opened and the contents partially used. The pattern shown above is for use on vertical surfaces

results can be obtained with paint-spray attachments for vacuum cleaners. There are handy, lightweight spray units that have built-in vibrator-type motors. One has a triple-nozzle turret, Fig. 1, giving a fan spray for large, flat surfaces, a circular spray for general painting of small articles, and a fog spray for insecticides.

Most spray guns are designed to operate either directly from an air compressor, Figs. 5 and 6, or from a pressure tank. The latter may be connected to a compressor, Fig. 11, or it may be a prefilled, replaceable tank fitted with a reducing valve to dispense air at desired working pressure, Fig. 8.

A compressor generally is operated by an electric motor, Figs. 1, 2 and 4, but units driven by a small air-cooled engine, Fig. 3, also are available. In some sprayers the motor is directly connected to the compressor, Figs. 1 and 4. In other types the compressor is belt-driven as in Figs. 2 and 6. Most homeowners will find it best to purchase a kit consisting of gun, compressor and hose. Compressors may be of the diaphragm type, Fig. 2, or the piston type, Fig. 3. The former is the least expensive and will serve all the needs of the average homeowner. The diaphragm will last many hours and is simple and inexpensive to replace. Piston-type compressors are used for heavy-duty work. Most light-duty guns have an attached paint cup but there is one which is made for quick attachment to any quart can of paint, Fig. 7. This gun can be operated from a vacuum cleaner, or from a special electric air blower which is available.

2456

For heavy-duty jobs painters often use a gun with a remote paint cup, or container. Paint is forced to the gun by air pressure. A gun not weighted by a paint cup is much lighter and easier to manipulate. Large remote paint containers, of 1 to 5-gal. capacity or more, often hold enough paint for an entire job.

Variations in spray guns: Spray guns differ as to the way paint is fed to the nozzle. In a suction-feed (or siphon-feed) gun, air passing over the fluid tip causes a partial vacuum and thus permits atmospheric pressure on the paint to force it up to enter the air stream. This type of gun is identified by the fluid tip extending slightly beyond the air cap, and by an air vent in the cover of the paint cup on the gun. In a pressure-feed gun, Fig. 9, part of the air is diverted to a closed paint container to force the paint to the fluid tip. This type of gun is capable of spraying heavier liquids than is possible with a suction-feed gun. A remote paint container requires the use of a pressure-feed gun.

Spray guns that operate directly from small air

11 Here's a spray rig for the big jobs, such as painting a house or perhaps your car. The remote container holds enough paint for the entire job. Container keeps paint under pressure

12 When preparing to spray paint, measure the distance from the nozzle to the wall by this rule-of-thumb method (shown at right). Nozzle will be at just the right position

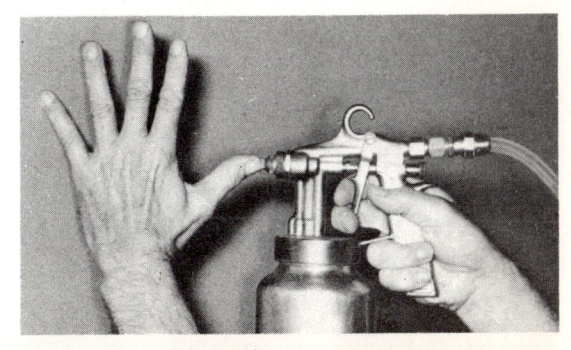

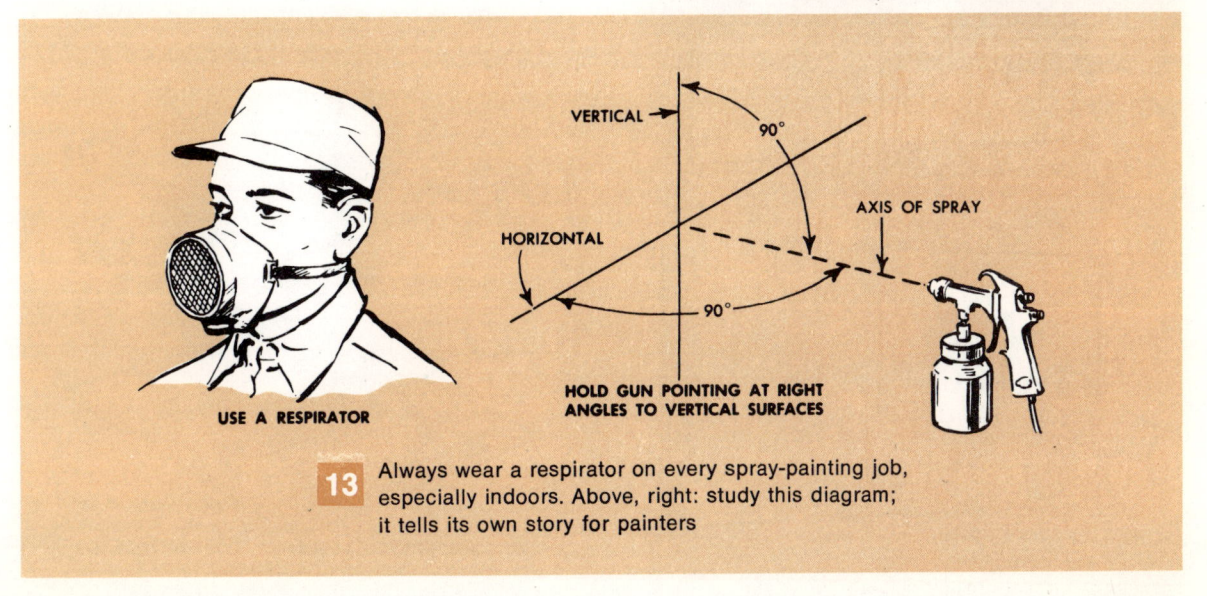

13 Always wear a respirator on every spray-painting job, especially indoors. Above, right: study this diagram; it tells its own story for painters

USE A RESPIRATOR

HOLD GUN POINTING AT RIGHT ANGLES TO VERTICAL SURFACES

2457

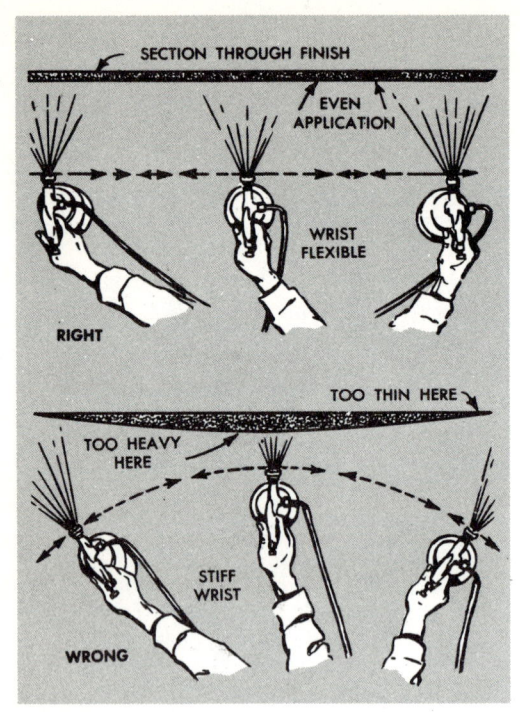

spray painting

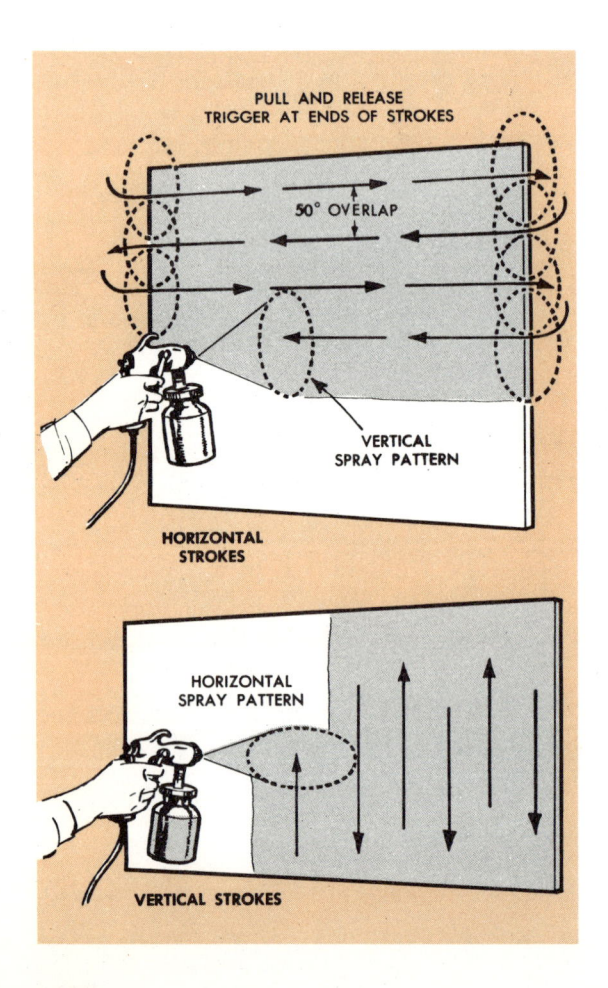

compressors having no pressure-controlling device are of the bleeder type made to pass air at all times and so prevent a pressure buildup in the air lines. Nonbleeder guns are used on controlled pressure lines where the gun trigger controls both air and paint flow. Guns mix air and paint either inside or outside of the nozzle, and are referred to as internal and external-mix types.

Preparations for spraying: Paints formulated for brush application can be sprayed with a pressure-feed gun. Some paints come in both brushing and spraying consistencies. Usually ordinary paints and lacquers must be thinned for use with suction-feed guns.

As a rule, paint should be sprayed at a temperature not less than 70 deg. F. The viscosity of a cold paint often makes it difficult to spray. Always strain paint to be sprayed through a 60-mesh screen or a piece of nylon hose, Fig. 10.

For operator comfort and safety, use a respirator, Fig. 13, to avoid breathing pigment particles. Never spray in a room where there is an open flame as nearly all finishing materials are highly flammable. Always provide ventilation, preferably by means of an exhaust fan in a window to draw paint fumes outside. Objects not to be sprayed should be removed from the room, or covered to prevent overspray from being deposited on them. Where considerable paint-

14 Above, the right and wrong ways to handle a spray gun when painting vertical surfaces. Keep the wrist flexible and maintain the distance between the nozzle and the surface

15 Spray techniques that work are diagrammed at the left and below. Note especially the use of both vertical and horizontal spray patterns

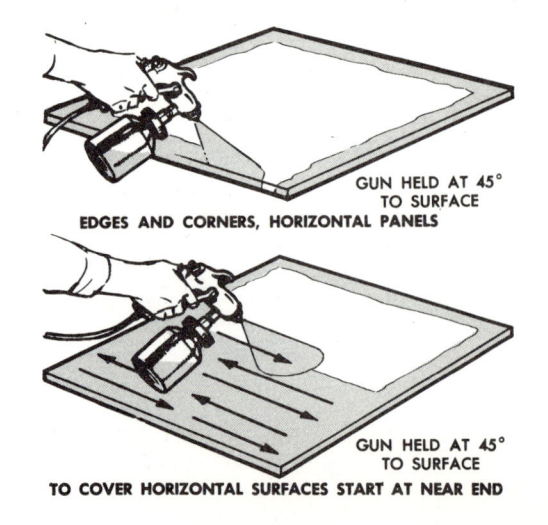

2458

spraying is to be done in a home workshop, provide a ventilated spray booth, Fig. 19.

Spraying techniques: You can acquire needed skills in handling a spray gun by practicing on newspapers taped to the side of a large carton. Experiment with the full range of fluid adjustment, starting from the nearly closed nozzle position that produces a pattern of about 1 in. wide when the trigger is pulled back fully. Many spray guns produce a fan-shaped spray that forms an oval pattern but some produce a round pattern, and others can be adjusted for either pattern. The longer dimension of an oval pattern is referred to as its width, Fig. 10.

As you adjust for a wider pattern and increase the flow of liquid, atomization becomes coarser. A pattern having a width of 6 to 8 in. when the gun is held 6 to 8 in. from the surface is practical for wall painting. For most other work the pattern should be of a lesser width. The air cap on the gun is turned to produce either a vertical or a horizontal pattern, Fig. 15.

Distance of the gun nozzle from the work surface should be between 6 and 8 in., which can be measured quickly by hand, Fig. 12. A lesser distance than this causes a heavier deposit of paint in a smaller area unless the speed of stroking is increased. For vertical surfaces, the gun should be aimed so that the axis of the spray cone is at right angles to the work surface, Fig. 13. This

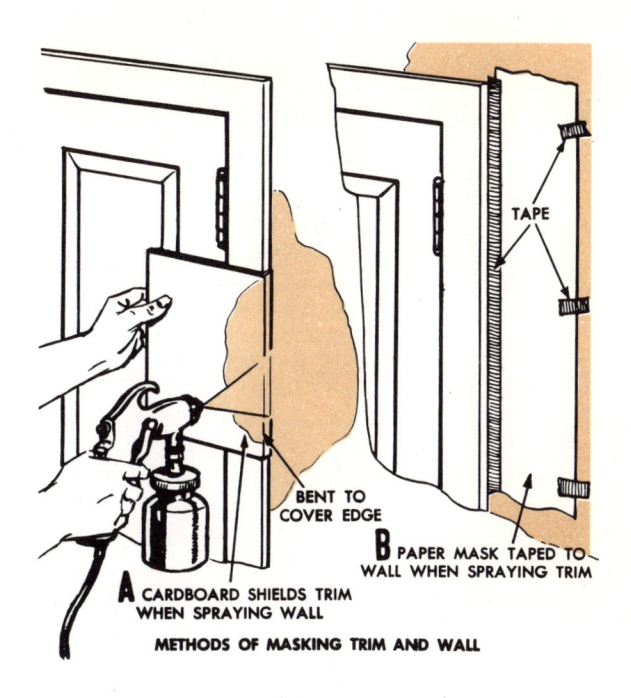

METHODS OF MASKING TRIM AND WALL

A CARDBOARD SHIELDS TRIM WHEN SPRAYING WALL — BENT TO COVER EDGE
B PAPER MASK TAPED TO WALL WHEN SPRAYING TRIM — TAPE

16 How do painters get that neat line where two colors meet? By masking as you see it done above. Use a newspaper or light cardboard as masking material. Masking tape is handy

17 The details below cover important points in the technique of spray painting. Note especially the two methods of handling an inside corner. Method B is less likely to cause over-spraying with running of paint. The angle nozzle makes it possible to spray without tilting the gun

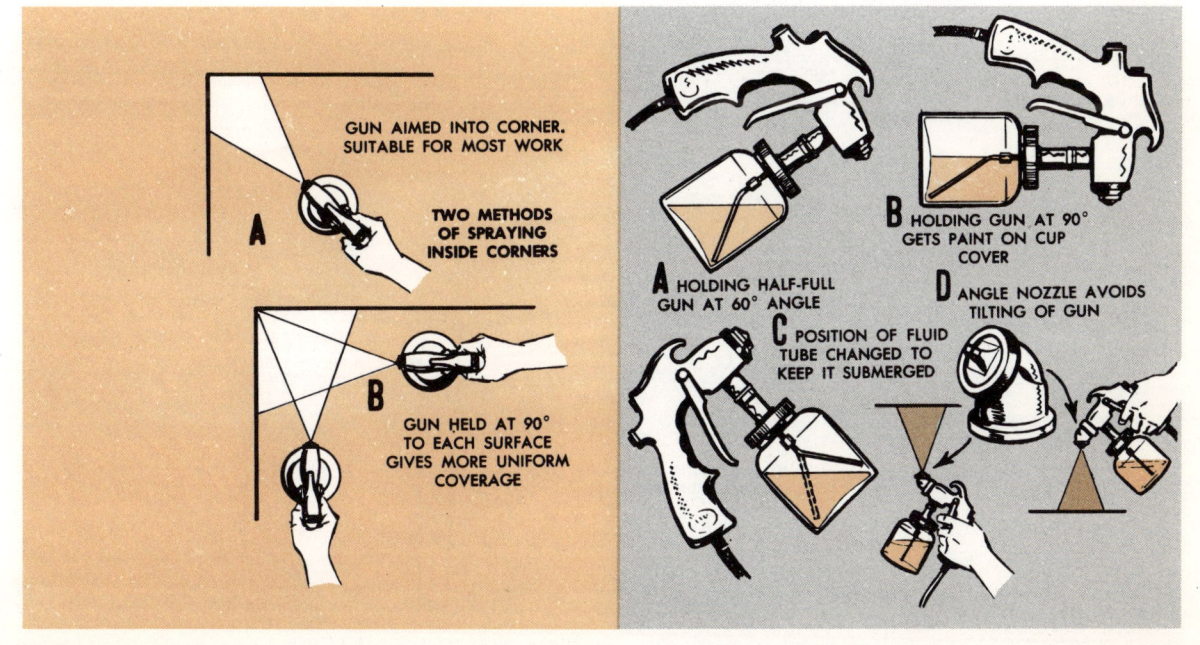

TWO METHODS OF SPRAYING INSIDE CORNERS
A GUN AIMED INTO CORNER. SUITABLE FOR MOST WORK
B GUN HELD AT 90° TO EACH SURFACE GIVES MORE UNIFORM COVERAGE

A HOLDING HALF-FULL GUN AT 60° ANGLE
B HOLDING GUN AT 90° GETS PAINT ON CUP COVER
C POSITION OF FLUID TUBE CHANGED TO KEEP IT SUBMERGED
D ANGLE NOZZLE AVOIDS TILTING OF GUN

spray painting

COMMON DISTORTED SPRAY PATTERNS

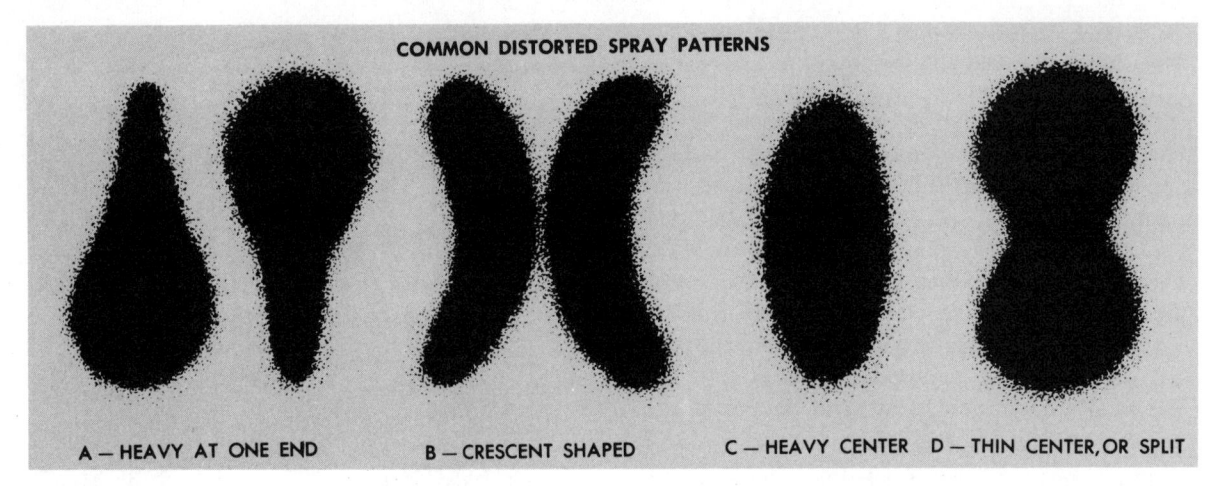

A — HEAVY AT ONE END B — CRESCENT SHAPED C — HEAVY CENTER D — THIN CENTER, OR SPLIT

paint with air, continued

18 Distorted spray patterns like these above usually mean that your gun needs a thorough cleaning—or perhaps new nozzle parts. Check it

produces a coating of uniform thickness. On each stroke the gun is moved parallel to the work, using a free arm movement and flexing the wrist at the ends of the stroke, Fig. 14.

Each stroke should overlap the previous one about 50 percent. A lesser overlap may result in streaks. When coating a panel with horizontal strokes the nozzle is adjusted to produce a vertical spray pattern, Fig. 15. Consecutive strokes are made in opposite directions.

SPRAY BOOTH

19 The spray booth at the left is a help in spray finishing. Below, the number sequence shows you how to proceed in finishing a table

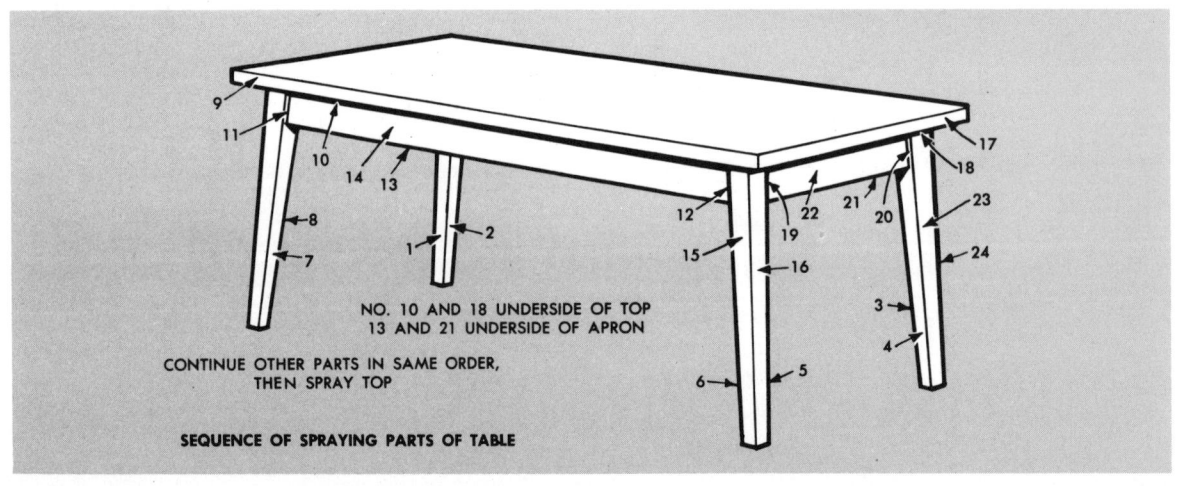

NO. 10 AND 18 UNDERSIDE OF TOP
13 AND 21 UNDERSIDE OF APRON

CONTINUE OTHER PARTS IN SAME ORDER,
THEN SPRAY TOP

SEQUENCE OF SPRAYING PARTS OF TABLE

2460

On long, narrow panels the strokes can be made vertically with the nozzle adjusted to produce a horizontal pattern, Fig. 15. When spraying large surfaces where horizontal strokes must be overlapped, the ends of the strokes are feathered. Similar feathering of adjacent strokes will build up the paint coat to proper thickness at the overlap.

On horizontal surfaces such as table tops the edges and corners are sprayed first, holding the gun at a 45-deg. angle, Fig. 15. Then the center area is sprayed. To finish an inside corner, usually it's best to work one side first then take the adjacent side, Fig. 17, left-hand details A and B. When applying clear coatings or stain in an inside corner each side should be coated separately to obtain an even coating.

Areas not to be painted, such as door and window trim, can be shielded with pieces of cardboard of suitable size, which are moved along with the gun, Fig. 16, A. Wall areas adjacent to trim can be covered by paper masks held with tape as in detail B. Window panes are similarly covered.

When it is necessary to tilt a gun, as for spraying table tops, ceilings, and the underside of shelving, the cup should not be more than half full. It then can be tilted up to 60 deg. without getting paint on the lid. See details A to D, Fig. 17. On most guns the position of the fluid tube can be changed to work special jobs. Where considerable spraying of horizontal surfaces is to be done, an angle nozzle, Fig. 17, detail D, can be used.

Distorted spray patterns: When spray patterns are distorted, Fig. 18, heavy at the top or bottom or crescent shaped, either the air cap or fluid tube is partially clogged, and requires cleaning. A heavy center pattern may be due to too low a setting on a spreader-adjustment valve, too low an atomizing pressure on a twin-jet cap, paint too thick, too much fluid pressure (with pressure-feed guns) or an excess flow of liquid beyond the normal capacity of the air cap.

A split or narrow-center spray pattern is caused by improper balance between air and fluid. This is remedied by reducing the width of the spray pattern or increasing the fluid pressure. A fluttering spray is caused by air getting into the fluid line, which happens when the cup becomes empty or the gun is tilted so the fluid tube is only partly submerged. It also can be caused by a loose fluid tube that allows entrance of air. On a suction-feed gun, jerky spraying can result from using too thick liquid, a clogged vent hole in the lid, a loose coupling nut on the lid, or a loose needle packing at the fluid valve.

Furniture finishing: In furniture finishing, a small spray pattern from 3 to 5-in. wide is best as it permits close control of overspray. For easy handling and accessibility to all parts, the work should be placed on a turntable, and spraying done in a ventilated and illuminated spray booth, Fig. 19.

To minimize spray dust on areas already coated, edges and out-of-way places are done first. Turnings such as table legs should be sprayed with vertical strokes and a horizontal spray pattern slightly wider than the legs. When spray-finishing a small table, Fig. 19, the legs are done first from the inside. For square legs, two sides of each can be sprayed from one position of the gun, the table being rotated for each leg. For round legs, all are first sprayed from the inside, then each is finished separately. Next, the edges of the table top are done, then the underside of the extending top and the apron and the outside of the legs. The table top comes last. On cabinets and casework, the inside is done first, then the outside.

Cleaning spray guns: Always clean your spray gun thoroughly immediately after using it. Fill an extra paint cup about one-quarter full of solvent used for the particular paint sprayed. Usually pint-size fruit jars make ideal extra cups for suction-feed guns, but metal cups should be used on pressure-feed guns. Solvents are as follows: water for water-base paints, turpentine for most paints and varnishes, alcohol for shellac, and lacquer thinner for lacquer.

With the compressor turned off, allow the fluid tube to drip a few seconds before wiping off excess paint from the tube and inside of the cap. Now turn on the compressor and spray solvent through the gun four or five times for two-second durations, against a newspaper or cloth to catch the spray. Then hold a cloth tightly against the nozzle and pull the trigger a few times to agitate the solvent violently inside of the cup and fluid tube. Next, wipe the cap and outside of the gun. Empty the remaining solvent into the paint cup to clean this. Be sure to get paint residue from the threaded portions of both cup and cover if these screw together. Remove the air cap, fluid tip and needle, submerging these in solvent.

Don't use a caustic alkaline cleaner as this can damage aluminum parts.

See also: brushes, paint; epoxy paints; house paints; painting.

Stagecoach fits on a coaster wagon

BY HI SIBLEY

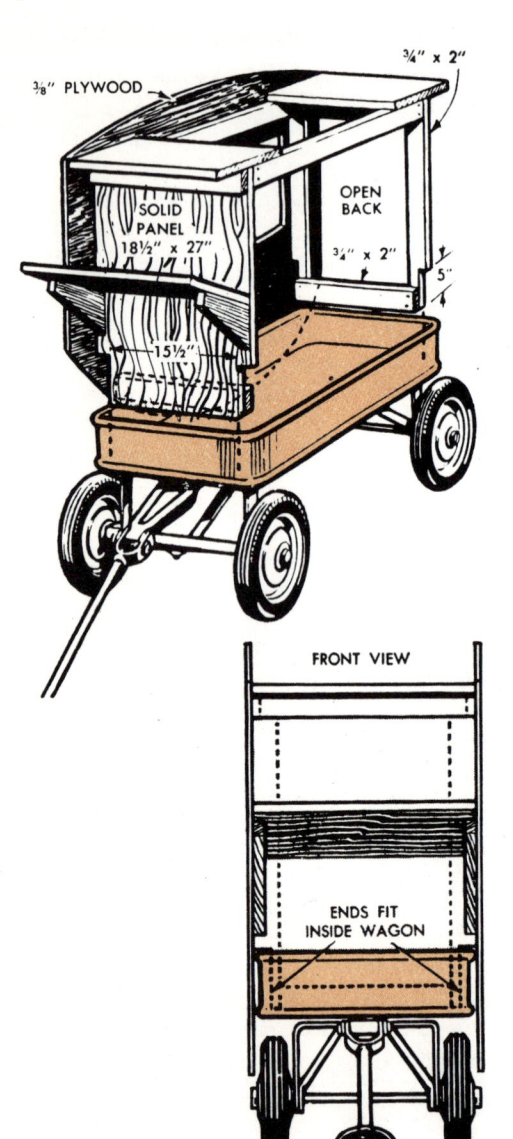

THE BRIGHT-YELLOW STAGE comes careening down the narrow mountain road with a whooping Apache war party in hot pursuit! High on his box, the stage driver yells encouragement to his team, and the guard riding shotgun fires away at the screaming redskins.

The stagecoach body is designed to merely rest in a coaster-wagon without fastening. When the wagon is needed for space-age games, the coach body is simply lifted out and stored in a corner of the garage. You can make both sides from a single panel of 3/8-in. plywood 40 in. x 72 in. Framing is cut from 3/4-in. lumber with a solid bulkhead in front on which the driver's seat and footrest are mounted.

Paint the coach yellow and use masking tape to add the black trim. Decals available at your paint store will make the coach look like the real thing. For use with a "two-horse" team, bind an extension to the wagon tongue and add a crossbar at the end.

See also: cars, sidewalk; ferris wheel; merry-go-round; parade floats; toys; train, children's.

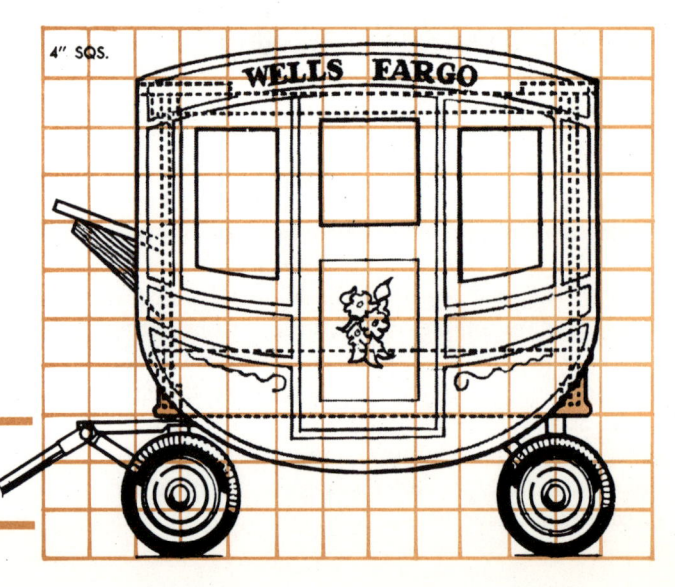

stages, puppet: see puppet theatres
staining, concrete: see concrete

2462

clever ideas

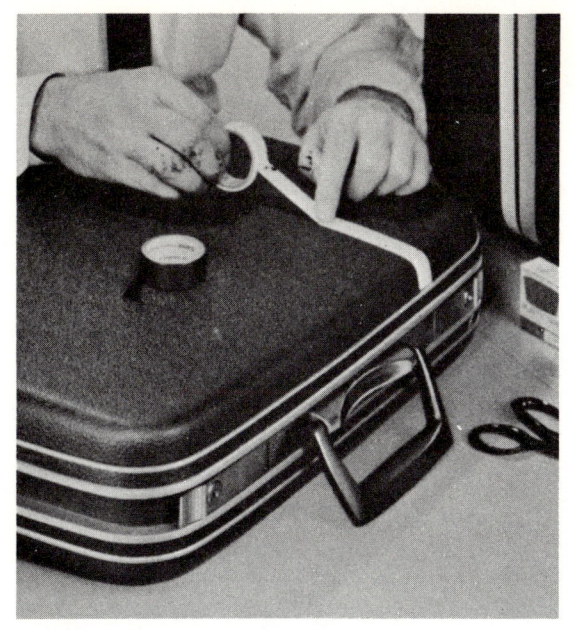

Going on a vacation? You'll find that you can save a lot of time when reclaiming your luggage after a plane or bus trip if it's marked with identifying strips of bright-colored, waterproof plastic tape. Use your imagination in applying the tape. If done carefully it can enhance the appearance of your cases.

No reel for storing your hose for the winter? Try coiling it inside a bushel basket. It's a neat solution to a difficult storage problem, and you can use the space in the center for sprinklers, shears and other small lawn tools.

Tipsy trays on stepladders can be locked securely in position if you drive a small screw hook into one leg of the ladder. Then locate a matching eye on the cross brace which supports the troublesome tray and slip the hook through the eye.

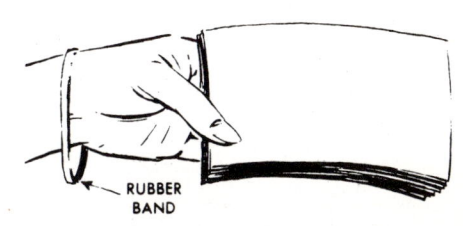

Here's a simple trick that comes in handy when you want to slip a rubber band over a stack of cancelled checks: Push the band up over your wrist, then pick up the checks and pull the band down off your wrist and over the entire stack.

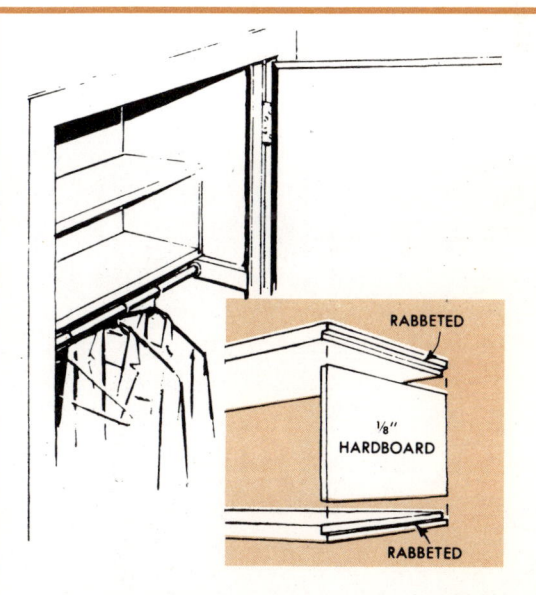

This extra shelf can easily be added to your closet without nailing by rabbeting the ends of the existing shelf and the new shelf to hold ⅛-in. hardboard spacers. Both shelves must bear firmly against the end walls to hold securely.

2463

staining, wood

Here's what you get in an unfinished pine chest of drawers, using the right stain for this popular wood

Wood stains and how to apply them

BY W. CLYDE LAMMEY

Staining not only colors cabinet woods attractively, but it also brings out all the natural beauty of the grain without changing its texture or characteristics

■ BASIC STEPS OF A FINISHING schedule on close-grained woods are sanding, staining and finishing with topcoats. Staining is the one in between, and often it doesn't get the close attention it deserves, especially when the finisher is working with high-grade cabinet woods.

When a transparent finish is to be applied to fine woods, the natural color of the wood can be changed and the delicate graining emphasized by skillful application of the right stain to bring out the best in the wood. Often changing the color simply means a uniforming of the natural colors of the wood by light staining, or a slight darkening or lightening of the whole unit such as a cabinet, table or chair, to obtain effects pleasing to the eye or perhaps to match existing furnishings.

To do a stain job takes something more than a brush or cloth and a can of stain; it calls for imagination, visualization and an appreciation of the individual beauty of the woods you are staining. Don't try to force a wood to be something it isn't; that is, don't attempt to force it out of character by staining. Pine, for example, looks like pine only when it's finished natural or colored with a proper stain made especially for finishing this particular wood. Use the right stain and topcoat, and you end up with the beautiful patina of old pine. But if you stain this wood to be something it isn't, such as mahogany, you generally wind up with an unsightly, smeary something that's neither mahogany nor pine.

There are, of course, some woods that are more amenable to such deceptions. For example, most pieces made from cherry, birch or black willow, either new or old, will take a presentable walnut finish if it's skilfully applied, using the right materials. White ash can be made to look like oak—if not examined too closely—and the lowly poplar can be made up to look like maple,

The trick is to apply the stain, then wipe off the excess until you get just the shade you want

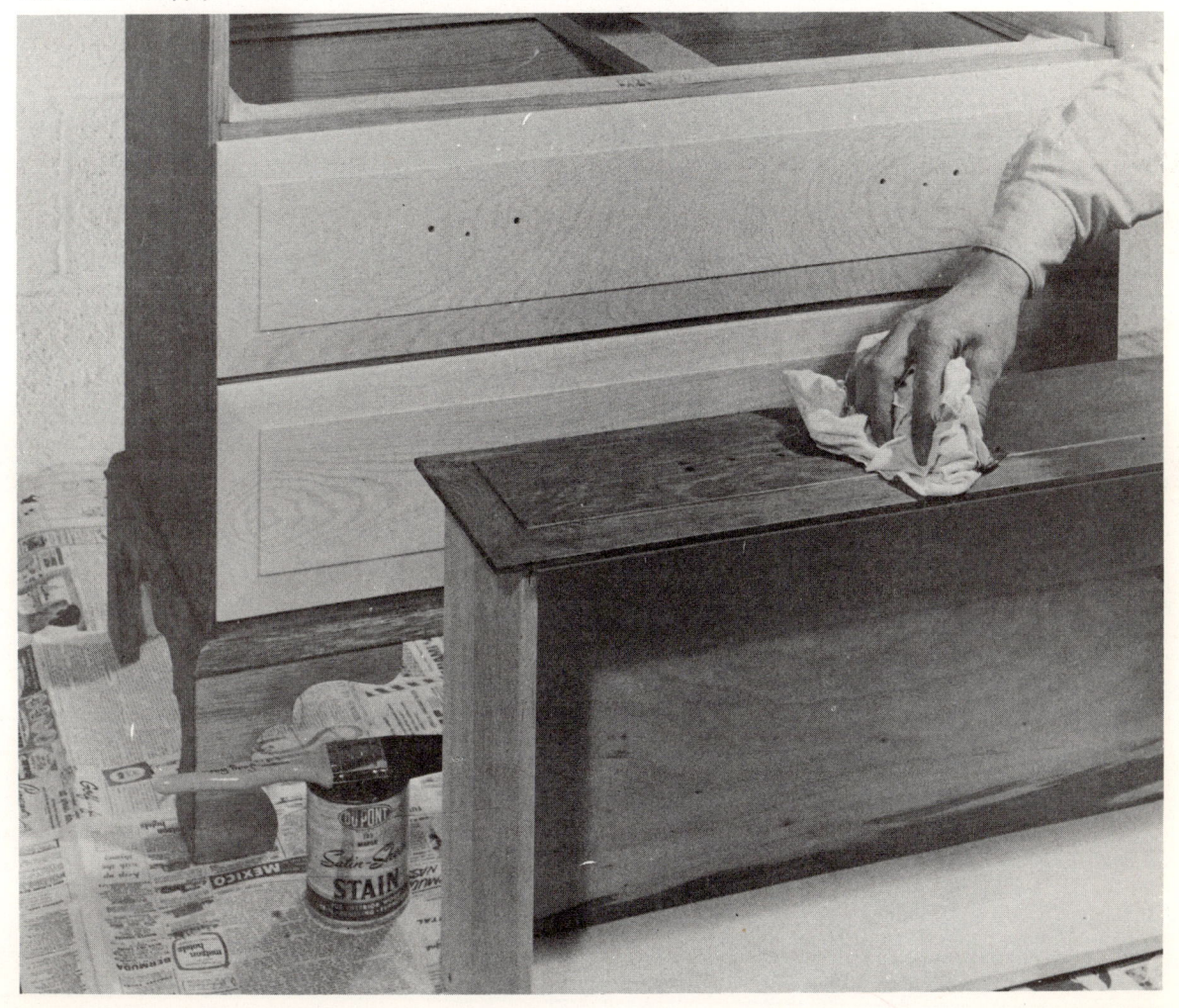

staining, wood

Most stains of the same type can be intermixed. Try mixture on a test panel until the color depth is that desired

staining, continued

Nearly all liquid stains can either be wiped or brushed on. Wiping on is usually best on moldings, gives a more uniform application

except to somebody who really knows his woods. In this sort of hybridization one may fool himself but he won't be likely to deceive the experts.

Real walnut can be colored the soft, reddish tone you often see on old work. But this finish does not conceal its true character and texture; it is instantly recognizable as genuine walnut. Likewise pine can be stained the light, reddish color often seen on old chests and the like; or it can be stained to the darker, brownish tones characteristic of some of the old colonial finishes. But pine it still is, even to the most casual glance.

All the common staining materials—with the possible exception of what are known as varnish stains—penetrate the wood in varying degree. And nearly all stains in liquid form will penetrate more deeply if warmed before application. (*Caution:* Never warm stains of any kind directly over a flame. Heat water in a pan and place the stain container in the warmed water.) When using most commercial stains you will be directed (in the instructions on the container) to apply the

Roller-staining works fine on wood paneling. Roll it on, wait for partial set, wipe off and that's it

stain as it comes from the can, with frequent stirrings. When necessary, thin such stains only as directed.

Prepared stains are of several types. The most common are generally referred to as penetrating stains, oil (pigmented) wiping stains and the non-grain-raising stains (NGR). The colors are usually specified as "walnut," "maple," "brown" or "red mahogany," "light oak," "dark oak" and so on. Nearly all these stains can be intermixed to obtain lighter or darker shades.

If you require very close control of the depth of tone—as is necessary on some types of work —it's usually best to use a wiping stain. This material can be brushed on or applied with a clean cloth. After application, it's allowed to dry until the coating begins to lose its gloss (usually about 10 to 15 min.) and then the excess is wiped off to obtain the depth of color desired.

If it turns up a trifle too light, you let the coating dry overnight, then apply a second coat, allow to flat and wipe off again. In some in-

For light sanding before staining, glue felt to wood blocks and rounds cut from dowels. With these you can smooth flat and curved surfaces

2467

staining, wood

staining, continued

stances you may find it desirable to go through this same procedure a third time to get just the depth of color you want. But *don't* apply this stain and then allow it to dry without wiping off the excess.

On the other hand, if it turns out a little too dark after wiping and drying the first application, you can lighten the tone by rubbing out lightly with fine steel wool, 3-0 or finer. Do this carefully or you may undo all you've done to this stage, and may have to repeat the process.

But before you do all this staining, there's a precautionary step or two to take. Suppose, for example, you are about to stain new wood such as that in a project you've made yourself from scratch, or one of those better quality ready-made pieces that comes to you in the "white," that is, unfinished. Before you touch any stain to the wood go over every surface to be colored inch by inch, running the tip of your finger lightly over every part, across the grain. In this way you'll discover rough places or "hills" and "hollows" that may escape your eye even in the best light.

These surface defects must be dealt with before staining; otherwise you're in trouble. There may be a small area, or areas, where the grain ends up at an angle to the surface to be finished. Then you're likely to find tiny, hairlike projections of wood fibers —"whiskers," the refinishers call them. Such an area usually will soak up stain like a sponge and leave you with a darker blob that's near impossible to equalize with the adjacent surfaces. These upended fibers may slip past your eye but not the tip of your finger.

ridges and depressions

Also, there may be low ridges and depressions to search out and eliminate. Such surface defects will show up disappointingly under almost any finish—opaque (paint or enamel), glossy, rubbed-effect, semigloss, or even a self-leveling finish that dries flat. Of course, the ready-mades (unfinished pieces) are presumed to be thoroughly sanded, with flat surfaces and no fibers sticking up to fool you. But don't take the chance; finger-check the surfaces before staining. Likewise make one last finger-check on any made-it-yourself project. It may save you a lot of trouble later on.

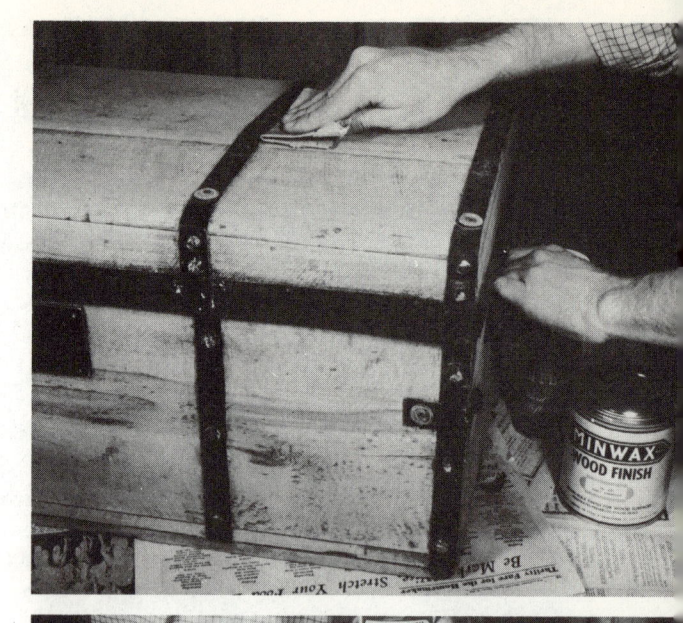

Suppose you're going to refinish an heirloom or an antique for which you've shucked out a month's salary. After you've removed the dirt and paint accumulations of the years, you may find it's made of a half dozen different kinds of wood, several of which you can't identify with any certainty. Some are light in color, some dark, and some in between. What to do about it? Obviously it must be stained. But what stain?

Or maybe the piece hasn't ever been painted, but has its original clear or stain finish. *Careful* is the word here! Perhaps you should forget about refinishing for the moment and see what can be done with the old finish. If the latter appears to be in reasonably good condition—no bad checks or areas worn down to bare wood—wash it lightly with soft, soapy water, wringing out the washcloth until it's little more than damp. Start in an inconspicuous place; if the finish lightens appreciably when dampened, *stop right there*. The finish is probably shellac or French polish; it may lighten and turn spotty if you wet the surface.

Otherwise continue with the wash, wiping the dampened surfaces with a dry cloth as you go; allow to dry a few hours and take a close look. If you like what you see, then let well enough alone. Waxing should bring back that old finish, almost like new. Use a wax especially prepared for use on old finishes.

But suppose you *do* take off the dirt and old paint down to the bare wood and are confronted with the problem of refinishing a piece made from several differing varieties of woods. Usually it's best to pick out the darkest piece of the several woods and take it from there. Should there be only one dark piece, you might try bleaching it out to match the lighter parts. But this is not always safe; you may end up with a surface that looks more like a chessboard than a side, top or front of an orthodox chest or table. It's nearly always safer to try matching the lighter woods to that darker piece or pieces. In this case you have to judge which stain to use

Below on this page is an attractive chest before finishing and after sanding. On the opposite page, top, the chest is being carefully sanded in preparation for refinishing. Center photo shows the "ragging on" of a combined stain and finishing material consisting of penetrating oils. In the lower photo, opposite page, the chest is nearly finished. Notice how the wood grain is brought out

2469

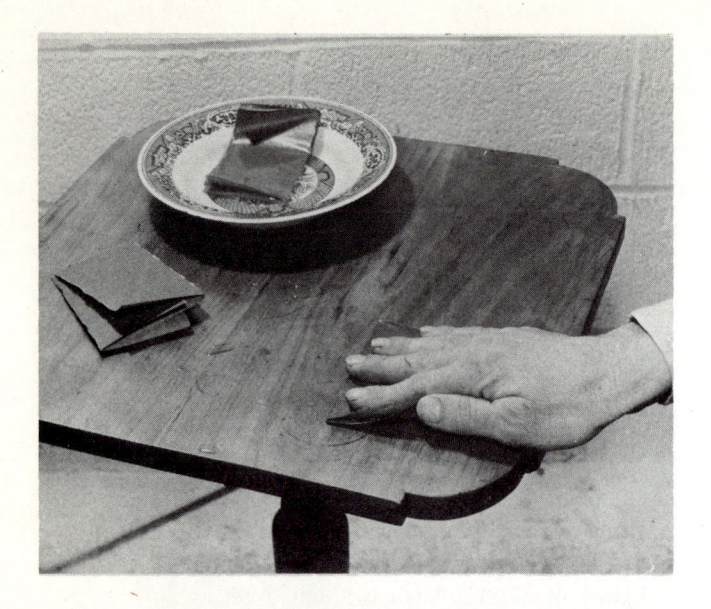

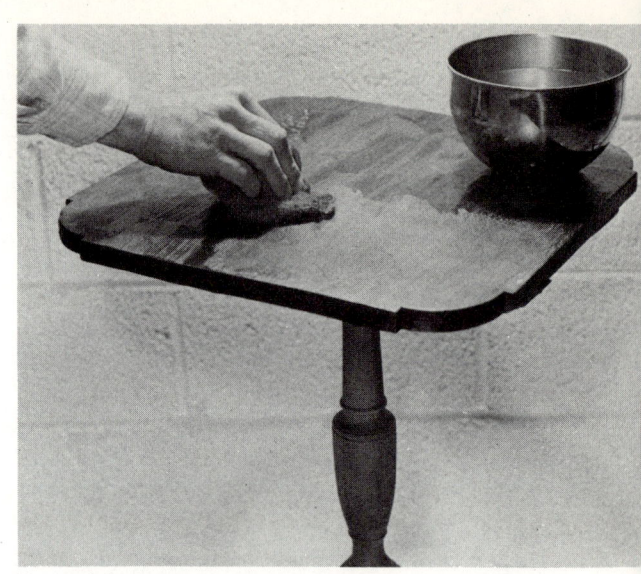

staining, wood

Above, left, you can see many defects but maybe there are some you can't see. A fingertip test will catch these. Above, steel wool and a solvent usually get small blemishes. Left, keep the brush well filled and stroke it lightly over the surface

staining, continued

solely by the color of the piece, or pieces, you are going to try to match. It isn't always easy to decide, but usually you can come pretty close by using one of the reddish or brownish stains, such as red or brown mahogany or walnut.

A pigmented wiping stain generally is best. You have better control and you can always remove the stain with a solvent if it doesn't turn out to suit. Run a line of the stain along the dark piece, wipe off the excess, and let the piece dry so you can see the effect. If you like what you see then continue the procedure on all the surfaces.

If, for example, two adjacent pieces are of a varying shade, apply stain to both, then wipe the darker one first, allowing the stain to remain on the lighter one a few minutes longer. By proceeding in this fashion you can usually come up with an attractive stain job on almost any old piece made of conglomerate woods.

Actual application of a stain is quite simple, but there are a few precautions, whether you wipe it on with a cloth, brush it on or spray it on. In factories and refinishing shops, professionals usually spray-apply stains but unless you rent or borrow a sprayer you're left with the cloth or brush. Either works with the wiping stains, but as a rule any of the others such as the NGR stains are usually best applied with a brush. In any case you have to work fast and watch closely in order to obtain a uniform application. When applying stain to a large, flat surface such as a chest top or tabletop, allow the brush or cloth strokes to overlap slightly and keep going until the surface is covered. Then, after allowing that few minutes drying time, begin wiping where you started staining.

Use a light, quick sweep of the brush or cloth on end grain and wipe immediately. Some finishers apply a very thin wash coat of shellac or sealer to end grain to slow down absorption of the stain. On open-grain woods such as oak and mahogany, refinishers and finishers often combine stain with filler, intermixing the two until they get just the right consistency and tone. This usually works out well on old work where the remover may have taken off much of the original filler.

When staining work where you have to be especially particular about final results, have the piece in good light—outdoors when possible—so that you can see what's what. Stains don't always show their true colors under artificial lighting, especially under incandescent lights.

If you do rent a sprayer for application of the stain, run test panels until you have the nozzle set to give you a relatively fine mist. Whenever possible, do this on the same wood as that to be spray-stained. Be sure beforehand that the container and nozzle of the gun are clean, with no residues of paint remaining in either. Just to be sure, wash out the container with a solvent such as lacquer thinner; take the nozzle apart and clean it. Then reassemble the gun, fill the container about half full of the same solvent, and blow it all out through the nozzle.

When staining by spraying it's the usual practice to hit corners and edges first. Follow immediately by staining the flat surfaces with uniform back-and-forth strokes of the gun, holding it the same distance from the surface and keeping the wrist rigid so that the nozzle is held at the same angle throughout the length of the stroke. Release the trigger at the end of each stroke to avoid a double application at the finish ends. Remove any dribbles or sags by dabbing with the wiping cloth; don't let these dry even partially.

Stain applied with a spray gun usually sets up a bit faster than that applied with a brush or cloth, so keep a close watch and wipe off early enough to remove any excess.

Some finishers like the stains that come in a tube, like toothpaste. Just how you proceed in applying these stains depends on the instructions on the container. Read these carefully and follow through in all details.

Non-grain-raising (NGR) stains are just what the name implies; they are light liquid stains that do not raise the grain of the wood as do the older water-soluble stains, which are no longer commonly used. Colors are brilliant, true and fade-resistant. They are suitable for spray or brush application.

The varnish stains are compounds of stain and varnish and serve the dual purpose of staining and finishing in one application. Other widely used finishing materials combine a stain with penetrating oils which provide a stain and finish in one or more applications. The latter finishes are generally topped with a final coat of special wax.

See also: finishes, wood; paneling, hardboard; paneling, plywood; paneling, wood.

WHICH KIND OF FINISH IS BEST FOR WHICH KIND OF WOOD?

	Natural	Stained	Blonded	Colortoned	Antiqued	Enameled
Mahogany	AA	A	B			
Walnut	AA	A	A			
Cherry	AA	A				
Maple	B	AA	AA	A		
Birch	B	AA	AA	A	A	
Oak	B	B	AA	AA	B	
Sycamore	C	B	B	A	A	AA
Elm	C	A	A	A	B	A
Ash	C	A	A	A	B	A
Pine	C	AA	A	AA	A	A
Teak	AA					
Gumwood	C	B	C	B	A	AA
Tropical Hardwood	B	B	AA	AA		

AA—Ideal; A—Excellent; B—Good; C—Acceptable.   Blank space indicates undesirable finish for the species of wood

stairs

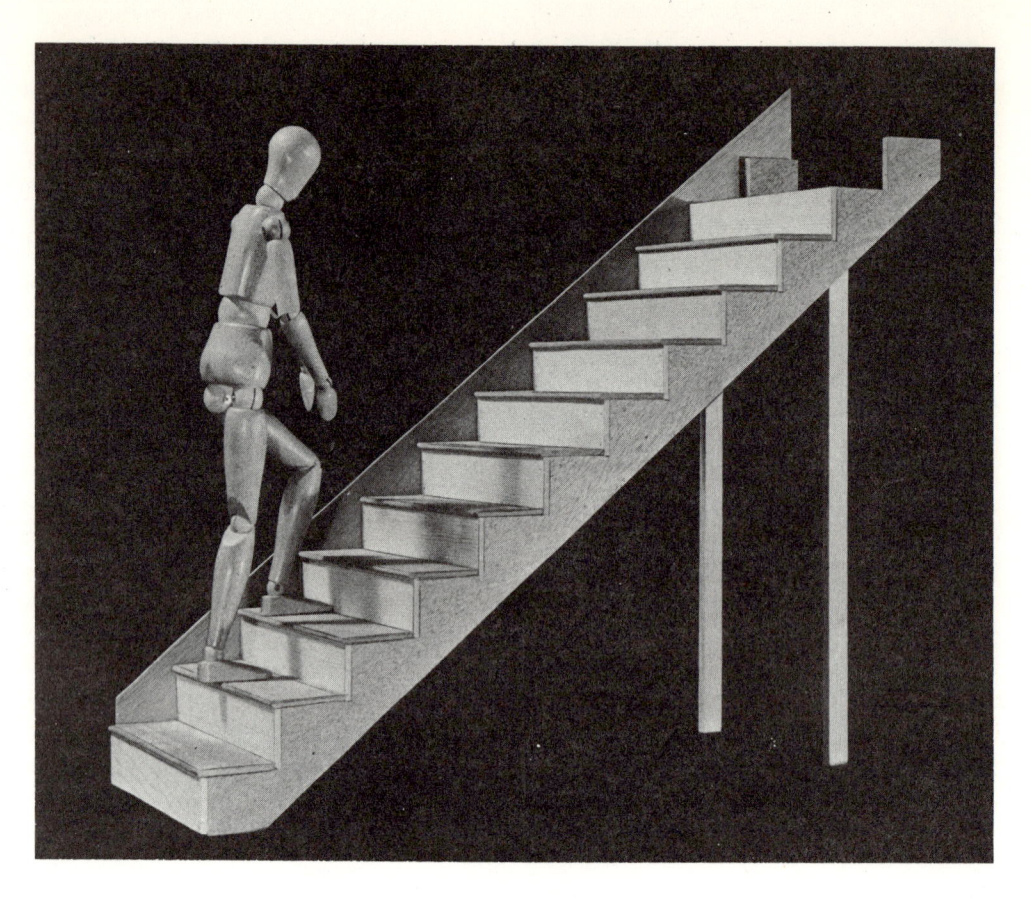

Secrets of building stairs

BY R. J. DeCRISTOFORO

■ THE SECRET IS IN PLANNING the job. Whether you're building a second-floor sun deck, remodeling an old two-story house, or are about to build a new one, there are facts and formulas you must know before you can provide a stairway properly scaled for safe, comfortable usage.

A ramp or incline is, in many cases, the safest and easiest way to walk from one level to another. But since the maximum pitch for comfortable climbing is about 15 deg., ramps take so long to *get* there that they're impractical for cramped indoor space. So we use stairs that let us raise the pitch to 30 or 35 deg.

That 30 to 35 deg. angle-from-horizontal is ideal, though stair pitch *can* be as little as 20 deg. or as great as 50 deg. An example of the former

On the wall side of the stairs nail a 1 x 2 into the studs, then nail the step-cut stringer to this and to the studs also (where the riser and treads are removed as is shown). Do this on both sides if you are building a between-the-walls stairway

stairway lift: see elevator
stairways, enclosing: see building

2472

might be the vast staircase to a grandiose public building where the flats (called treads) are almost too wide to negotiate with a normal stride. You've probably encountered the 50 deg. pitch—or steeper in the attic stairs of old houses, where the vertical spaces between treads (called risers) are so great you tend to trip on the way up or pitch forward on the way down.

A good relationship between tread and riser is based on the length of an average person's climbing stride, and this runs somewhere over 16½ in. and under 18 in. Thus, the sum of one tread plus one riser should fall within this range. Proper riser height is around 7 in., so the tread should be 10 to 11 in. wide—not including the nosing (that part of the tread that projects beyond the riser and should never exceed 1¾ in.).

In cases where you have no control over the pitch, and your stairway must be steeper than you'd like, you must increase the height of the riser and narrow down the tread. At 50 deg., for example, risers 9½ in. high and treads 8 in. wide still fall within the recommended "stride range." Carried beyond a certain point, though, a ladder would be more practical than a stairway.

Okay, let's consider an actual installation. You know you've got to get from the lower floor to the one above; how can you do it best within the space you can spare for a stairway? Though the solution hinges on the application of a simple formula, a surprising number of professional builders duck the problem by calling in a "stair expert"—a fellow who probably knows no more than *you* will by the time you finish this article.

First: measure the vertical distance between the lower finished floor and the upper one. This is the *total rise*. Divide this by 7 (which represents the ideal *unit* rise) and you've got the number of risers you'll need. Ignoring any fraction, divide the total rise by this number to get the *actual* (as distinguished from the ideal) unit rise. Example: Total rise—8 ft.; 7 into 96 in. = 13.71; 13 into 96 = 7.384, the actual height of each of the 13 risers.

Now, to find a standard tread width, subtract the unit rise from 17½ in. This is the *unit run*. To find the *total* run (the actual length of floor space the stairway will require) multiply the tread width by the total number of risers, minus one—in the preceding example, 12.

Should you end up with an impractical total run for the space you've got, some compromise is in order. Better make a scale drawing based on the total rise and total run you have to work

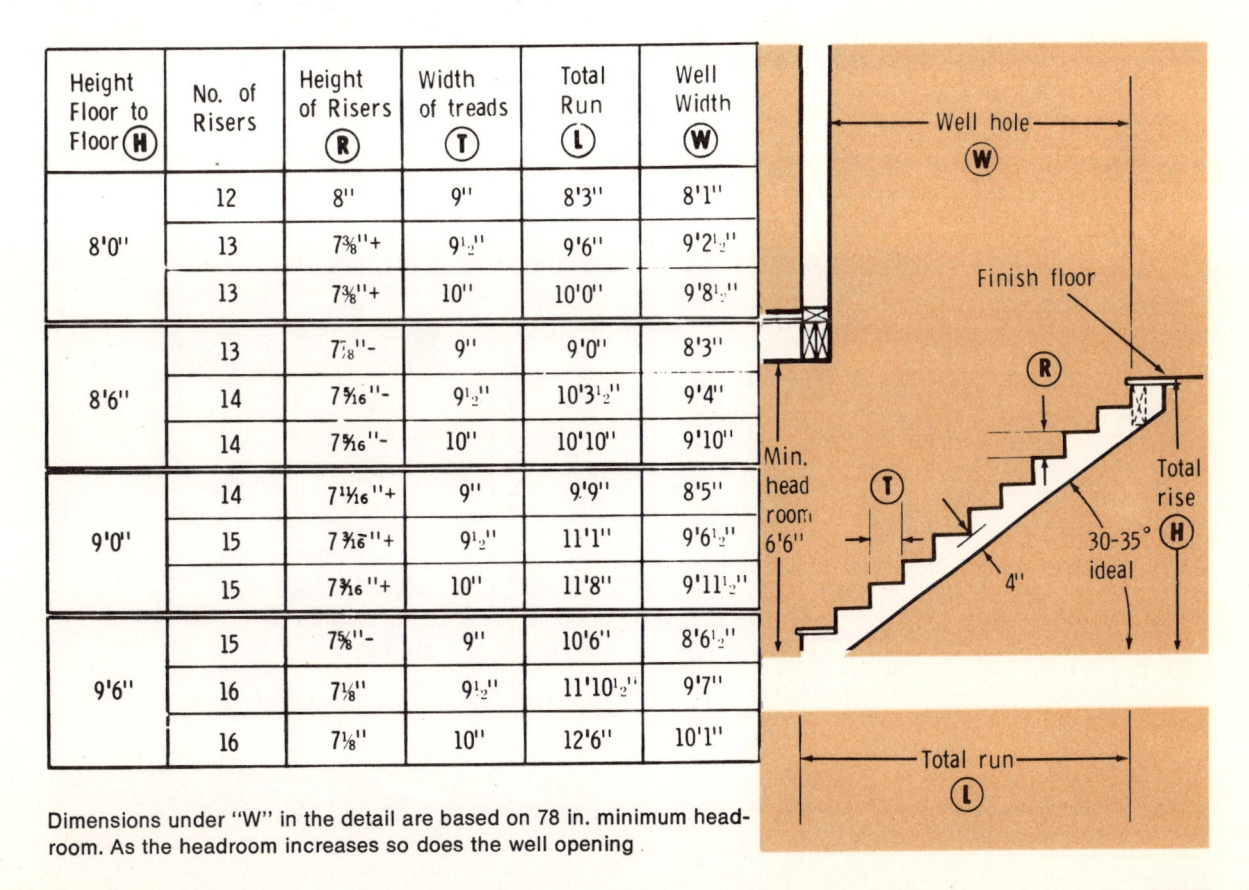

Height Floor to Floor (H)	No. of Risers	Height of Risers (R)	Width of treads (T)	Total Run (L)	Well Width (W)
8'0"	12	8"	9"	8'3"	8'1"
	13	7⅜"+	9½"	9'6"	9'2½"
	13	7⅜"+	10"	10'0"	9'8½"
8'6"	13	7⅞"-	9"	9'0"	8'3"
	14	7 5/16"-	9½"	10'3½"	9'4"
	14	7 5/16"-	10"	10'10"	9'10"
9'0"	14	7 11/16"+	9"	9'9"	8'5"
	15	7 3/16"+	9½"	11'1"	9'6½"
	15	7 3/16"+	10"	11'8"	9'11½"
9'6"	15	7⅝"-	9"	10'6"	8'6½"
	16	7⅛"	9½"	11'10½"	9'7"
	16	7⅛"	10"	12'6"	10'1"

Dimensions under "W" in the detail are based on 78 in. minimum headroom. As the headroom increases so does the well opening.

stairs

HOW TO LAY OUT STRINGERS FOR CUTTING

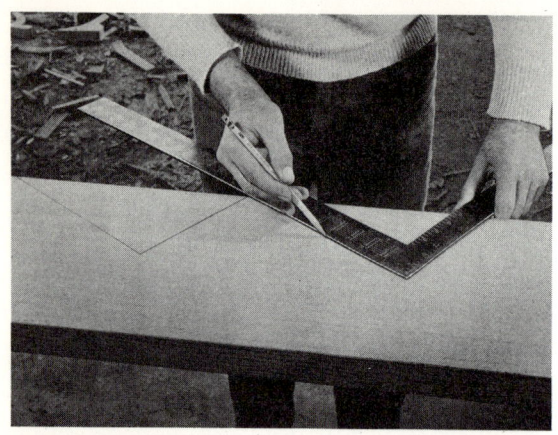

Use of a framing square assures the correct angle between the risers and treads. Use the tongue of the square for the unit rise, the blade for unit runs

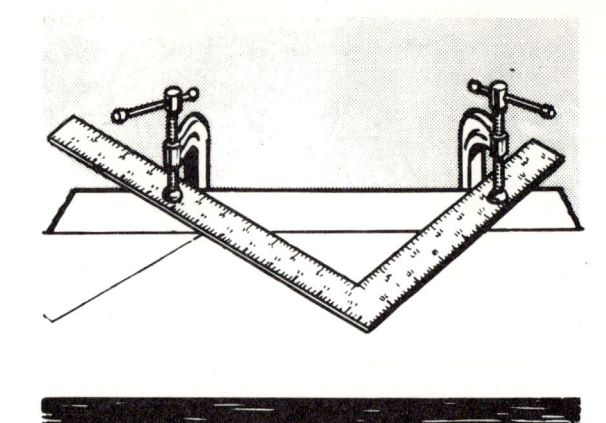

For uniformity and speed clamp the square to scrap stock having one straight edge. Then slide along the edge of the stringer to each trace-around position

Or you can make a layout jig having a right-angle triangle with sides equal to the tread width and riser height. Screw this to a stop strip as pictured. Place the stop against the edge of the stringer, mark and slide to the next position

A carriage-type stringer is built up of triangular blocks cut from 2 x 8 stock and nailed to a 2 x 4 stretcher. Cutting of the blocks can be done accurately on your bench saw. As pictured here one block has been lifted to show the procedure

UNDERCUT STRINGERS FOR OPEN-RISER STAIRS

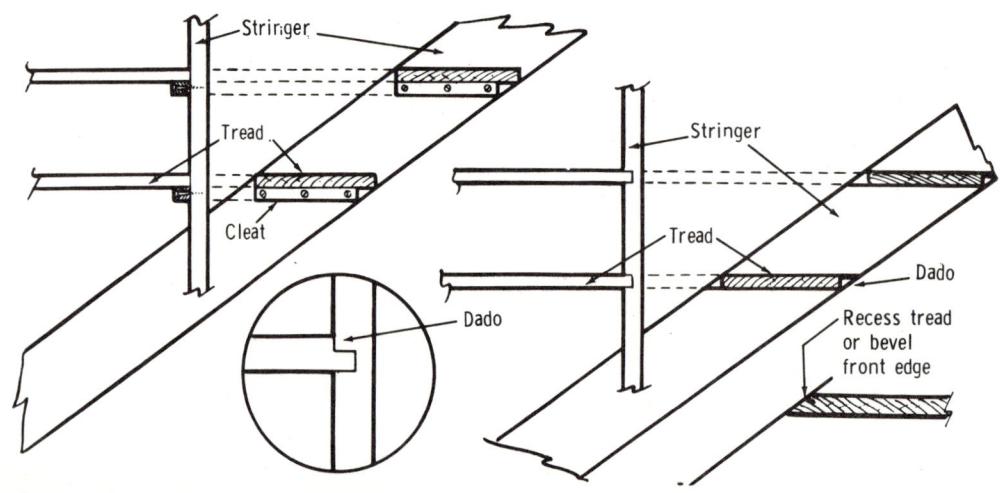

Utility stairs are often built without notching the stringers. Here you can either support the treads on cleats or house them in dadoes as detailed. Such stairways are often built to attics, basements or sundecks

with—or a scale model, like the one pictured.

Since you don't want to have to stoop as you climb your stairs, *headroom* is your next consideration. Measure along a plumb line dropped from the lowest ceiling point to the tread beneath. This distance should never be less than 6½ ft.—7 ft. is ideal wherever possible.

The *width* of the stairway depends on its intended use. For a single person at a time, it needn't be over 24 in.; for two people—walking together or passing in opposite directions—you'll need a width of 36 to 42 in. The minimum width isn't recommended for an inside stairway.

stringers support the treads

The boards that are set at a ramp-like angle between upper and lower floors to *support* the treads are called stringers. Stringers are to treads what joists are to floorboards. Most often, they're notched into a sawtooth pattern to form bearing surfaces parallel to the floor. This pattern is laid out by means of an ordinary steel square, or one of the right-angle jigs illustrated. The distance between the point of the "teeth" on the layout is called the "bridge" measure. To determine how long a stringer you'll need, multiply this figure by the number of risers.

Stringers are usually cut from 2 x 12 stock, using a handsaw—or a portable circular saw moved as far into each cut as possible, then followed with a handsaw. It's a good idea to clamp or nail the two stringer boards together and cut both at once, so they'll be identical. Other types of stringers are the uncut utility ones, or the top-quality housed type as detailed. The latter provides the squeak-free sturdiness and "finish" required for costly homes. Here the tapered grooves for the wedge-held treads and risers come factory cut in ready-made stair kits.

When the steps run up between two walls, they're called close-string stairs. If there's a wall on one side only, they're open-string stairs, and should have a handrail or balustrade along the open side. In some open-string applications in modern settings, such a hand rail would interrupt the "spatial flow," so the stairs are made extra wide and a rail is attached at the *wall* side, instead. Whether it's a wall-mounted rail or a row of balusters topped by a rail, the proper height remains as shown in the detail.

So far, we've spoken in terms of the simple straight-run stair. In some cases you won't have enough wall or floor space to accommodate the full march of treads you'll need for a given rise. At such times, you must bend the stair, either

ANCHORING STRINGER TOP

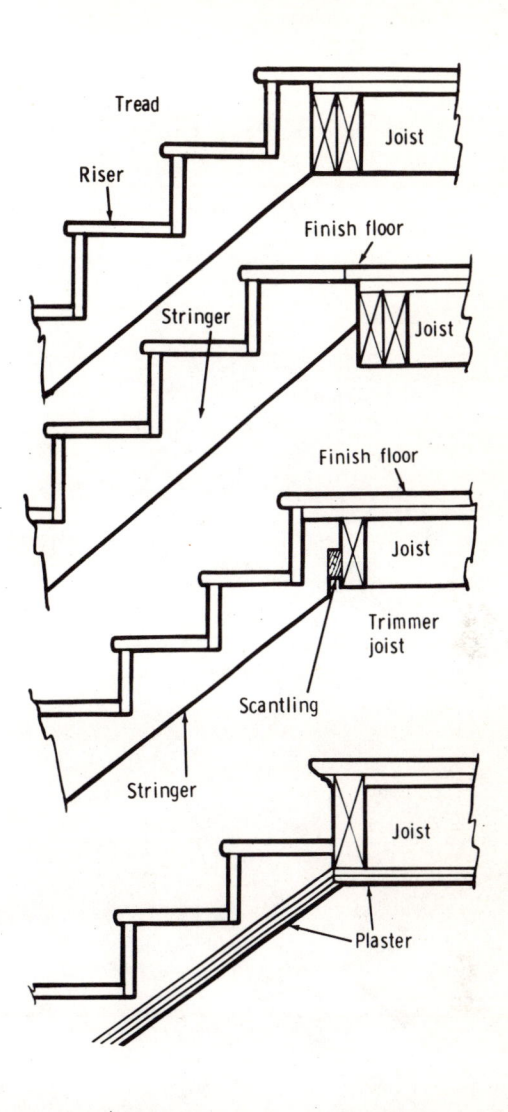

NOSING DESIGNS

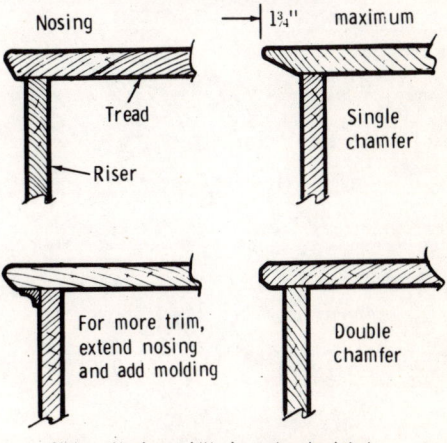

Note: Nosing width is not calculated in tread width when planning stairs

2475

stairs

stair-building secrets, continued

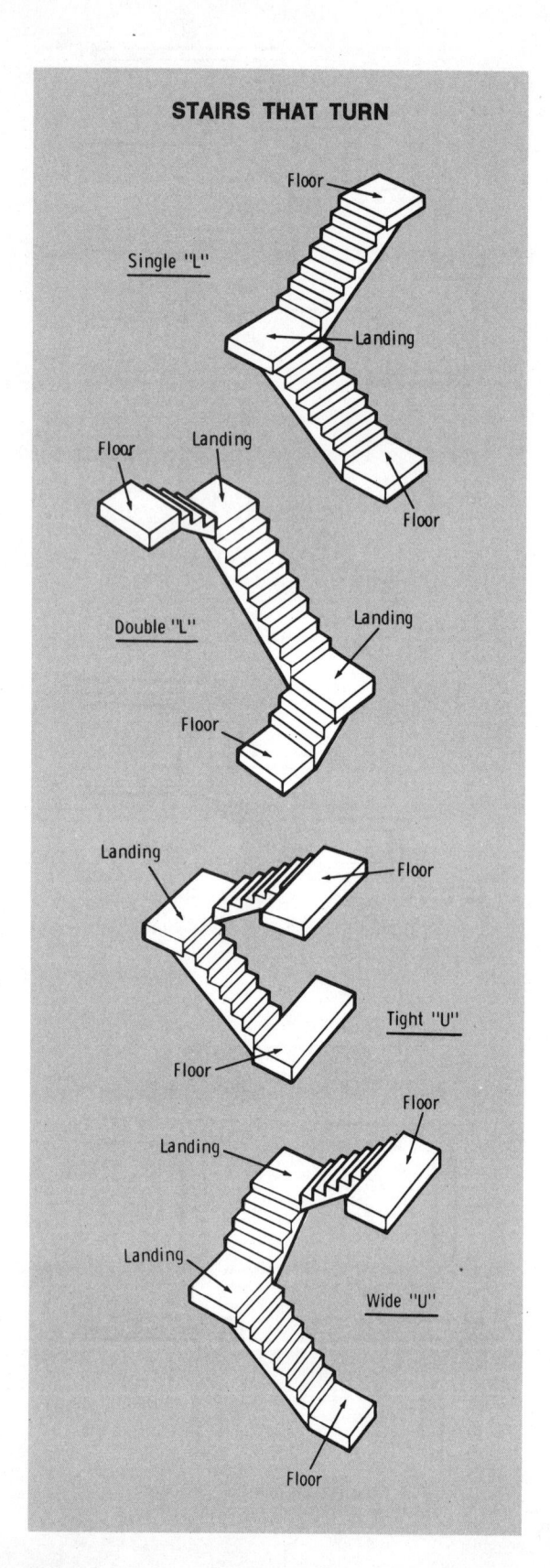

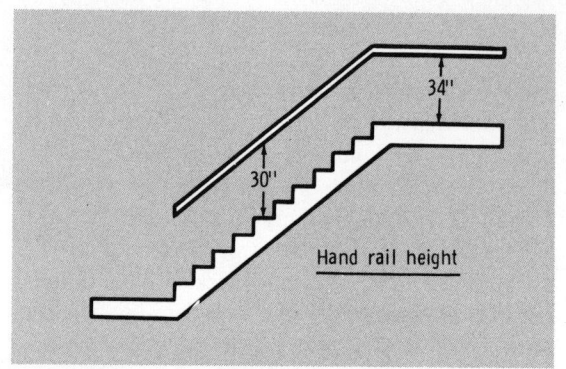

STAIRS THAT TURN

- Single "L"
- Double "L"
- Tight "U"
- Wide "U"

Hand rail height — 34", 30"

For safety all open-string stairways should be provided with a continuous handrail. For a comfortable, sure grip all the way up and down, the handrail heights should approximate those given in the detail

around a corner to form an L, or completely back on itself to form a U. Samples of such stairs are illustrated. Note that the bend always involves a platform, or landing. Years ago, the high ceilings of vast Victorian homes taxed the capacity of stairways, and builders tried to squeeze maximum lift from them by having steps continue around turns, without a landing. This was done with pie-wedge treads that fanned around a corner by tapering down to nothing at the newel post. Such cramped, narrow treads caused serious accidents when they were placed toward the top of a long flight.

Treads are usually 1 to 1¼-in.-thick hardwood. On utility steps 2-in. pine is often substituted. Outdoors, water run-off must be provided for. You can simply drill holes in the treads or use narrower boards, leaving ¼-in. openings between them.

See also: building; elevator; floors; measurements; remodeling ideas.

Housed stringers—seen in high-grade work—have ½-in. grooves on inside face of the wall stringer. The treads and risers are both wedged from behind and below to assure a tight, squeakless fit

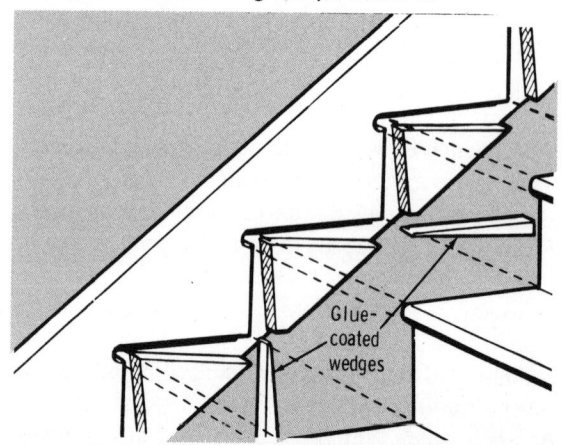

Glue-coated wedges

2476

clever ideas

Tired of hunting for paper and pencil every time you have to write a note to the milkman? Mount a small blackboard and chalk holder near the door and you can jot down your order where your milkman can see it at first glance.

Hidden hangers for "floating" bookshelves disappear completely when books are in place. Made of light sheet metal, these paper-thin brackets should be spaced no more than 2 ft. apart along the shelf to provide proper support for the books.

If you lose the cap to a plastic glue bottle, a slip-on pencil eraser makes an excellent substitute since it fits the spout exactly. The eraser can also be used to spread the glue.

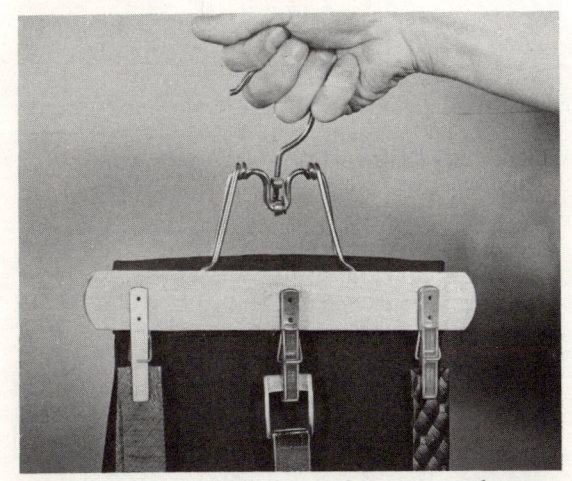

This nail carrier is a minutes-only project which can be made by cutting a hand hole in a 1 x 8-in. board and nailing a number of 1-lb. coffee cans on each side. For smaller nails, you might substitute fruit or vegetable cans.

Double the capacity of wooden trouser hangers by fastening three plastic clothespins to each side with small screws. These will hold belts and ties neatly. In an emergency, they'll even support a pair of slacks.

The weak point in most coffeemakers is the pin assembly—when this wears out, the whole base must be replaced. To lengthen its life, leave a short cord plugged into the base at all times and plug an extension cord into it.

stake plates

Stake plate has many shop uses

BY WALTER E. BURTON

■ BENCH-TYPE STAKE PLATES can be adapted to a wide variety of uses in home or appliance-repair shops. The plate shown with this article was made from an old sadiron. If you don't have a sadiron, a square of steel will do just as well.

home-shop plate

The one pictured, made from the sadiron, has only round holes. But if you go to the extra trouble of squaring several holes, you can use any number of anvil heads and stakes of the type used in the art-metal crafts. Blind round holes can be drilled to take various sizes of dapping punches and the sadiron can serve as an anvil on which to bed a doming stage or perhaps a dapping die. By machining suitable mandrels for insertion in a hole pattern in the plate, you can improvise a bender for forming the more common bends in light ornamental ironwork.

hollow anvils

For the more practical household and appliance-shop uses, you can make the anvils needed from drill rod, which, for light work, need not be hardened. The photo and details show a representative selection. Note that both stakes detailed have holes centered all the way through. The holes also can be counterbored, the smaller hole coming in about halfway from the shouldered end. In this way the stake is self cleaning. As a rule, holes in the plate should be drilled clear through.

solid anvils

It's always handy to have a number of solid anvils of different diameters and lengths. These fit the counterbored holes in the plate and are

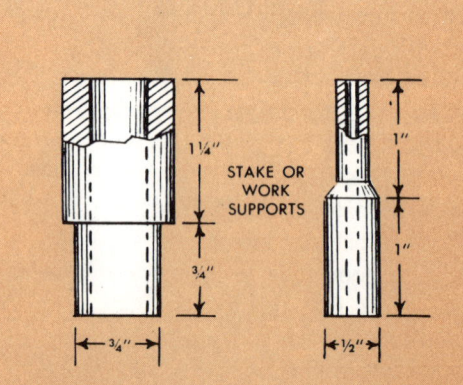

Stakes, above, can be just about any size, any turned shape required. Smaller sizes can be of drill rod for light work without hardening

Plates, below, can be made from mild steel or tool steel to any convenient size. Dimensions given for hole sizes are only representative

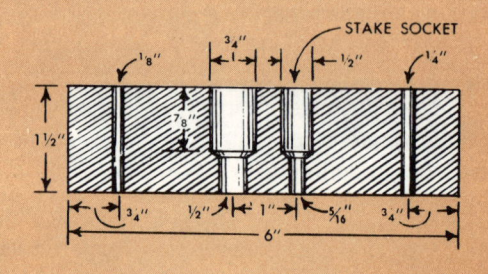

---

stalking game: see archery
stalls, auto: see auto repair
stamps, rubber: see rubber stamps
stand, bench saw: see bench saws
stand, spotlight: see light stand
stand-up drawing board: see drafting equipment

2478

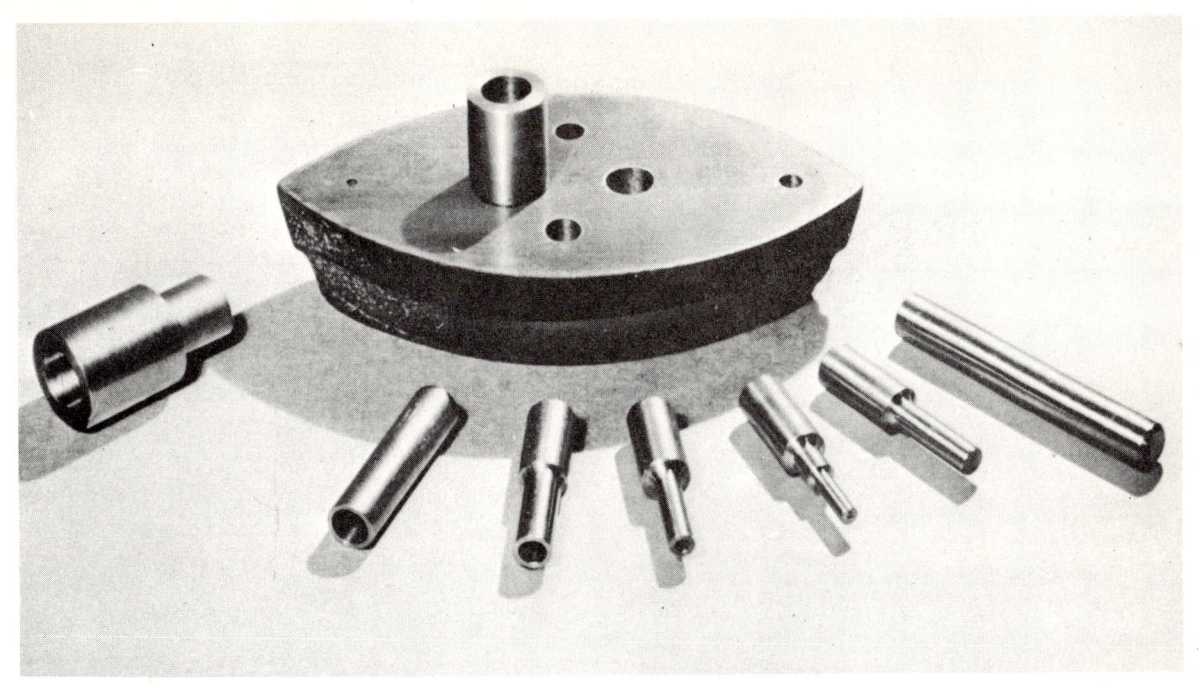

A sadiron plate, with a representative selection of both solid and hollow anvils, is handy for appliance repairs

useful for a variety of operations involving hammering and peening. There's no need to turn these or have them shouldered at a machine shop. They can be cut from drill rod and the holes drilled in the plate to the given diameters.

anvil and plate sizes

Make the plate any size to suit the purpose, using 1-in. flat steel if you require something larger than the sadiron pictured. The more holes in the plate of various sizes the greater the extent of its usefulness, especially in a repair shop. On large plates it's a good idea to leave an area clear of anvil holes so that this area can be used as a surface anvil or even as a surface plate for simple layout operations with a surface gauge. The dimensions of the through holes and counterbores in the plate, as well as its overall size, given in the detail to the left, are only representative.

uses of stake plate

With an assortment of anvil sizes and types at hand a stake can be used for riveting, peening, setting or tightening hinge pins, pattern punching for hole arrangement, driving various sizes of pins in or out with pin punches, straightening wire, round and square rods, bending sheet metal and light band iron. Also the units can be adapted for punching holes in sheet metal with a hardened punch.

See also: benders; drilling; punch; sheet metal; shrink plate.

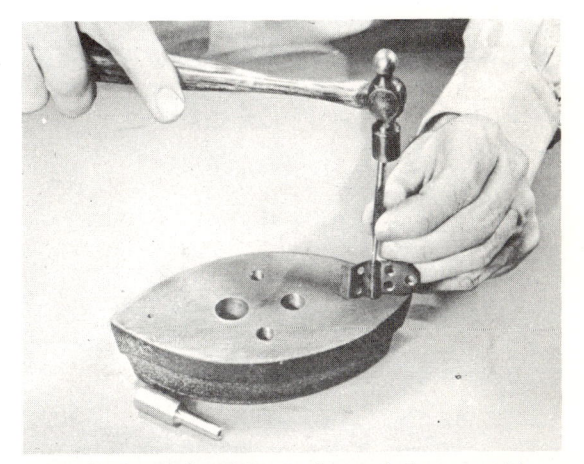

A handy-size stake plate can be made from an old sadiron, above. It's heavy enough and hard enough for peening rivets, setting hinge pins, and for light work as a surface anvil. Below, shouldered stakes are shown being drilled for use with the plate

clever ideas

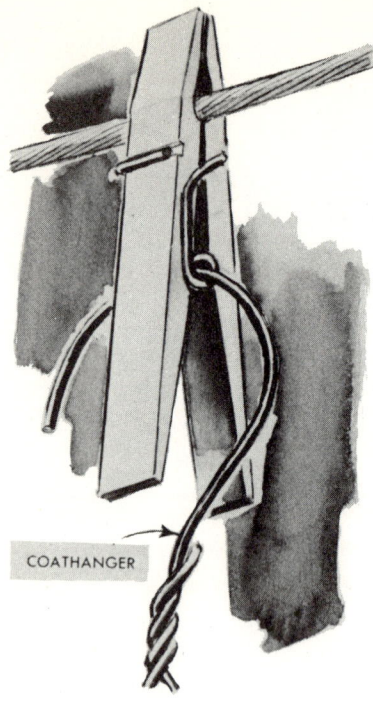

Here's an easy way to prevent blouses and wash dresses from blowing off the clothesline. Fasten the clothespin to the line in the usual manner, and then slip the hook of the clotheshanger through the loop in the spring.

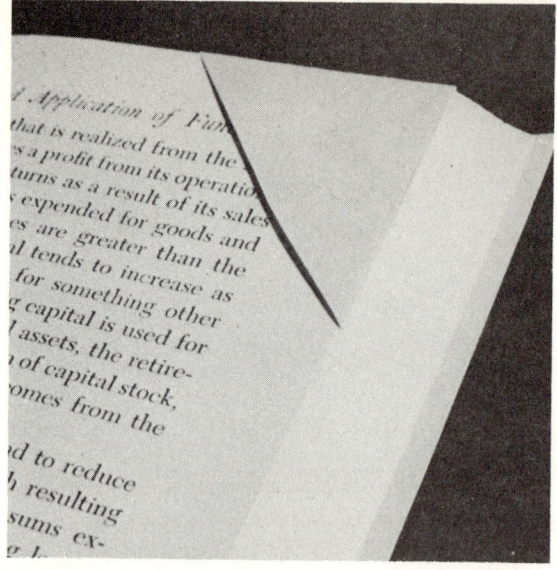

It's inconvenient to lose your page when you are reading an exciting book, and bookmarks have a tendency to become dislodged. Here's one that will stay put. Just cut the corner off a used envelope and slip it over the page of the book. Having two sides of the page to cling to and no projecting edges, it's not likely to come loose. These markers are also easy for the kids to decorate, and make nice gifts for them to give to friends.

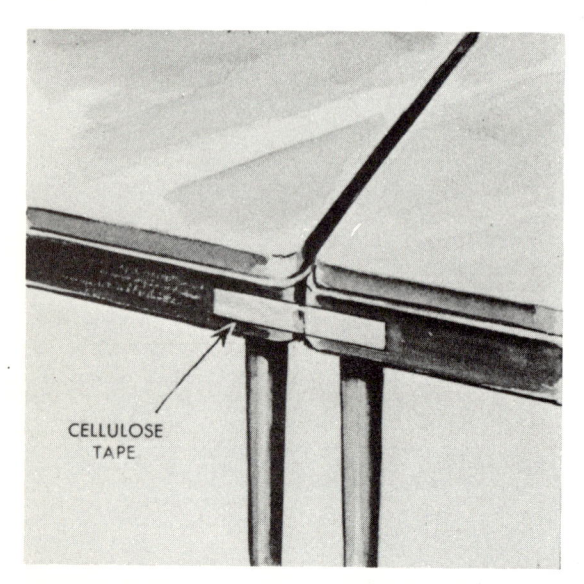

Ever wish you had a big card table instead of two small ones? The two can be joined together temporarily, as when using them for playing cards or serving food, by applying a 6-in. strip of cellulose tape along the sides as shown. When the setup is no longer needed the tape is merely peeled off without marring the finish in any way. Try this idea the next time you throw a party.

This potted "rose bush" is yours for the doing. Cut any small wild shrub having several branches, prune it to size and tape artificial roses and leaves to the branches as shown. Use dark green cloth tape for this purpose. Mount the rose bush on a wooden block that will fit in the pot. Then fill the pot with gravel and you will have a nicelooking rose bush that requires no care.

Window sills are usually too narrow to take potted plants, and even if they do fit they have a tendency to mar the finish. You can make an extension from ¼-in. plywood that will make room for the plants and protect the sill as well. Cut the shelf to fit the sill and scallop-cut the outer edge. Trim the stop ¼ in. and slip the plywood under it as indicated. Screw-fasten the stop.

A hand support board like the one shown is a real help when doing oil paintings by the numbers. It is a 4-in.-wide board cut a few inches longer than picture width and fitted with ½ x ½-in. cleats nailed across the ends to raise the board off the work and prevent smearing.

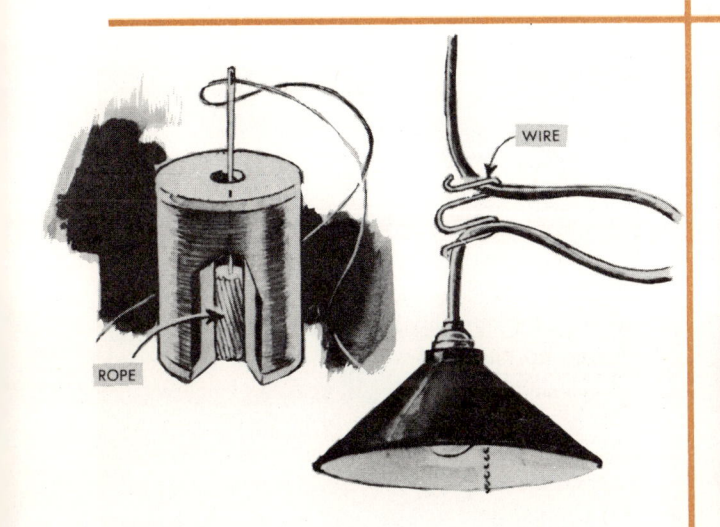

The built-in pincushion, above left, lets you store sewing needles right with the thread so that both are always handy. Simply press a short length of clothesline into the spindle hole of the spool.

To raise a droplight having a cord that is too long, form an M-shaped clip from a short length of stiff wire or paper clip and loop the cord through it, as shown above, right.

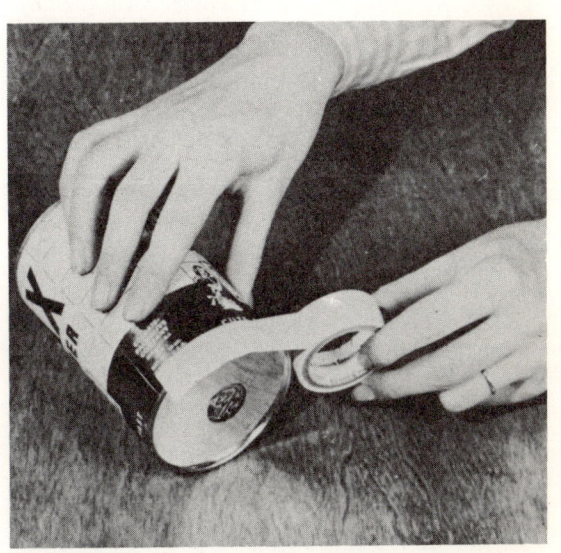

Are you annoyed by rust stains that are left on sinks and tubs by cleanser cans? Then wrap a wide strip of adhesive tape tightly around the bottom rim each time a new can is placed in use, pressing the tape firmly against the metal at the bottom of the can. This tape treatment will also stop the can from scratching countertops. In most cases the tape can be used more than once, by moving it from an empty can to a new one.

2481

starting, auto, cold weather

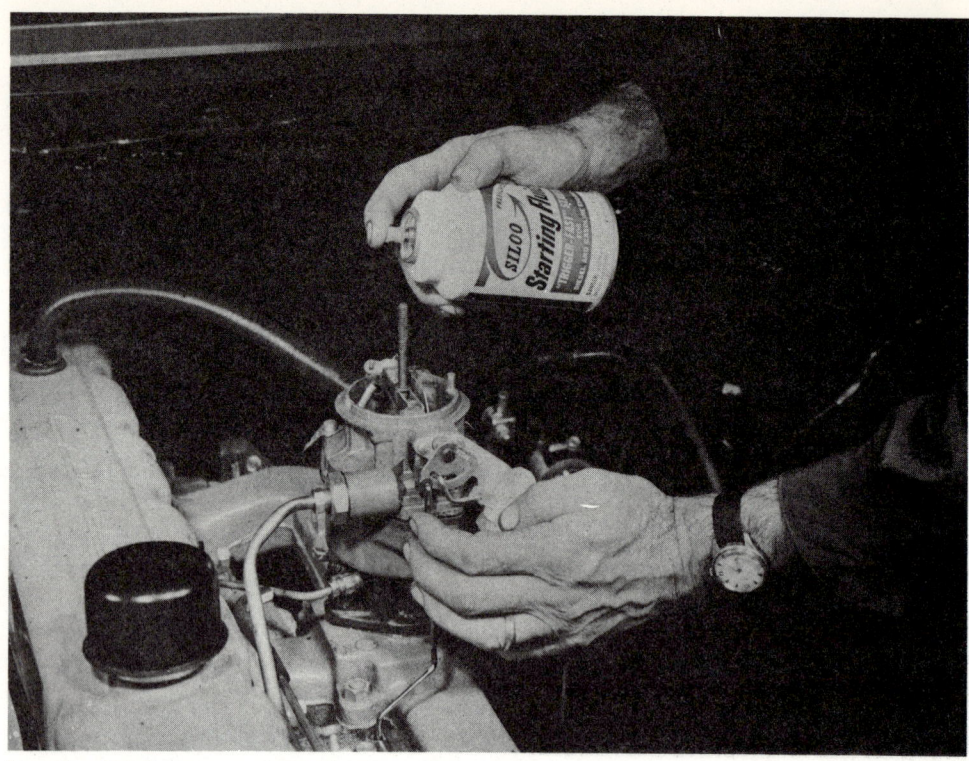

Speedy—but dangerous. Aerosol-powered ether sprays demand the ultimate in caution

Hot tips for cold starts

BY MORTON J. SCHULTZ and
HARRIS EDWARD DARK

■ ON A FRIGID WINTER MORNING, there are few sounds more disheartening than the slow, labored groans of a cold engine refusing to start.

Dumping the problem in the lap of a competent road serviceman is an appealing idea, but on a bad morning he may not show up for hours. Instead, if you understand the problem, you can probably get yourself going just as well. You can, after all, do just about anything he can when he's away from his shop.

Road servicemen throughout the U.S. cold belt use pretty standard cold-start procedures: If your car won't crank, they first hook up a booster battery. If your engine doesn't respond at once, off comes the air filter so the choke can be held either open or closed (opposite the position it was found in) while the engine is given another whirl. If this fails, the distributor cap is removed and the engine cranked again to see if the points are making and breaking. If they aren't, an adjustment is made. The last resort is the tow truck.

Once in the shop, your car will almost always get a sparkplug job. If you won't stand still for complete replacement, it'll be cleaning and regapping. Meanwhile, somebody's probably hooked up the battery to a fast charger—and this can damage it if it's still at zero or below.

By the time you drive out of there, you may have spent good money for plugs, points, battery charge, oil change, carburetor adjustment or one of the many cold-weather additives or gimmicks for sale at garages. One thing you *won't* drive out with is a guarantee your car will start on the *next* cold morning. So it pays you to know what you can do for yourself.

You pinpoint the cause of cold weather no-start much the same way a doctor diagnoses a patient's ailments. You first find the reason for the car's malfunction, then try various cures in the likeliest order.

But, as with any patient, an ounce of prevention is worth all the cures you can try. That car should have been winterized and tuned before

2482

the cold weather hit—and should have another tune-up performed midway through the winter. If you've neglected this care and have yet to experience a cold-weather starting problem, consider yourself in luck. But don't press it. Midwinter service may not prevent no-start, but it gives you top odds.

Such cautions aren't much comfort, however, while you're sitting in that refrigerator-on-wheels, wondering how to get it started. Still, for the sake of this article, we must assume your car's been properly winterized, since we're going to cover only *cold weather problems*.

Now let's go back to that fatal moment you turned the ignition key. Those lifeless growls strongly suggest an ailing battery.

Reports from AAA's Emergency Road Service department put batteries at the top of the list of no-start causes. Normally, battery trouble is the cause of 25 to 46 percent of their emergency calls; but during cold snaps, the national battery figure has jumped to nearly 70 percent—proof

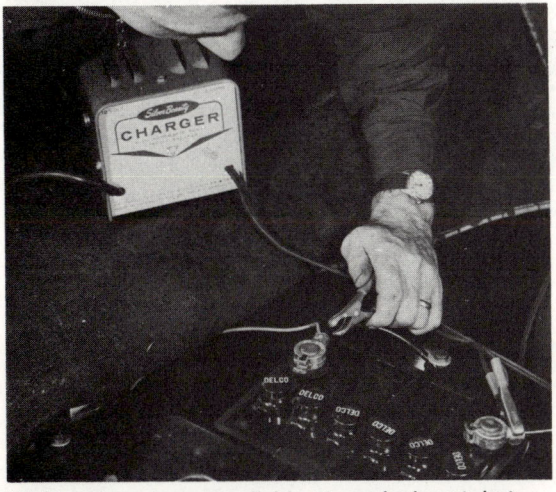

Trickle chargers are available at nominal cost, but may be limited to a single class of battery. Costlier models are more flexible. These can prove an effective cure for cold-start problems

Battery terminal pads fit around the post under the clamp. The most desirable ones are treated to neutralize acids. They also change color to signal when it's time for you to replace them

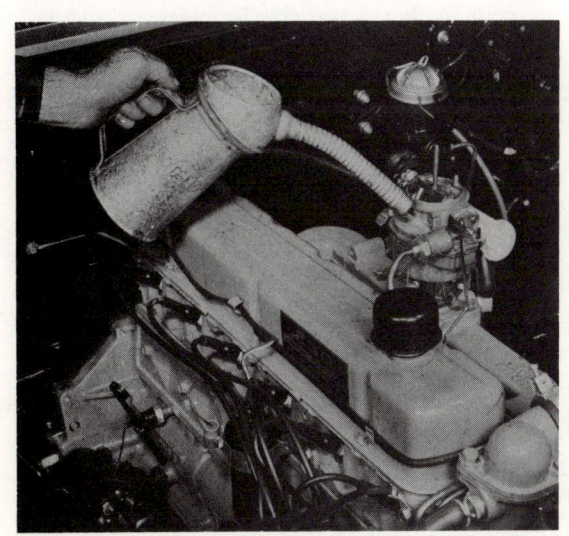

Warm water poured over the carburetor fuel bowl can be just the thing to help free frozen parts. A long, flexible spout such as on this can helps direct water and keep it from the carb throat

Very hot water is required if you're trying to melt ice in the fuel pump. A result of moisture accumulating in the gasoline, fuel-pump ice keeps gas from reaching the carb and is a common problem

starting, auto, cold weather

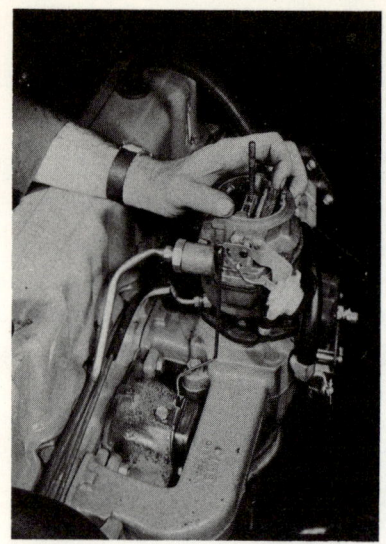

Position the choke plate opposite to the way you found it. And as you do, feel for restrictions in movement that may warn you of the accumulation of gummy deposits

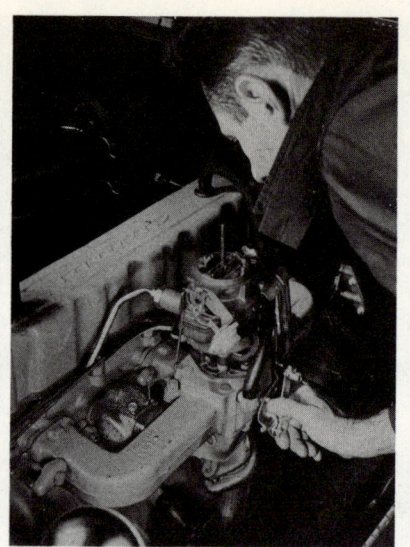

Operate the throttle linkage to verify that gas is getting into the carb. But be careful not to overdo it; you'll find it's easy to flood the engine

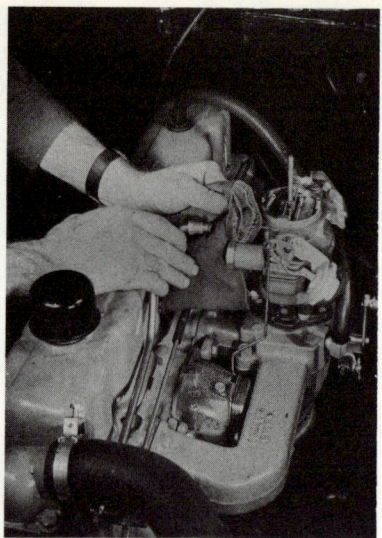

If fuel isn't getting into the carb throat, detach the fuel line and crank the engine. Gas dampening the rag shows it's getting this far, so ice is probably in carb

that winter takes a heavy toll of battery efficiency.

Even a new battery can fail you at low temperatures. At zero degrees, a fully charged battery is only about 50 percent efficient. And it's not only the cold that saps a battery's strength all winter long: you're putting a heavier drain on it with prolonged use of accessories such as the heater, defroster—and headlights that must be switched on much earlier in the day. It's likely, too, that you're doing much more short-range driving, giving the battery less chance to rejuvenate itself.

A battery in top condition, then, is vital. The most important thing is to keep your battery at full charge. Why? To prevent freezing. When a battery is partly run down, the acid has moved from the electrolyte into the plates. Since it's the acid that acts as antifreeze, the greater the discharge, the more likely the battery water will turn to ice. Any battery with less than three-quarter charge can freeze when the mercury takes a dive.

It's important to note that 12-volters, being more easily run down, are in greater danger of freezing. This is a major paradox of the automotive industry. In the early '50s, Detroit engineers recommended a switch to the 12-volt system because of the increasing electrical loads in modern cars. But the new 12-volt batteries were made practically the same size as the 6-volters they replaced, so as not to increase the bulk, weight or cost. The result: In doubling the number of cells, the design *halved* the ampere-hour capacity. The new 12-volt batteries had much less lead, active material, water and acid *per volt* than the old type.

Consider these figures from an engineer in Delco-Remy's Design and Application Section: Under a test load of 300 amps at 0 deg. F., a typical 6-volt battery reaches its "out" point in 3.8 minutes. Under the same conditions, an equivalent 12-volter reaches its out point in exactly *one* minute. It's the ampere-hour capacity that counts, here. And the electrolyte of a 12-volt battery is much weaker at out point (and thus more vulnerable to freezing) than a 6-volter's electrolyte. A good 6-volt battery will cease cranking while there's still a safe "antifreeze" value in the electrolyte. The 12-volter, on the contrary, will keep cranking up to a point of near-total discharge.

The record of the 12-volt system hasn't been good in recent years. By 1956, most American cars had made the switch. Since that time, the annual reports from AAA's emergency service show that battery and electrical failures have taken a wide lead over all other causes of stall-calls. Is it only coincidence that the battery grabbed top spot in the years since the 12-volt system became standard?

This sidelight only points up the importance of keeping a full charge during cold weather. Even so, it's a wise precaution to have a booster

As a temporary solution, if you can't thaw ice from the fuel inlet screen, remove it. Wrap it in a rag and drive on, saving the screen in your pocket or glove box

A spare battery and a set of jumper cables is the common way to overcome cold-weather starting problems. If you can't use the battery in a friend's car, carry a spare. Whenever you're at home, however, keep the spare in a warm place in the basement. Cold hurts it even more than the car battery, since it isn't under constant charge

on hand. A booster, of course, is nothing but a good, fully charged reconditioned battery, and a set of jumper cables. A used 12-volt battery can be had for a few dollars. You might save a couple of dollars by buying a 6-volter; it will work on a 12-volt system, and as we've seen, it'll hold a charge better than its big brother.

To use your booster, hook the two batteries in parallel—that is, positive terminal to positive terminal and negative to negative. The jumper cables are also negative and positive, and must be properly connected to their respective battery posts. Many are marked with plus and minus signs; others are color-coded—a red cable is always connected to the positive battery post.

If you connect the two batteries wrong in a generator-charged car, it isn't too serious. The engine just won't respond until you switch the leads. But in a car with an alternator, a wrong hookup—even for a second—can send current back to ruin the diodes and voltage regulator.

Keep the booster fully charged and store it where it won't freeze or overheat—the cellar's fine. If you tote the booster and cables along as insurance when you park in a lot or on the street, remember to tuck the battery back in a heated niche when you get home. A frozen booster is as useless as a frozen car battery.

In the absence of a booster, there are a couple of tricks that might get a car with a cold battery started. First, try to warm up the battery by turning on all accessories (heater, radio, headlights, etc.) for about 30 sec. This will cause current to begin its flow—a flow that might thaw the battery somewhat. Then, with the accessories turned off, try starting the car. Crank the engine for no more than 15 sec., let it rest for a minute or two, and then try again.

If this doesn't start the engine, remove every other plug in firing order (to keep the engine in balance). This may reduce cranking resistance enough to get the battery to turn the engine over. It works best with an eight-cylinder car.

If the engine does start, let it run for a minute or two with your foot holding the accelerator pedal a quarter- to halfway to the floor so the battery thaws out and gets some charge. Then, shut off the engine and replace the plugs.

If none of these methods is successful, you'll have to remove the battery from the car, bring it inside and set it in a tub about half-full of warm (not hot) water. As the cold battery chills this water, replace with hot (but not scalding) water. It'll take about an hour to warm the battery sufficiently, but when it's replaced in the car, it should spin the engine.

On occasion, the cause of those low, lifeless growls is not the battery at all, but the battery cables. Any corrosion that might develop between cable and battery post could choke off a winter-weakened charge.

Remove the cable from the battery and scrape

starting, auto, cold weather

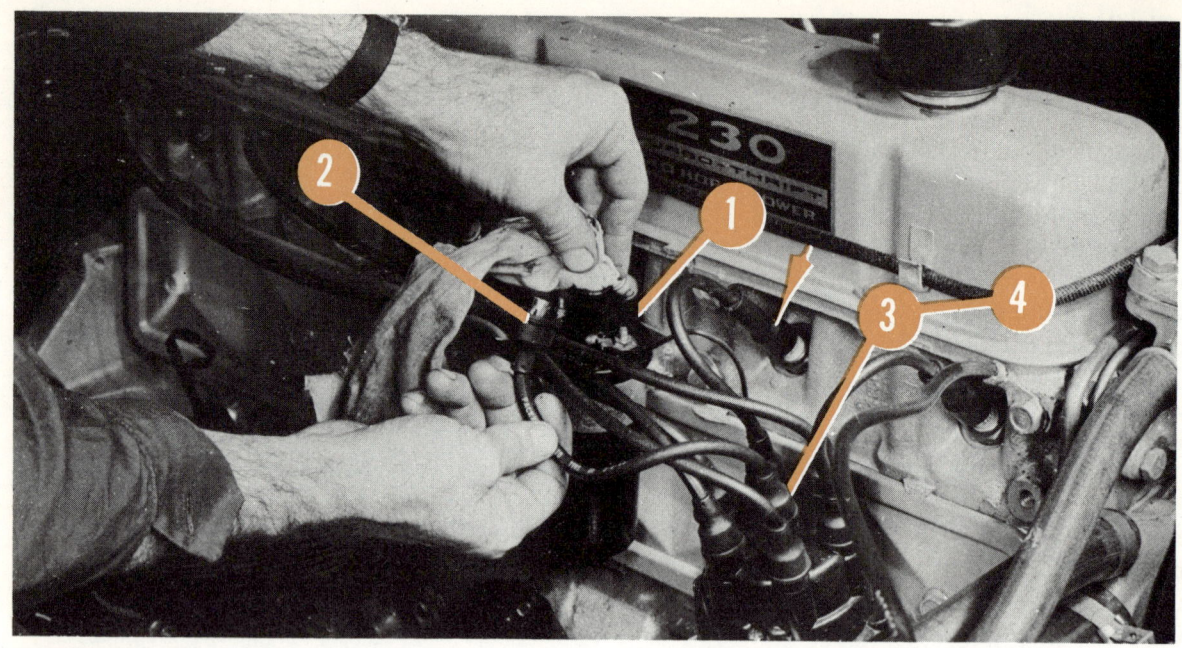

A dry ignition system is absolutely essential for reasonably reliable cold-weather starting. Four of the most important "dry" areas are the central tower of the coil and the primary voltage to that tower and also the corresponding locations at the distributor end of the primary lead. Rubber sparkplug boots (arrow) are meant to keep dampness out. Pull each of the leads and make sure they are fully effective

out the inside of the terminal with a pocketknife. Also scrape the battery post. When replacing the cable, make sure connections are tight, not only at the battery but also where the ground cable connects to ground on the block or frame, and where the "hot" cable connects to the starter.

Now let's assume that when you try to start the engine it cranks just fine, but doesn't start. You can rule out the battery as the cause. The next logical diagnosis might be a faulty fuel system.

Any time of year, three things are needed to start a car: the proper fuel mixture, a hot spark, and good compression. Check now to make sure you have all three, beginning at the fuel system. You can be getting either too much gas or none at all. And the chief cold-weather cause of either condition is a binding choke plate. That's why this is the second thing a road serviceman checks.

If your car has an automatic choke, you'll have to remove the carburetor air cleaner and operate the choke plate by hand. If the plate is stuck shut, a gummy shaft may be keeping it from moving, thus letting too much raw gas flow into the cylinders, flooding the engine. On the other hand, if the plate is stuck open, the cylinders are not getting enough gas.

You can usually free the plate of an automatic choke by working it back and forth with your fingers. (With a hand choke, try working it by cable from the dash.) To start an engine flooded by a closed choke plate, work the plate to an open or partially open position. With an automatic choke, you'll have to *hold* it open while someone else stomps the accelerator pedal to the floorboard (to unload the carburetor), and then cranks the engine while his foot's still on the pedal. The engine will usually start on the second or third try, since air is now pouring into the carburetor and diluting the raw gas in the cylinders. If the engine doesn't start, it's probably

Check ignition spark by holding the terminal near the plug or block while the engine is cranking. Watch for a nice, fat spark to jump the gap

too badly flooded; let it sit awhile before trying again.

If the choke plate is stuck open when you first examine it, close it with your fingers. Crank the engine. After it starts, go back to the choke and open it slightly to prevent flooding.

But what if your check of the choke plate finds it moving freely? The trouble may still be in the fuel system, so give the throttle linkage one or two quick pulls. You should get a spit of gas into the carburetor (you can see, hear or smell it), which tells you that fuel is getting to the cylinders. This fact eliminates the fuel system as the cause of your problem.

If no gas is getting to the carburetor, there's a stoppage either at the entrance to the carburetor or somewhere back in the fuel system. To find out where it is, follow the steps shown in the photos at the top of page 2484. If your check indicates an ice clog, remove the filter screen from the carburetor port and wash it. Now, pour a kettle of *warm* water slowly over the carburetor fuel bowl, which contains the needle valve and float.

If no fuel shows up on the rag it means that the gas is being blocked somewhere along the line to the carburetor. The trouble is probably ice in the fuel line, in the fuel filter (if you have one) or in the fuel pump. To thaw out these parts, pour *hot* water over them.

But, how do you thaw them when there's no hot water handy? An alternate heat source—one that's *always* available (though not of top efficiency)—is *you*. If you can pinpoint the ice clog, simple hand-warming may melt it enough to let fuel pass. Water, being heavier than gasoline, settles in the low spots of the system. So look for a likely dip or loop in the fuel line and grip this spot in your fist. Of course, in cold severe enough to ice a fuel line, you may not be able to stand contact with bare metal long enough to do much good, but it's worth a try.

Is there an electric outlet handy? Then borrow your wife's hair dryer. The newer models, with a flexible hose and a capacity of 250 to 400 watts, are especially helpful.

How about ether sprays? Certainly there's enough talk about their use; they're touted as extra-helpful because of ether's affinity for water as well as its extreme volatility and flammability. The claim is that ether dries up condensation and melts ice that often forms in the carburetor.

To start with, let's recognize that it works. A squirt or two of ether into the carburetor can well make the difference.

But there's a lot more to the ether question than whether it works. It's well to consider that you, bending over the engine as you hold an aerosol can of ether starting fluid, are holding a bomb in your hand! This vapor is *so* very flammable that it's explosive. And that isn't all. Ether is rarely used as a hospital anesthetic today, but whenever it is used, extreme care is taken to protect the patient—and staff. One doctor pointed out that a user who sprayed his hand in subzero weather would freeze it. An eye specialist said an accidental blast in the eye can permanently "frost" the cornea.

The use of ether isn't particularly unusual among fleet mechanics—but those who use it also use lots of caution. One fleet maintenance chief says his men have great success starting cold diesels with ether, but he wouldn't think of using it on a passenger-car engine. It can sneak along valve guides and collect under the rocker-arm cover, he says, and when the concentration is right: *blam!* Other equally horrendous results are possible with the many other sources of

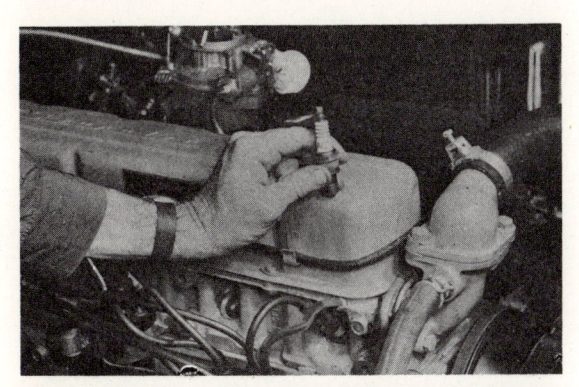

The plug gap can be closed up slightly even without a plug tool. Just rap the ground terminal sharply against a firm surface a couple of times

A matchbook cover can serve as a makeshift emergency feeler gauge. Close the plug gap to the thickness of the cover stock—but check the accuracy later

2487

starting, auto, cold weather

YOUR AREA	WINTER TEMPERATURES	OIL TO USE
Alaska, No. Canada...	VERY COLD / −10 and under	5W or 5W-20
Montana, Minn., Maine...	COLD / −0 to −10	10W or 10W-30
Kansas, Ohio, Maryland...	NORMAL / −10 to +32	20W or 20W-40
So. Calif., Texas, Florida...	BALMY / Above 32	Oil you normally use

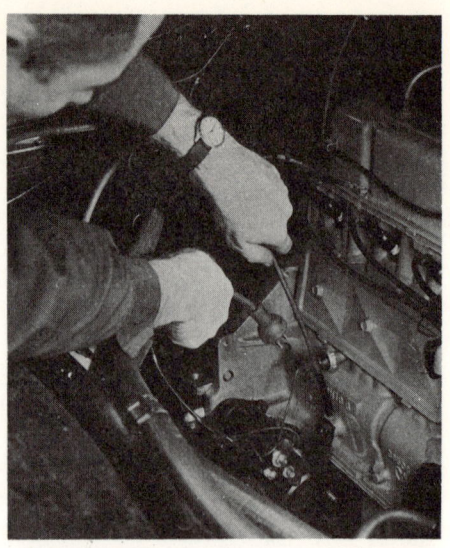

A dipstick warmer amounts to nothing more than a heating element. It costs about $5 or so. Plugged in overnight it assures that congealed oil won't inhibit starting in the morning. The chart gives a guide to the best oil, depending on your location and prevailing winter temperatures

sparks around an engine. And there's always the hapless victim who unconsciously lights up a cigaret.

Yet this stuff is sold without restriction. There are rarely more than a few restrained words of caution on the label. So let this be your warning:

There are plenty of other effective—and safer —ways to get the car started. Steer clear of ether sprays unless you're desperate. If you insist on using them, stay out in the open, use only a little, and take every precaution you can think of. And get that can away from the car, especially the glove box, when warm weather approaches. It can explode at as little as 120 deg.

Another type of product is sold to cut down on icing in the fuel system. It's a liquid containing chemicals that prevent condensation woes; you add a can to every other tankful of fuel. There's something to be careful of here, too. The liquid picks up a lot of sediment, and this is carried to the fuel system's filters. These should be cleaned quite often during the three or four-month period that you use such a fuel antifreeze (often called "dry gas").

As long as your battery's in good shape, there's little reason to suspect your ignition system of being the cause of cold start problems. After all, sparks can't freeze. One thing that would cause hard starting, though, is wind-driven snow or sleet that settles on the distributor cap and plugs, wetting them down. The photo at the top of page 2486 shows how to dry them out.

Some motorists swear by a spark intensifier. This item, when introduced into the system at the distributor or coil, supposedly builds up the current going to the plugs, giving them a hotter jolt.

Such gadgets can't hurt anything, but many mechanics dispute their worth, contending that a properly tuned ignition system is the only guarantee one has against ignition breakdown.

Suppose your ignition system does fail, though —not because of cold weather necessarily, but because of a faulty part whose failure is speeded by the cold. How can you at least get the car to a shop?

The first thing to do is make sure the trouble is really with the ignition. Disconnect an ignition wire from a plug and hold it near the block while someone cranks the engine. If you get a fat, crackling spark about ½ in. in length, there's nothing wrong with the ignition except, possibly, moisture at the plugs. (If you get no spark, you'll have to check the entire system right then and there, isolate the bad component and replace or repair it. You won't get the car started if there's *no* spark at all.)

If, however, the spark is weak, you can try

one method of getting started: Remove two or three plugs and close their gaps as at the bottom of pages 2486–7. When you put the plugs back, you may find that the shortened gaps permit the weak spark to jump them and start the cold engine.

At any temperature below zero there's danger of your crankcase oil becoming solid as lard. This can add up to enough friction to make it impossible for the starter to turn the engine over. Not too many years ago, it was common practice to pour kerosene or diesel oil into crankcases to thin the engine oil. This would almost certainly damage modern engines that require extreme-pressure lubricant.

Fortunately, it's never necessary, with today's motor oils. Extreme-pressure capability is now available in a wide range of oils of both the regular viscosity (5W, 10W, 20W, 30, and 40) and newer multiviscosity types (5W-20, 10W-30 and 20W-40).

If quick starts at low temperatures were your only consideration, the thinnest oil you could buy —5W—would be your choice. But once you're on your way your main concern is what happens to that oil at *high engine* temperatures—temperatures that vary little from summer to winter. At 210 deg. F., 5W oil gets extremely thin—so low in viscosity, in fact, that car manufacturers warn you not to drive faster than 60 mph with it in your crankcase—and even that speed can be risky. The newer 5W-20 multigrade oil, however, has a viscous polymer solution added to prevent such thinning out. Your choice between the two types (as a winter oil in very cold climates) has to be a compromise: for short, low-speed winter drives, 5W is okay. But change your oil before you head for the open road and speeds upward from 50—even at the risk of a few hard starts en route. See the chart on page 2488 for other recommendations.

gadgets can help

Whatever oil you choose, there are devices to keep it from thickening, or to thaw it once it has thickened. These are called engine heaters; plug them into an electric outlet overnight. Then you get the kind of hot start you'd expect in July.

One of the most popular types is the dipstick warmer, shown on page 2488, but there are others. One is a 650-watt water-jacket heater which is immersed through the head into the block coolant. It fits most engines and sells for a few dollars. For engines this regular size *won't* fit, you can buy a special model at a higher price.

There's also an 850-watt external-tank heater which connects between the lower water jacket and the car's heater hose. This type has a siphon percolator that circulates heated water throughout the system. It fits all liquid-cooled engines and is thermostatically controlled. There is also a 1500-watt model that warms up an engine in less than an hour.

Some types of dipstick warmers and other engine heaters are equipped with a cigar-lighter adapter. When away from an outlet, the device is plugged into the car's cigar lighter.

Prolonged use will, of course, run the battery down.

try a lamp makeshift

In the absence of an engine heater, a makeshift measure is a photoflood lamp in a reflector beneath the car near the crankcase. This is too expensive, though, for any but emergency use; these lamps throw off a lot of heat, but have a limited life, ranging from 4 to 6 hours. Far longer-lasting is an infrared heat bulb. But don't dangle any lamp under the hood. It's of dubious value and you could bake the plastic-insulated wiring.

To keep a battery from freezing, there are several types of plug-in heaters on the market. Better still is a trickle charger, like the one on page 2483. Hooked up overnight, it will keep the battery fully charged, a more effective means of preventing freezing than mere warming. Some work on either 6 or 12-volt batteries and have automatic shutoffs to prevent overcharging. Forget chemical additives; they're of no proven value in keeping a battery warm and charged. But a trickle charger with either a coolant or crankcase immersion heater is like a heated garage around the family bus.

The final cause of cold weather no-start can be the driver himself—the type who insists on flooding his engine although all mechanical parts may be operating.

To start an engine in cold weather, depress the accelerator to the floor once or twice to prime the carburetor. Then, holding the accelerator halfway to the floor, turn on the ignition and hit the starter for about 15 seconds. If the car doesn't start, release the starter. After a minute or two, try again. Should you flood the engine, keep the accelerator *against* the floor on the next try.

See also: auto repair; batteries, auto; carburetors, auto; chokes, auto; driving, snow; electrical system, auto; ignition system, auto.

starting, auto, hot weather

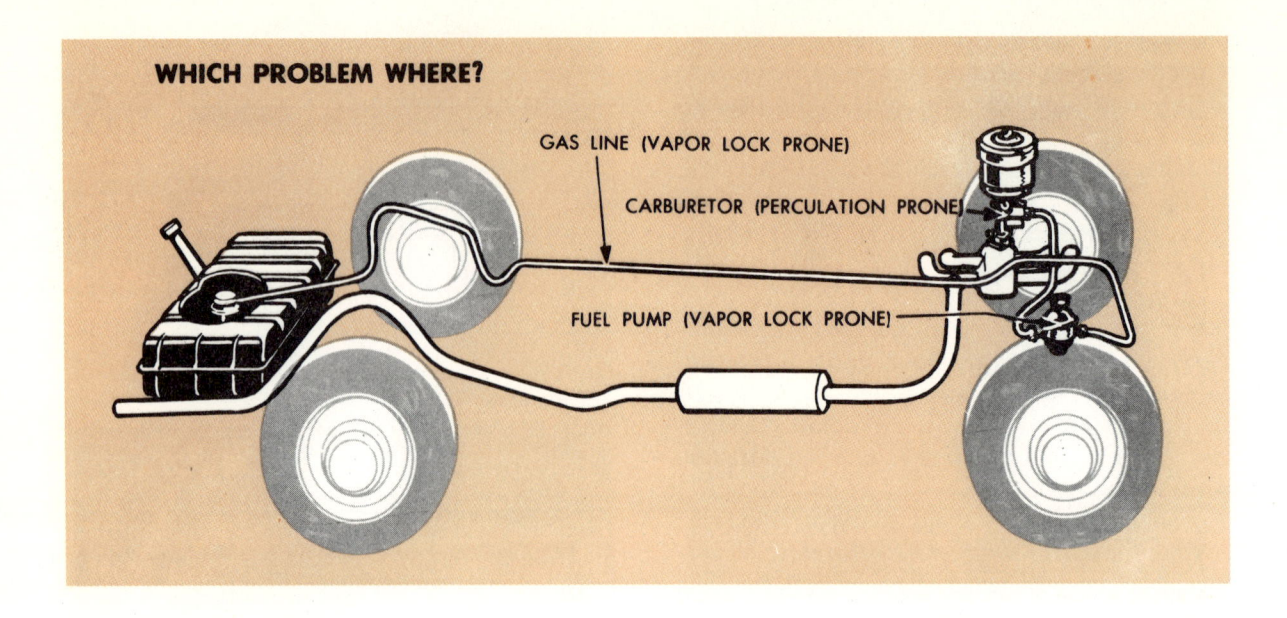

WHICH PROBLEM WHERE?

GAS LINE (VAPOR LOCK PRONE)
CARBURETOR (PERCOLATION PRONE)
FUEL PUMP (VAPOR LOCK PRONE)

Cool tips for hot starts

BY MORTON J. SCHULTZ

■ A SATURDAY MECHANIC might be forgiven for considering that the traditional summertime car complaints—stemming from fuel percolation or vapor lock—are outdated today. Modern engine design and the oil companies' practice of blending gasoline according to an area's climate should make those old problems about as common as a Stanley Steamer on the Interstate system.

But a car owner is well advised, even with all the modern advances, to beware of an excess of confidence. Those who take the trouble to investigate will find that the first warm day of summer usually brings a rash of various complaints—all with the same symptoms—to the professional mechanic. And that similarity in the symptoms is the key that shows there's still a basic problem that is widespread among car owners.

The pros tell of a spurt of business right after the first warm day each summer. Customers tell of bad sparkplugs, bad ignition coils, failing fuel pumps, or clogged gasoline filters. But checking over the cars commonly reveals no genuine problem. Yet, overwhelmingly, the owners have experienced some sort of stalling or no-start during the heat of the previous day.

In fact, there are nearly as many people who have trouble getting started in the summer as there are in winter, although for different reasons. Some garage owners report they encounter more problems today with fuel percolation or vapor lock than they found even before the development of anti-percolation devices and climate-blended fuel.

Two explanations are probable:

• Simply because of the general improvements in reliability in recent years, drivers—although they usually recognize the possibility of these special summertime problems—are no longer attuned either to their possibility or to the appropriate countermeasures for such troubles.

• Modern cars with their high-compression engines, restricted radiator area, and in many cases airconditioning, generate lots more heat under that gleaming hood.

Of those two possibilities, the first may well be the better bet. Many authorities hold that the increase is more in complaints than in occurrences —suggesting that the basic difficulty is that motorists simply don't recognize these hot-weather problems as readily as they did in earlier days.

That suggests that an educational effort is in order—to bring more of us back to the level of understanding that we had decades ago regarding hot-weather problems. If the average motorist can learn to keep cool in the face of summer starting or stalling problems, he may save the cost of a needless mechanic's bill.

The first point to clear up is that vapor lock and percolation *aren't* the same thing, though the

starting system, auto: see electrical system, auto

A strong aroma of gasoline encountered when you lift off the air cleaner shows that the engine is experiencing the enforced flooding effect that comes from fuel that has been percolating from the float bowl into the carburetor and then into the manifold

Modern carburetors have anti-percolation devices like that indicated by the pointer. On this two-barrel Rochester carburetor, the device is spring-loaded and operated by foot pressure on the accelerator. Even such devices can become clogged, however

symptoms are similar. Depending on its blend, gasoline can begin to boil at a temperature of from about 80 to 100 deg. When this happens, either percolation or vapor lock can result. It depends on where the boiling action takes place, whether the resulting condition is vapor lock or percolation.

Vapor lock is the vaporization or boiling of gasoline anywhere in the car's fuel system *before* that gas reaches the carburetor. The air bubbles, or vapor created by the boiling action, prevent, partially or completely, the supply of an adequate amount of fuel to the carburetor. Naturally, with an insufficient amount of gas or no gas at all, the engine will begin to chug-chug along or will stop running entirely.

Percolation, on the other hand, is confined only to the carburetor. Everything might be in top shape throughout the rest of the fuel system until gas reaches the carburetor. Here, however, the carburetor itself might be hot enough to boil and vaporize the fuel. Not only does your engine tend to run hotter in summer, but there's that sun beating on the hood.

As the carburetor bowl gets hotter and hotter, the fuel it contains begins to boil. If the temperature reaches a point just over the boiling point of gas, the fuel begins to vaporize and these fumes move up the bowl nozzle into the air-horn.

Being heavier than air, the vapors fill the airhorn and bleed past the throttle valve into the manifold. If the temperature gets to a high enough pitch, bubbles of gasoline actually rise in the nozzle and overflow into the air-horn, much like boiling water bubbles up and over the spout of a coffeepot. Whatever the case, vapor or bubbles, a condition similar to engine flooding takes place.

In short, then, when vapor lock occurs, your engine doesn't get sufficient gas. When percolation occurs, it appears to get too much, in the form of vapor or gas bubbles.

As we've already indicated, the consequences of a vapor lock or percolation condition are similar to those caused by other malfunctions. Indeed, your woes might not be the result of vapor lock or percolation at all, but a failure in the ignition system, a bad fuel pump or a clogged fuel filter. We'll assume, however, that your ignition has been properly tuned, and you know your fuel pump is OK and your fuel filter is clean.

We'll also assume that you've just completed a run of several miles, the engine is well warmed up, you've stopped for a bite to eat, you go to start the car, but it won't kick over. Or, you're driving along on a hot day and suddenly the car starts to buck and roll, eventually stalling, and won't start again.

Your first tip-off as to whether your problem is vapor lock or percolation is the *way it happened*. Percolation occurs most often after a hot, *slow* drive. Under these circumstances, the carburetor gets little air circulating around it. On a fast drive, there's plenty of air blowing through the

2491

starting, auto, hot weather

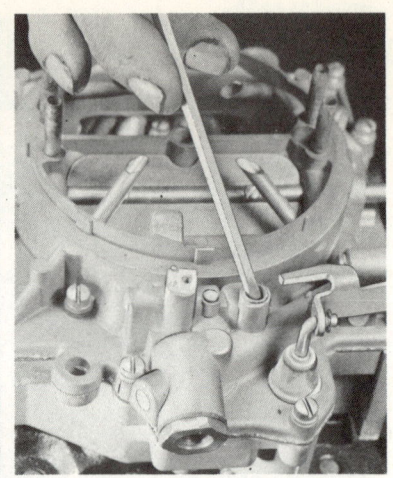

Service the anti-percolation device with the engine idling and no pressure on the accelerator pedal. First, use a ruler to check the clearance between the vent hole and spring. Readjust as required by bending the spring tang (left) down to reduce clearance or up to increase it. To replace a spring that has lost its tension, remove the top cover (center). While the spring is off the carburetor, check the vent hole (right). If it's clogged, pressure in the carburetor can escape readily into the carburetor throat and cause the engine to stall

tips for hot starts, continued

engine compartment. Vapor lock, on the other hand, can occur under fast or slow driving conditions. So if you were tooling along the turnpike before the stall, you're pretty safe to rule out percolation. But if you've been bumper-to-bumper in beach traffic, you can't be sure.

The low hood line on some modern cars can contribute to percolation problems by reducing the air flow and trapping heat around the engine. Although the body design is fixed and beyond an owner's control, pads can be removed from under the hood to improve cooling

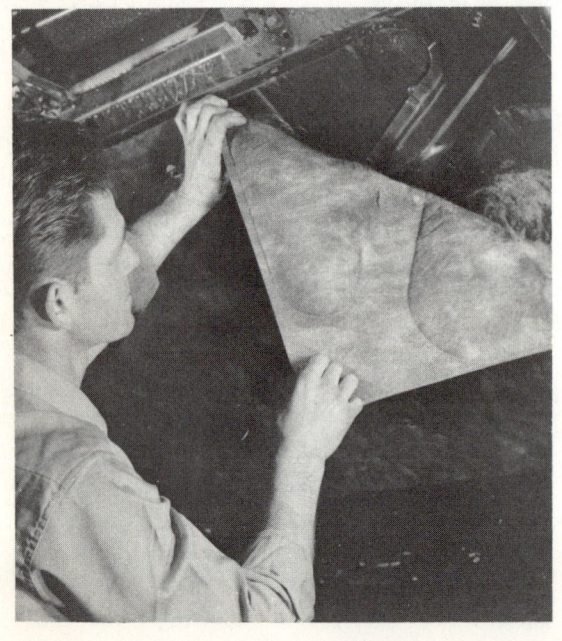

At least, not until you lift the hood and take off the carburetor air cleaner. A strong odor of gas fumes says your trouble is percolation. In some cases, if vapor has built up to a really high pitch, you might see a cloud wafting off into the air. A constant odor of gasoline in the car during the summer might also denote a percolation condition.

Percolation problems aren't as common today as they were in the past because of some built-in safeguards. Gasoline, for example, is different from summer to winter. Gas supplied to service stations during the winter is blended with so-called light ends, which makes it more volatile for easy starting.

If winter fuels were used during the summer, they would boil at a much lower temperature because of this lower volatility point. Thus, oil companies have developed a summertime fuel containing additives to make gas less volatile.

California Oil Co. says, for example, that its regular winter fuel is designed to burn at 90 deg. and the summertime equivalent is designed to burn at 96 deg. High-test gas made by Calso has a range of 88 deg. in the winter and 95 deg. in the summer.

This, though, doesn't mean that summer gas couldn't percolate if the temperature were high enough. Besides, you might live in a part of the country where the volatility of fuel supplied by oil companies is constant throughout the year. This is a possibility in cooler, northern climates. Yet even Minnesota and Montana are often seared by hot spells.

The *construction* of a modern-day carburetor also provides a safeguard against percolation. Each has some type of venting arrangement which, if not clogged or out of whack, permits vapor to escape.

Venting systems differ from carburetor to carburetor, though all work on much the same principle. The most common term for such a system is "anti-percolation device." The spring-loaded type shown on page 2492 is typical. As you drive along at highway speed, your foot on the gas pedal exerts enough pressure to keep a cam pressing against a flat spring that caps a vent hole. Once you get in traffic, though (where the chances of percolation increase), the lesser amount of foot pressure on the accelerator—or no pressure at all when you stop for a light—permits the spring to pop up. Any pressure that has built up in the carburetor can then escape through the vent.

Being mechanical, it's possible for this anti-percolation device to get out of adjustment or for the spring to lose tension. It's also possible on some carburetors for the vent hole to become clogged.

At the first sign of percolation, this device should be checked in accordance with the specification for your carburetor. This specification tells how much clearance there should be between the spring and the vent hole when the tension is off (usually $\frac{1}{32}$ in.). Adjustments can usually be made without removing the carburetor from the car (see p. 2492).

If the spring won't cover the hole when you step on the accelerator, it has lost tension and should be replaced. This entire assembly can be bought at a supply house or from a dealer who stocks your type of carburetor.

There is another mechanical part of a car that could lead to percolation if it's inoperative—the manifold heat-control valve. If the valve is stuck in the closed position, too much heat will react on the fuel after it passes through the carburetor. This excess heat causes the fuel to vaporize excessively and gives rise to a percolation condition. So, if your car has a manifold heat control valve, make sure it's working and well-lubricated.

Now, if the anti-percolation device and manifold heat-control valve are in good shape, you should seldom experience percolation. If you do, your best bet is to try to cool off your carburetor. This may involve stripping off the hood pad, as shown on page 2492, or inserting thicker gaskets between carb and manifold, this page.

If percolation persists you might want to investigate the availability of a new fan with more blades on it to circulate more air throughout the engine compartment. This also helps to prevent vapor lock.

Vapor lock is sneaky and potentially dangerous. Sneaky because it hits when you least expect it. Potentially dangerous because it could happen in traffic.

Let's suppose you're driving along without a care, but deep within the fuel system devious things are taking place. Maybe the design of the fuel line runs it too close to a manifold. Little by little, the gas going through that line is becoming heated.

Eventually, little gas and much vapor is pass-

The carburetor can be moved up away from manifold heat by using several carb-to-manifold gaskets as spacers, stacked on top of each other under the carburetor. This can be just enough to keep fuel from reaching the boiling—and percolating—point

Fiber blocks of varying thicknesses are available to help move the carburetor away from the manifold. These are for four-barrel carburetors. The thicker model (upper) requires the car owner to replace regular mounting bolts with longer versions

starting, auto, hot weather

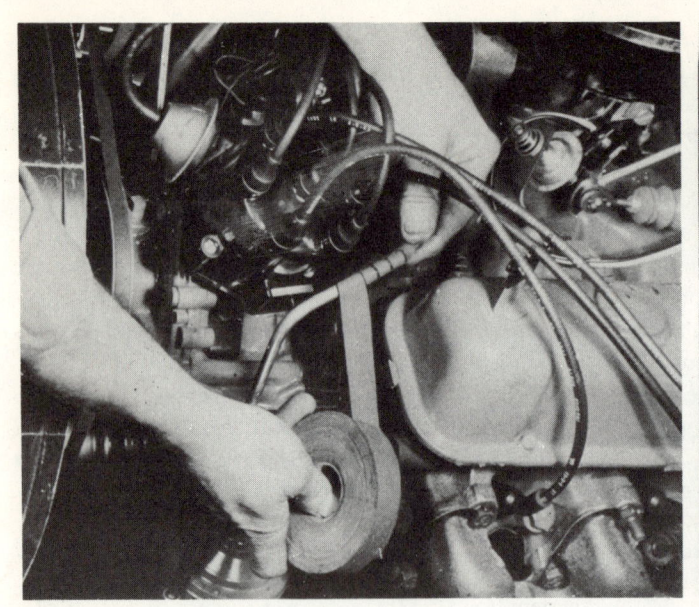

When vapor lock is the problem, cooling off the fuel line is the answer. But it isn't necessary to wait until it cools off itself. When the line runs in an especially hot spot it can be insulated with asbestos tape as at the left. Cold water poured over both fuel line and the pump (right) is another quite effective solution. Efficiency of the method is speeded up if you wrap the line and pump in a heavy cloth which soaks up the cold water and cools the line and pump even more effectively. The procedure may have to be repeated

tips for hot starts, continued

ing on to the carburetor. Suddenly, you feel a loss of power, the car starts backfiring and the engine cuts out. Or, there's no warning at all—the engine just ups and quits, and won't restart.

When vapor lock occurs, the fuel line may be positioned too close to the manifold or an engine hot spot. Asbestos wrapping, shown on this page, will help protect the line from that heat.

But if your fuel lines don't seem to be receiving too much heat, check the fuel pump. Heat concentrated on this part—from a manifold pipe above it, for example—could be causing gas to vaporize as it passes through the pump. This is not a common occurrence in late-model cars. Most manufacturers have separated the pump from any heat-giving source. Some have placed the manifold on one side of the engine block and the fuel pump on the other. Others have put a deflection shield on top of the pump to divert heat if that part is near a heat generator.

However, if you do suspect the fuel pump, you can fabricate your own deflection shield from aluminum or sheet metal to isolate the pump from the heat source. Attach it to any convenient location, such as to the manifold bolts themselves, between the pump and the heat source.

If your car remains vapor-lock prone despite your efforts, make a habit of carrying a thermos of cold water on hot trips. Give the fuel lines and pump a shower. Might as well splash the carburetor, too, in the event of a percolation condition.

Any car hit by vapor lock or percolation will eventually restart, of course, if you let it cool down for several minutes. But why risk even this inconvenience if you can help it? Here are a few more tips:

• Make sure that the cooling system is operating efficiently and at the lowest possible temperature. Undue heat can be generated from this system if it's clogged.

• Make sure the fan belt is in good condition and properly adjusted.

• Consider the use of a low-temperature (150 to 160-deg.) thermostat in the summer to provide a greater circulation of water throughout the cooling system and, consequently, less heat.

• Insure that a pressure-type gas tank cap, if your car is so equipped, is operating properly. Make sure the vent holes are open by blowing through the cap or blowing it out with an air hose. This vent lets off excess vapor pressure built up in the fuel system because of heat. Tanks without such caps are internally vented, so adding a vented cap is merely extra insurance against a plugged vent where you can't see it.

See also: auto repair; batteries, auto; carburetors, auto; electrical system, auto; heat valves, auto; ignition system, auto.

Project-a-plan

Here are the famous Project-a-plans—the *Popular Mechanics* system that makes you an artist in minutes. The method is simple. Cut the Project-a-plans from this page, following the dotted lines. Then coat each drawing with shellac, clear nail polish or even vegetable oil. Then mount each little drawing in a cardboard 35-mm slide frame. Put the frame in a slide projector and project it on the material on which you want to draw—poster board, plywood, etc. Set the material up against the wall like a screen, and make certain the projector is at right angles to the board. You can make the drawing any size you wish by moving the projector. Trace the enlarged outline on the material and you're all set. You can use this system for making signs and posters, enlarging designs for jigsawing and many other projects that require artwork.

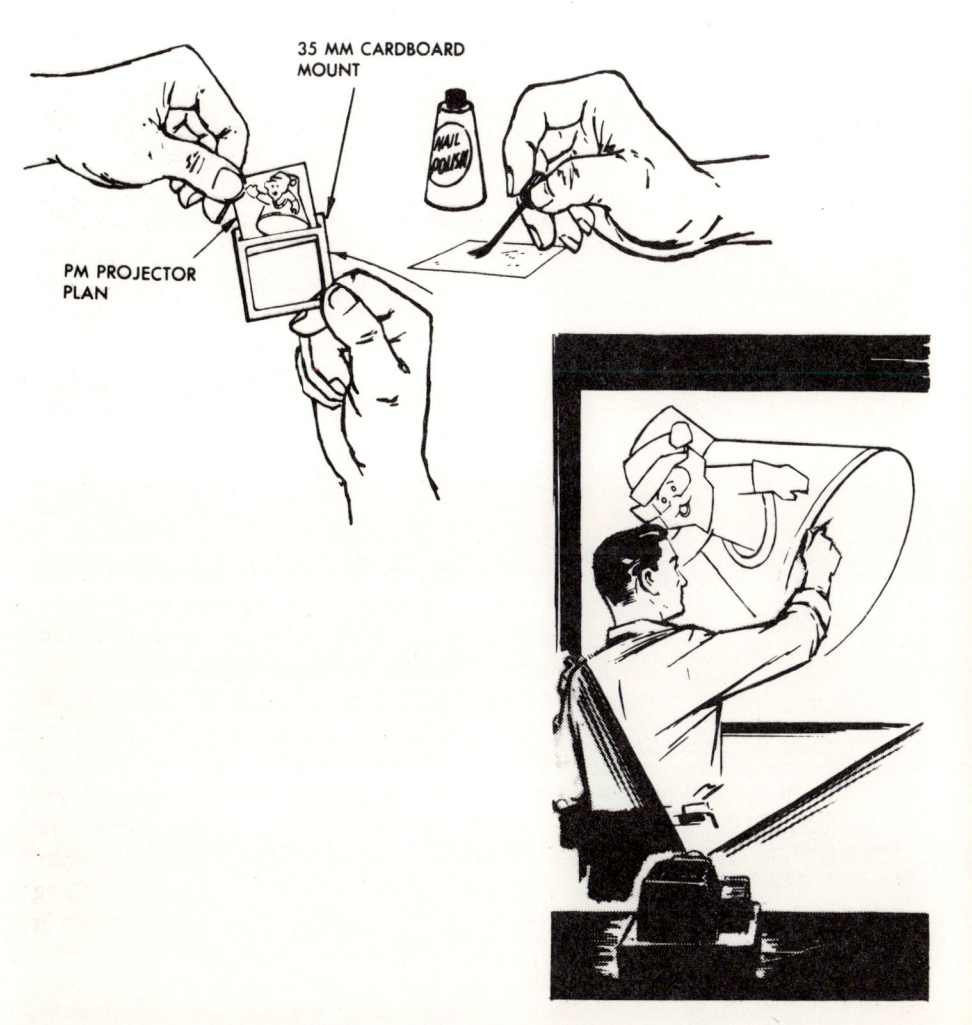

SEE "CARVING SIGNS WITH ROUTER TEMPLATES," PAGE 2352

2495